HUMAN GROWTH AND DEVELOPMENT

for health & social care

Hilary Thomson & Carolyn Meggitt

Hodder & Stoughton
A MEMBER OF THE HODDER HEADLINE GROUP

Acknowledgements

We are indebted to our friend Jean Manuel, who sadly died before the production of this book, but whose writing for earlier books was a valuable source of information.

Thanks to Jean Waterworth, Health Visitor, who contributed a number of articles and was always willing to share her expertise and enthusiasm.

This book is dedicated to our children Doy, Guy, Laura, Leo and Jonathan

For the reproduction of copyright material, the publishers would like to thank the following: fig 2.2: Health Education Authority; fig 2.13: Sally and Richard Greenhill; fig 3.2: Eric Grave/Science Photo Library; fig 3.3a: Pictor Uniphoto; fig 4.5: G.I. Bernard/Oxford Scientific Films; fig 4.19: Tom Bruce; fig 6.2: Robertson & Robertson; fig 6.3: Hulton Getty Picture Collection Limited; fig 6.9: Popperfoto.

The publishers would also like to thank the following for their cooperation in taking the photographs: Kiera MacDonald (fig 2.12), Phil, Wendy and Ben Coombe (fig 4.6), Geraint and Mathew Edwards (fig 4.12), Gillian and Emily Fisher (figs 6.4 and 6.7).

ISBN 0 340 683627

First published 1997
Impression number 10 9 8 7 6 5 4 3 2 1
Year 2001 2000 1999 1998 1997

Typeset by Wearset, Boldon, Tyne and Wear.
Printed in Great Britain for Hodder & Stoughton Educational, a division of Hodder Headline Plc, 338 Euston Road, London NW1 3BH by the Bath Press, Bath

Contents

PART

I

Physical Development

CHAPTER 1

Stages *of* Physical Development

There is a distinction between growth and development. Growth is an increase in size and complexity, whereas development describes the acquisition of skills. There are different methods of measuring growth and development, which are considered below.

The main stages of physical growth and development of the individual move from conception through infancy; childhood; adolescence; adulthood; to old age.

Growth

Growth is a characteristic of all living things and can be simply defined as an increase in size and structural complexity. At a cellular level, there are three stages to growth:

1 *Cell division.* Cells divide by a process known as **mitosis**. This results in the formation of two 'daughter' cells from each cell. The daughter cells contain the same number of chromosomes as the original cell (46 in humans) and are genetically identical. Figure 1.1 gives a diagrammatic representation of the process.
2 *Cell expansion.* Cells expand irreversibly by taking up water and/or synthesising new material.

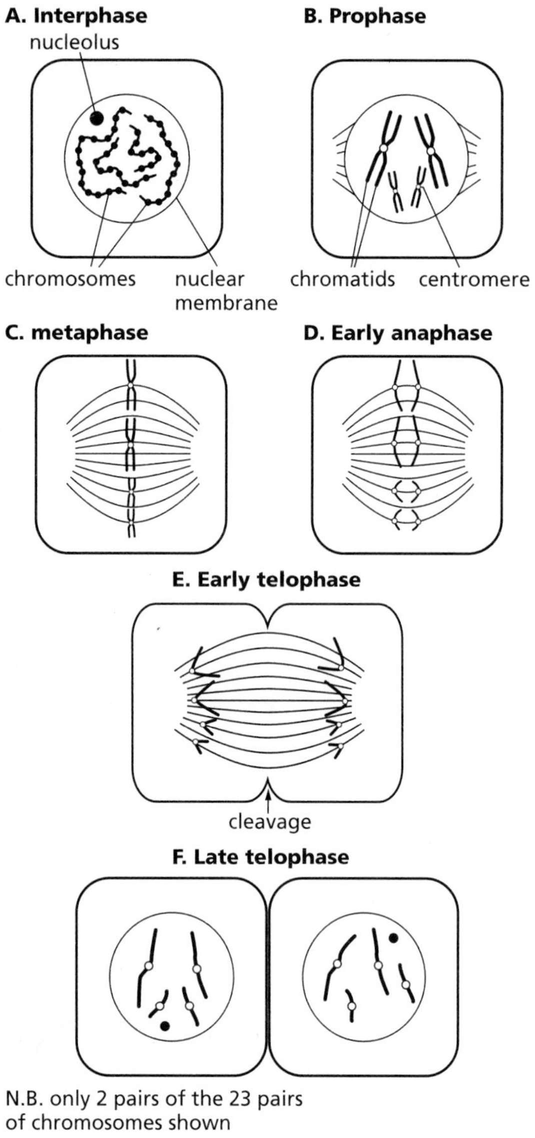

A. Interphase
nucleolus
chromosomes
nuclear membrane
B. Prophase
chromatids
centromere
C. metaphase
D. Early anaphase
E. Early telophase
cleavage
F. Late telophase

N.B. only 2 pairs of the 23 pairs of chromosomes shown

Figure 1.1 Diagrammatic representation of mitosis

3 *Cell differentiation.* This is the specialisation of cells into particular types. For example, liver cells, muscle cells, blood cells etc.

– activity –

1 Use a microscope to observe cells undergoing mitosis (for example, use a prepared slide of onion root tip). Try to find each of the stages shown in Figure 1.1.
2 If possible, watch a video of the process of mitosis, so that you can see the chromosomes actually moving.
3 To form **gametes** (i.e. sperm and ova), cells divide by **meiosis**. This results in cells with half the number of chromosomes which are all genetically different. Look at the description of this on page 40 and then explain how it differs from mitosis.

(See Appendix A for answers.)

MEASURING GROWTH

Human growth can be measured by height (or length in babies), weight or head circumference. Data from these parameters can then be expressed in various types of **growth curve**. The **actual** or **absolute growth curve** is the parameter plotted against time (Figure 1.2a). This shows the overall growth pattern and the extent of growth. The steepest part of the curve corresponds to the most rapid rate of growth. The **absolute growth rate curve** is produced by plotting the *change* in parameter against time (Figure 1.2b). This curve shows how the rate of growth changes with age. The highest point shows where growth was most rapid.

activity

The absolute growth curve (Figure 1.2a) shows four distinct phases of increased growth. During which phase is weight gain most rapid? (See Appendix A for answer.)

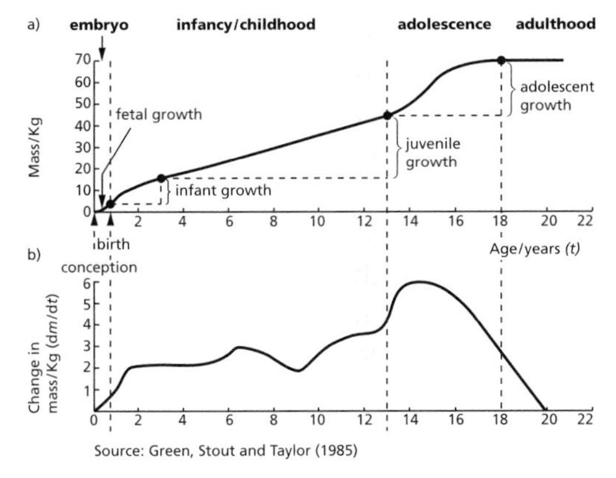

Figure 1.2 (a) Absolute growth curve for humans (b) Absolute growth rate curve for humans

Differential growth

During human growth, the organs increase in size at different rates. This is known as **allometric growth**. Nervous tissue grows most rapidly during gestation, and subsequent growth is slow. The skull and brain usually reach adult size by the fifth year. The long bones of the limbs grow fastest after birth. This **differential growth** in different parts of the body results in changes of proportion during development (Figure 1.3).

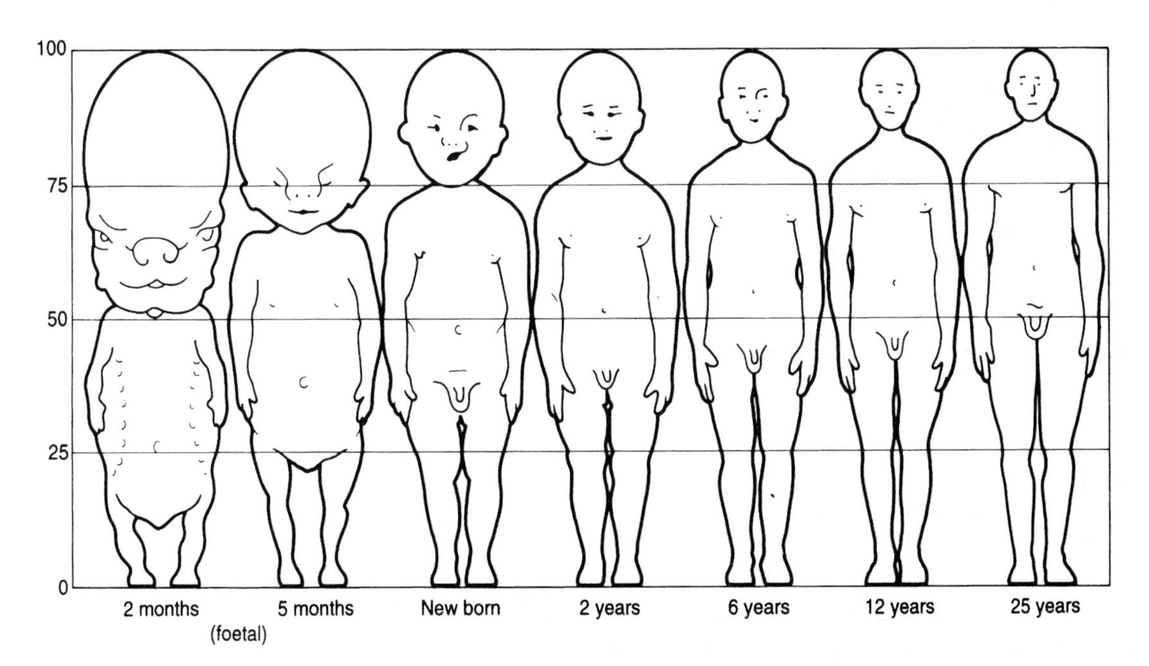

Figure 1.3 Disproportionate growth of different parts of the body throughout life

activity

1 Figure 1.4 shows the differential growth of some tissues. Summarise the information shown, and suggest why each of these tissues shows these growth patterns.
2 A simple test is used to determine when children in the Third World are old enough for a particular vaccine. The children are asked to reach over their heads to touch their left ear with their right hand. If they can touch their ear, they are old enough. If they cannot reach, they are still too young. Describe the changes in the proportions of different parts of the body which enable this test to be used. (See Appendix A for answer.)

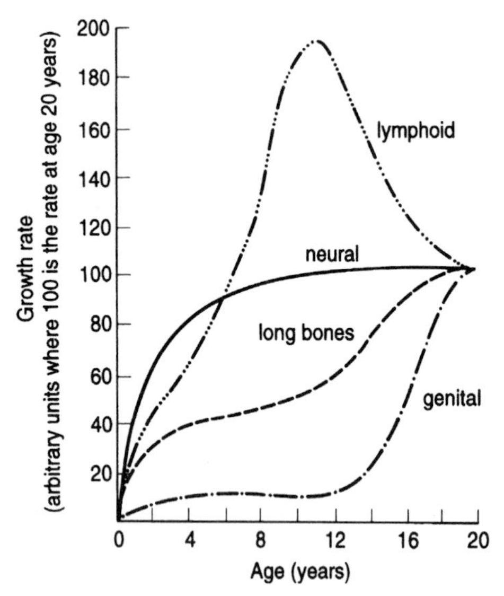

Figure 1.4 Differential growth rates in some tissues

Just as growth follows predictable patterns, so physical development proceeds in a set order, with simple behaviours preceding more complex skills (Figure 1.5). For example, a child will sit before they stand.

A **norm** is a fixed or ideal standard. Developmental norms are sometimes called **milestones**. Each child will, of course, develop in their own unique way, and using norms helps in understanding patterns of development while recognising the wide variation between individuals.

Development

Development is concerned with the acquisition of **skills**. These can be divided into two main areas:

1 *gross motor skills:* these use the large muscles in the body and include walking, running, climbing etc.;
2 *fine manipulative skills:* these involve precise use of the hands and figures for pointing, drawing, using a knife and fork, writing, doing up shoe laces etc.

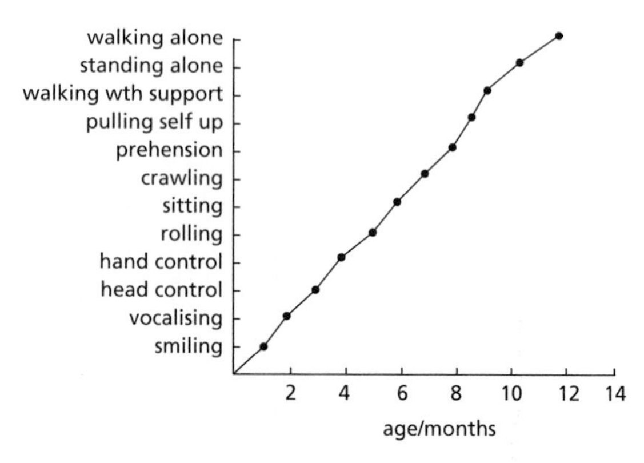

Figure 1.5 Some developmental milestones in the first year of life (from Smith Bierman, Robinson after Johnson, Moore and Ross)

activity

1 Discuss the advantages and disadvantages of the use of developmental norms.

2 Two different methods can be used to try to determine **growth norms**:

- *longitudinal study:* a number of individuals are measured (for example, height, weight and head circumference) at intervals from their birth until early adulthood
- *cross-sectional study:* at one set time, a number of different individuals of various ages, from birth to early adulthood, are measured

The data obtained from either of these studies can be used to produce growth curves such as those shown in Figures 1.2 and 1.6. Make a table to show the relative advantages and disadvantages of each type of study.

3 Look at the **centiles** in Figure 1.6 which are used to measure variation about a norm. For example, at 6 months, 10% of babies weigh 6.9 kg or less, and 90% weigh more than this. What percentage of babies are longer than 54 cm at 3 months?

4 If possible, attend a local clinic at which babies are weighed and observe these charts being completed. How does the girls' chart differ from the boys'?

(See Appendix A for answers.)

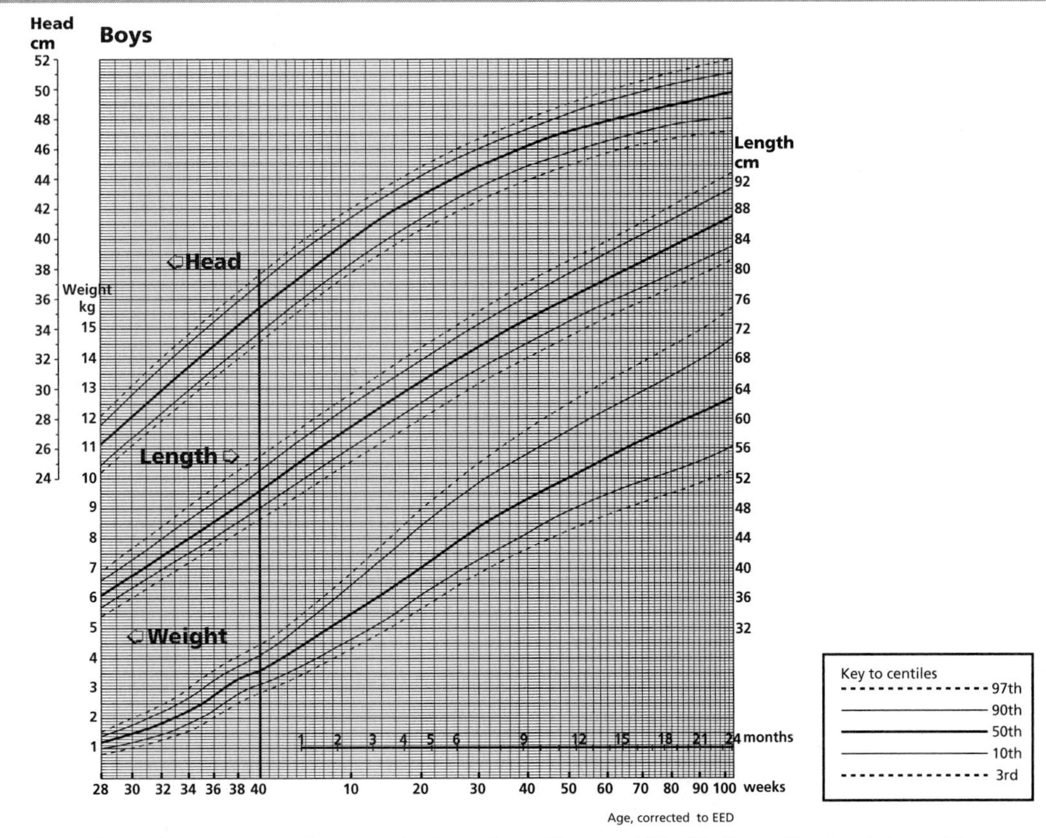

Figure 1.6 Page showing growth norms for boys from 'Personal Health Record'; a book issued in several health authorities to enable parents to record measurements

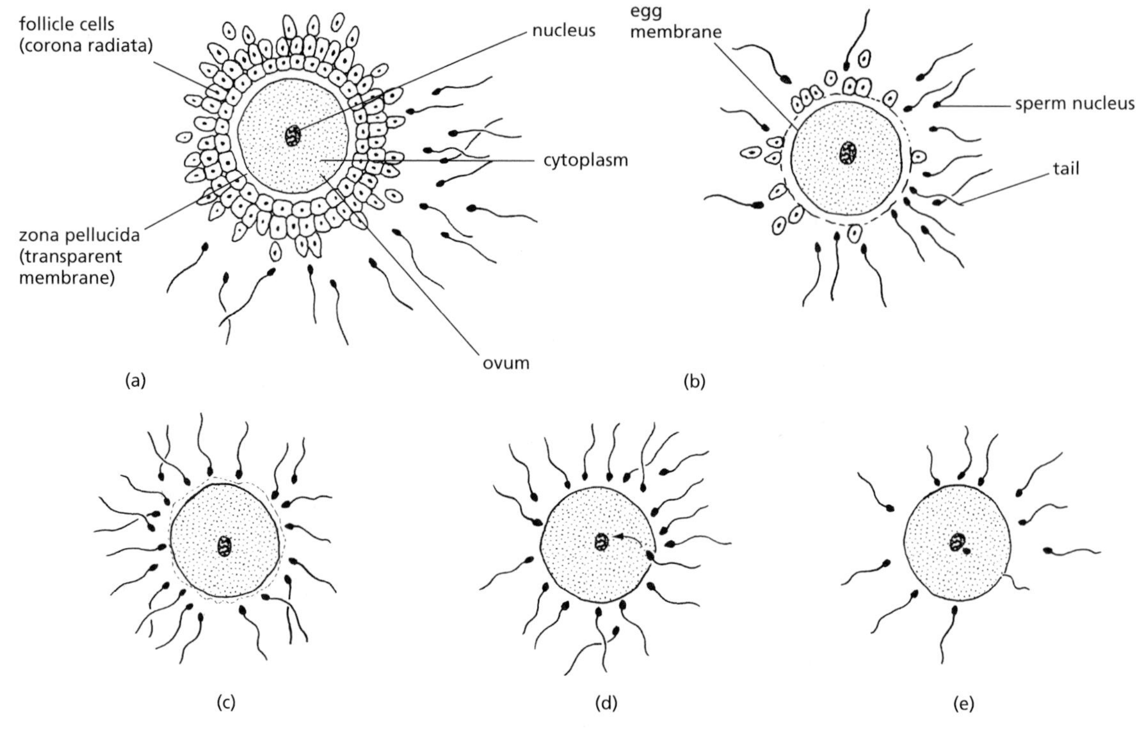

Figure 1.7 Conception

The physical development of a human is a continuous process, but for ease of description, and to aid our understanding, we can divide this process into a number of stages:

Conception to birth (0–40 weeks)

Conception

(For information on the reproductive system, readers should refer to pages 154–157 of Thomson et al. (1995) *Health and Social Care*, 2nd edition.)

When **fertilisation** occurs, the sperm penetrates the egg (**ovum**) and their two **nuclei** fuse (Figure 1.7). The resulting fertilised egg is known as the **zygote**. This process usually takes place in the **Fallopian tube** (Figure 1.8) 12 to 24 hours after **ovulation** (release of the egg from the ovary).

activity

1 Using diagrams, describe the events leading up to fertilisation, i.e.:

- the formation of the male and female gametes
- the ovarian cycle
- copulation
- stages (a) to (e) in Figure 1.7, including the **acrosome reaction**

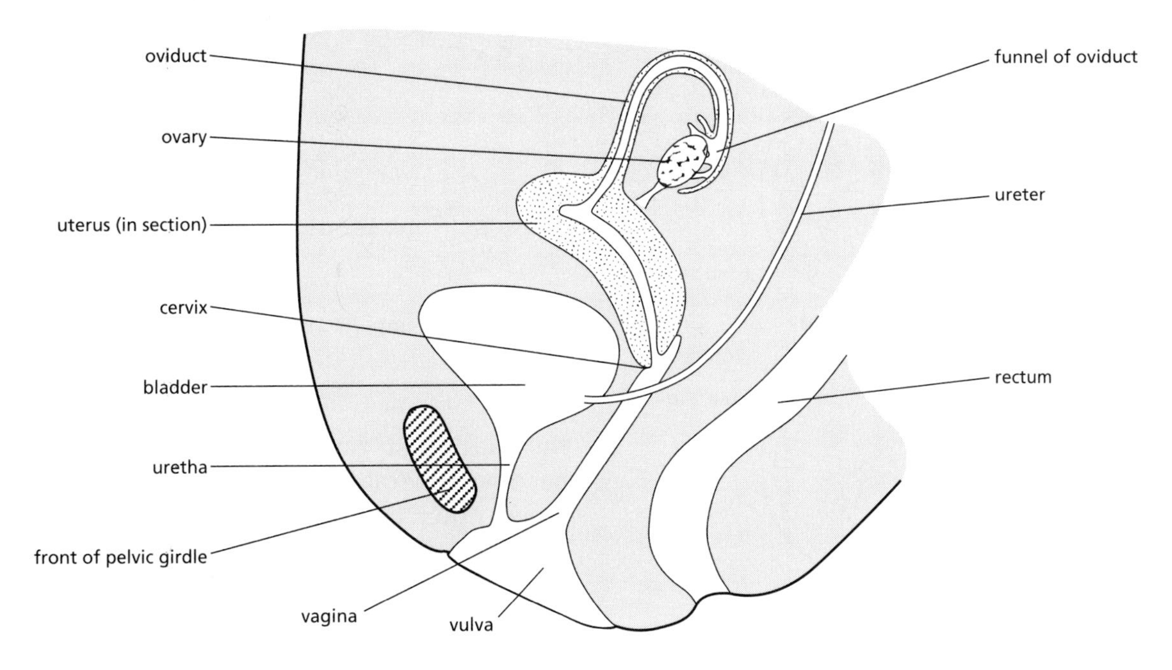

Figure 1.8 Female reproductive system

(If you are working in a group, you may each wish to take one of the above aspects and then feed back the information to the rest of the group.)

2 Microscope work:

- Look at a microscope slide of spermatozoa. How are the spermatozoa adapted to their function?
- Examine a section of the **testis**. Identify what you see
- Examine a section of an **ovary**. Make a series of annotated diagrams to illustrate the development of an ovum
- Find out how many chromosomes are present in:
  - the nucleus of a human ovum
  - the nucleus of a human sperm
  - the nuclei of a human zygote.

3 Produce a leaflet which gives a simple explanation of **in vitro** fertilisation. Find out about the availability of this on the NHS, and the costs of having this treatment privately. In your leaflet, give an indication of the success rate of the procedure.

(See Appendix A for answers.)

Development of the zygote

Immediately after fertilisation, the zygote undergoes rapid cell division. The first division, or **cleavage**, results in the formation of two cells (see 'mitosis' above) and takes about 36 hours (Figure 1.9). Within another 24 hours the second division is completed, resulting in four cells. These then divide to form eight cells which then divide to give sixteen cells and so on. A few days after fertilisation, these divisions have led to the formation of a solid mass of cells known as the **morula**. Because pro-

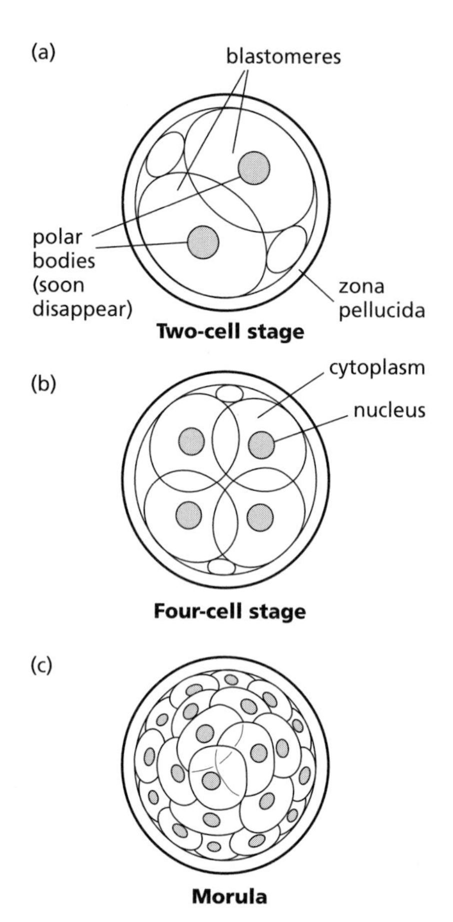

Figure 1.9 Formation of the morula

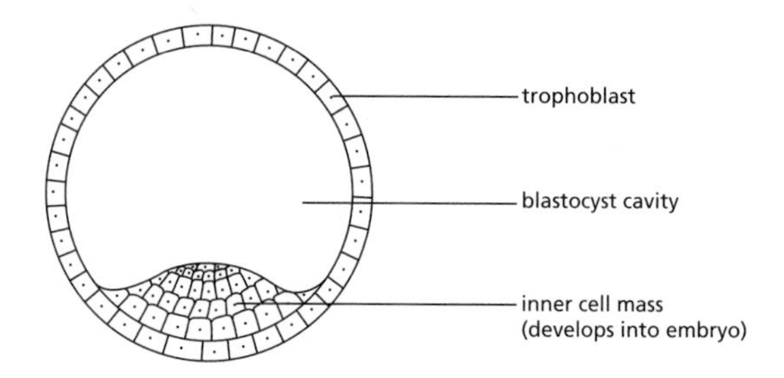

Figure 1.10 Simplified diagram of a human blastocyst

gressively smaller cells are formed, the morula is about the same size as the original zygote. As the morula forms, waving cilia assist its movement down the Fallopian tube and into the uterus.

As cell division continues, a hollow, fluid-filled ball is formed which is known as a **blastocyst**. As the amount of fluid in the blastocyst cavity increases, the cells become separated into two parts: a flattened outer cell layer known as the **trophoblast** which eventually goes on to form the embryonic part of the placenta, and the **inner cell mass** which is the origin of the embryo (Figure 1.10). About 7 to 8 days after fertilisation, **implantation** takes place. This is when the blastocyst becomes attached to the **endometrium** (the lining of the uterus). During implantation, the outer cells of the blastocyst secrete enzymes that digest the cells of the endometrium. Eventually, the blastocyst becomes buried in the endometrium. The uterus lining develops a rich supply of blood vessels and becomes increasingly muscular. The outer cells of the blastocyst form finger-like projections (**chorionic villi**) through which the exchange of nutrients, oxygen and excretory materials occurs (see the 'Development of the placenta and foetal membranes' section on page 12 below).

activity

What is meant by an **ectopic** implantation? (See Appendix A for answers.)

Development of the embryo

For the first two months of development, the developing human is called an **embryo**. During this time the beginnings of the principal organs are formed, and the embryonic membranes are developed.

Following implantation, **gastrulation** takes place. This begins at the end of the 1st week and is completed during the 3rd week. It involves the arrangement of the inner cell mass of the blastocyst into three layers:

1. the **ectoderm**, which forms the skin and nervous system
2. the **mesoderm**, which forms the muscle, bones, blood and other connective tissues
3. the **endoderm**, which forms the epithelial lining of the alimentary canal and respiratory tract, and a number of other organs.

(Throughout the following description of the development of the embryo and foetus, refer to Figure 1.11.)

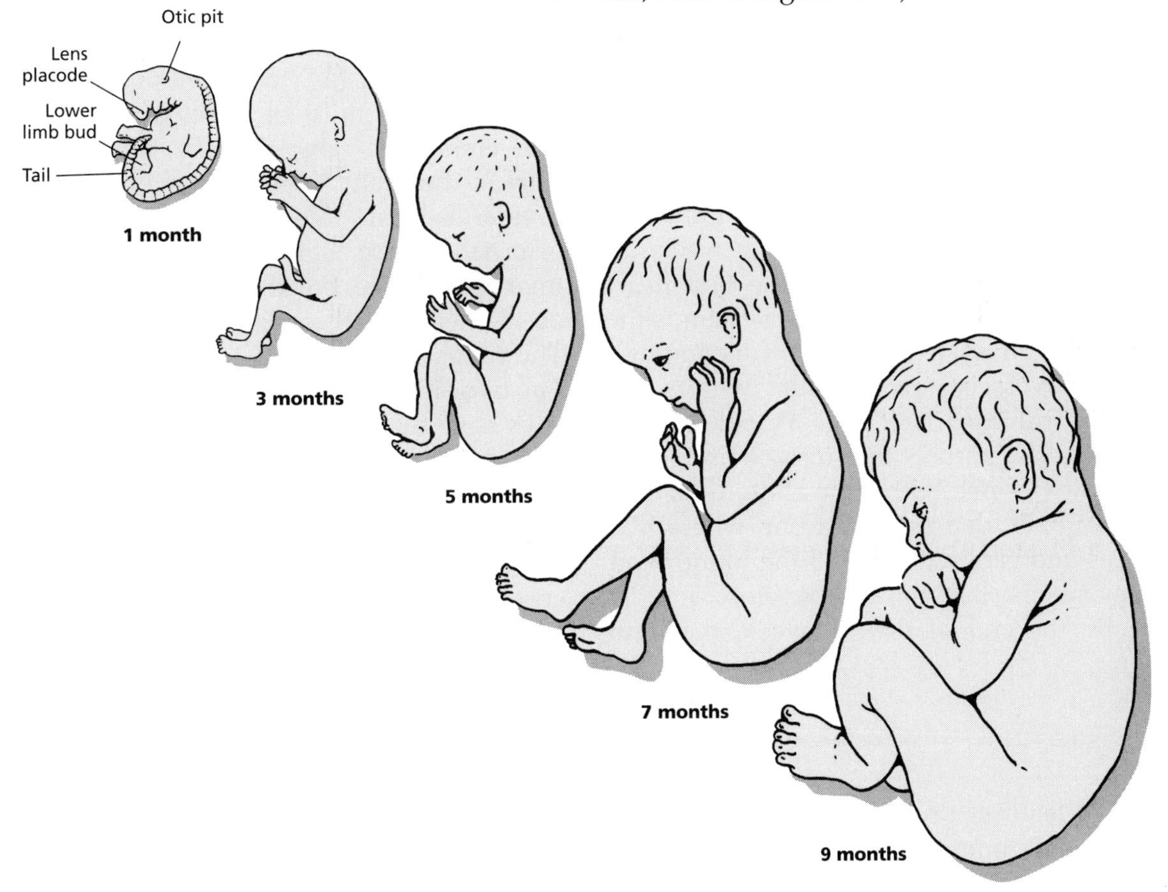

Figure 1.11 (a) development of the embryo and foetus in the uterus (drawing not to scale)

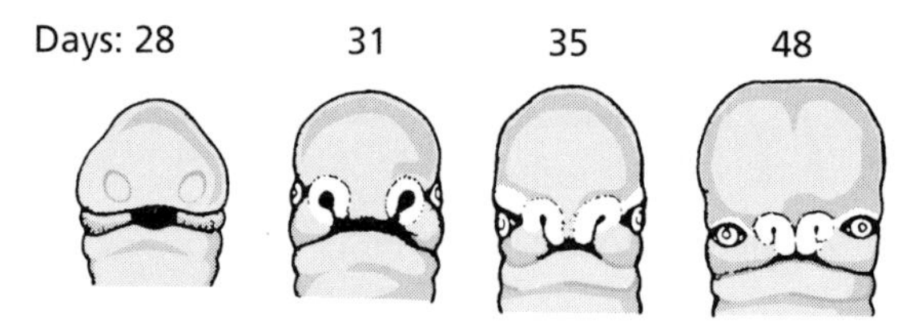

Figure 1.11 (b) development of the face
Source: Moore, 1988

In the 4th week, the limb buds appear as small swellings. The embryo has a 'C-shaped' appearance, with a prominent tail.

At the end of the 5th week, the embryo is approximately 2 mm long, and would therefore be visible to the naked eye. The spine is beginning to form, and the origin of the nervous system is just visible. Blood formation begins. Growth of the head is obvious due to the rapid development of the brain.

During the 6th week, the embryo grows to about 6 mm long (the size of a grain of rice) and the chest and abdominal cavities start forming. The tail becomes less noticeable and the four limb buds continue to develop. By the end of the 6th week, an ultrasonic scan can detect the first heart motions. (The cardiovascular system is the first organ system to start functioning.) Blood vessels are forming within the **umbilical cord** (see page 13 below) and the earliest parts of the stomach and intestine are formed within the **abdominal cavity**. Small depressions form where the eyes and ears will be, and the mouth and jaw are also beginning to develop.

By the end of the 7th week, the limb buds are clearly distinguishable as arms and legs. Ridges can be seen where the fingers and toes will develop. Blood vessels are present throughout the head and body, and they contain blood cells. The heart beats with sufficient force to move the cells through the vessels. The liver, kidney and lungs are all developing. The brain and spinal cord and head are also all developing very quickly. The head is assuming its final shape but is bent forward over the chest and is very large compared with the body. The inner parts of the ears are forming. The eyes continue to develop, but they are still completely covered with the skin which will eventually become the eyelids. Although the nose is still not present, apertures can be seen where the nostrils will form. By now, the embryo is about 13 mm long.

By the 8th week, all the major internal organs have begun to develop, but the functioning of most of these is minimal. The embryo is now about 22 mm long. This is the main time of growth for the eyes and the middle and inner ears. The external ears are beginning to take on their final appearance, but they are still low set on the head. The heart is beating strongly. The lungs have grown but are still solid. The two sides of both the upper and lower jaws have fused, so that the mouth can be recognised. Shoulders, elbows, hips and knees can also be seen as the limbs continue to develop. Although the external genitalia have begun to form, sex differences are not yet obvious. The tail disappears completely.

activity

What features present in the embryo suggest that humans and other mammals, reptiles, birds, amphibians and fish have all evolved from a common ancestor? (See Appendix A for answer.)

Development of the foetus

From the beginning of the 9th week after conception until birth, the developing human is known as a **foetus**. This change in name is to signify that the developing human has now acquired definite human characteristics. Development during the foetal period is mainly concerned with the growth of the organs that formed during the embryonic period.

Weeks 9–12
By the 9th week, the foetus is developing muscles and so is starting to move. However, these movements are not yet detected by the mother. Bone formation (**ossification**) begins particularly in the skull and long bones.

At 9 weeks, most of the red blood cells are produced by the liver, but by 12 weeks they are being produced by the spleen. During this period, **urine** formation begins. It is excreted into the amniotic fluid (see page 12 below), and the foetus reabsorbs some of this fluid after swallowing it.

At 9 weeks, the foetus is about 30 mm long and weighs about 2 g. By 12 weeks, it is about 65 mm long and weighs about 18 g.

Weeks 13–16
Body growth is very rapid during this period. By 16 weeks, the foetus is about 160 mm long and weighs about 135 g. The formation of the skeleton is taking place rapidly, and foetal movement continues to increase, although it is still not sufficiently vigorous to be detected by the mother. By 16 weeks, the ovaries will have formed in females and primitive ova can be seen. The external genital organs continue to develop, and the sex of the baby is now obvious. The head is now rounded, and the neck is developed so that it can move freely. The mouth, nose, eyes and external ears are all properly developed. Fingers, toes, fingernails and toe nails are all present. A fine downy hair (**lanugo**) covers the whole foetus, including the face, and eyebrows and eyelashes start to grow.

Weeks 17–20
The growth of the foetus slows down during this period. The limbs grow at a relatively quicker rate until they reach their final relative proportions, and muscle is rapidly increasing. The skin becomes covered with a fatty secretion (**vernix caseosa**) which protects it from the chapping that could result from continuous exposure to the amniotic fluid (see page 000 below). **Brown fat** forms which is an important site of heat production, particularly in the newborn infant. Head hair may become visible at this time.

At the end of the 20th week, the foetus is about 255 mm (25.5 cm) long and weighs about 340 g.

activity

At around this time, the mother will first become aware of foetal movements (**quickening**). If possible, talk to a woman about her experiences of this. Ask her at what stage of the pregnancy she first noticed this. Did this vary from child to child? What did it feel like? Was the baby more active at certain times of the day or night?

Weeks 21–25
Growth is rapid during this period, and by the end of 25 weeks the foetus is about 34 cm long and weighs about 600 g. By 24 weeks, the cells lining the lungs have secreted a layer of **surfactant** which facilitates the expansion of the developing **alveoli**.

Weeks 26–29
By this time, the lungs have developed sufficiently to function if the foetus is born prematurely (see page 36 below). The central nervous system has also developed enough to bring about rhythmic breathing movements, and to control body temperature. By 28 weeks, the formation of red blood cells in the spleen ceases and begins in the bone marrow. Fat forms under the skin, which means that the foetus loses its wrinkled appearance.

Weeks 30–38
After 35 weeks, most foetuses will be plump. By 36 weeks, the circumference of the head and the abdomen are approximately equal. In a male, the testes will have descended into the **scrotum**. The lanugo will have disappeared from most of the head and body, but the foetus remains almost entirely covered with vernix except on the mouth and eyes. The colour of the iris is always blue at this stage.

The baby increases in weight by about 28 g per day from the 36th week until birth. At birth, it will be about 50 cm long, on average, and weigh about 3.4 kg.

activity

1 From the above information, make a table to show:

- the size
- movements
- sensory development (i.e. the development of the brain and nerves, the eyes and the ears)

of the embryo and foetus at 1, 3, 5, 7 and 9 months after conception.

Plot a graph from the figures given to show the increase in

- length
- weight

from conception to birth.

2 What physiological effects does pregnancy have on a woman? How do these effects help the foetus grow?

Development of the placenta and foetal membranes

The **placenta** is made up of cells derived from the mother and from the foetus. It is an organ in which the foetal and material blood systems come very close to one another. This allows the transfer of nutrients, oxygen and metabolic waste to take place. It also allows **antibodies** to pass from the mother to the foetus, ensuring the baby has **passive immunity** to certain diseases.

The **amnion**, a membrane which surrounds the embryo, secretes **amniotic fluid** to fill the amniotic cavity between the amnion and the embryo. This fluid supports the embryo and protects it from mechanical shock.

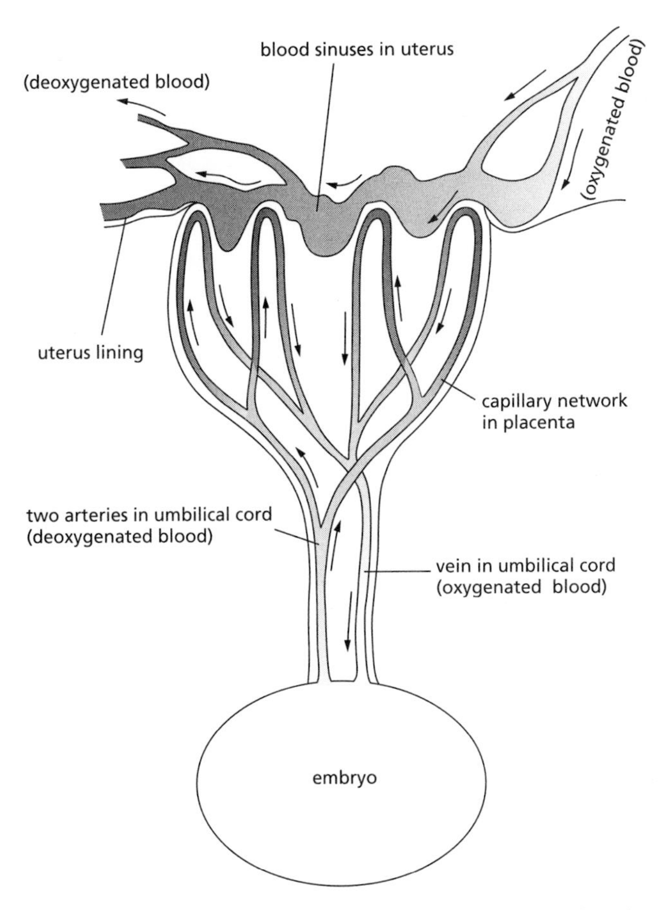

Figure 1.12 The relationship between the blood supply of the embryo and the placenta

The formation of the chorionic villi, finger-like projections which surround the newly embedded embryo, was described above (see the 'Development of the zygote' section on page 7 above). These increase rapidly in both number and size. By the 12th week, the chorionic villi at the site of the original implantation develop rapidly to form the placenta. The remaining villi gradually disappear.

Blood reaches the placenta from the foetus through the two umbilical arteries. It returns to the foetus through the umbilical vein (Figure 1.12). Processes from the placenta branch into blood sinuses in the **uterus** containing the maternal blood. This arrangement means that the foetal blood and the maternal blood are only separated by a thin membrane of about 2 μm across.

activity

1 Transport of substances takes place by **diffusion** (e.g. respiratory gases) or by **active transport** (e.g. nutrients). Explain what is meant by each of these terms. (See Appendix A for answer.)

2 The placenta also functions as an

endocrine organ, and it produces the following hormones. Find out what their functions are.

- chorionic gonadotrophin
- oestrogens
- progesterone
- human placental lactogen

3 Find out about the placenta and foetal membranes of both identical and non-identical twins.

Birth

Birth, or **parturition**, usually occurs at approximately 266 days or 38 weeks after fertilisation. This is usually calculated as 280 days or 40 weeks after the last menstrual period.

In the first stage of labour, the uterus starts to contract. These contractions become more frequent and intense until the cervix is fully dilated (Figure 1.13).

In the second stage, the baby is pushed downwards, usually head first, through the vagina (**delivery**).

The third and final stage is the delivery of the placenta (**afterbirth**).

– activity –

1 Watch a video of a baby being born, and if possible interview a mother informally to find out about her experience of giving birth.
2 Write an account explaining how hormones bring about the onset of labour.

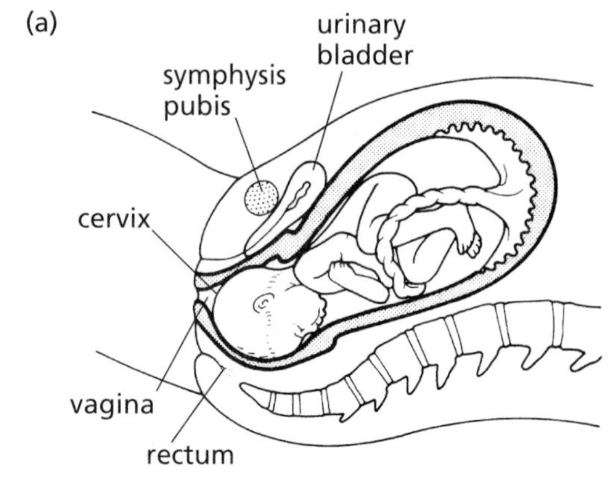

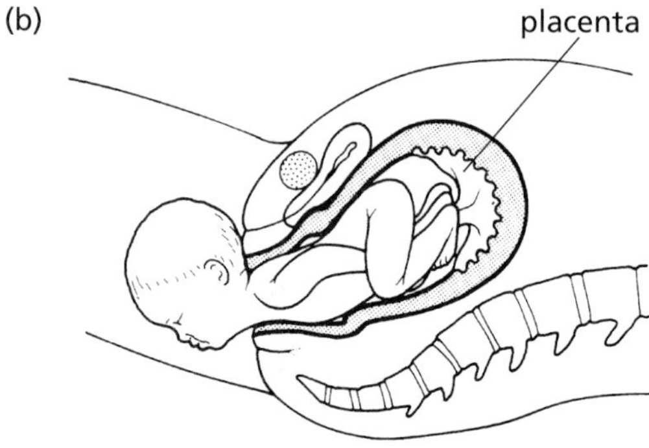

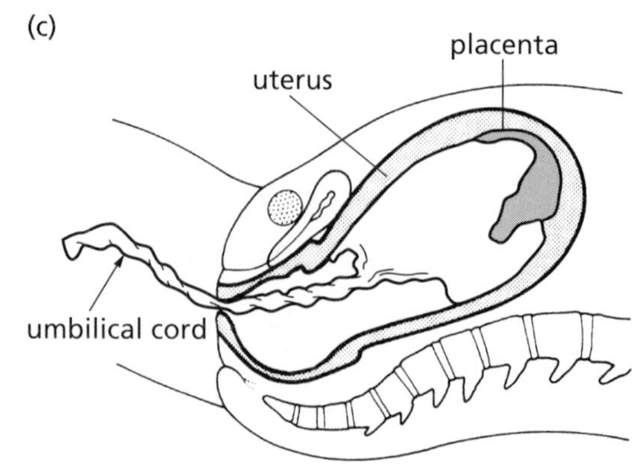

Figure 1.13 Stages of birth (a) first stage (b) second stage (c) third stage

Age	Physical ability
Newborn	Innate reflexes: sucking, stepping, gripping, Plantar reflex, startle reflex
2 months	Can lift head when lying face down
3 months	Holds rattle placed in hands. Turns head to sound
4 months	Puts hands together
5 months	Can reach for, and grasp an object
6 months	Sits (hands used for support). Rolls over. Transfers object from one hand to the other
7 months	Sits without using hands for support
8 months	Leans forward to reach for objects when sitting
9 months	Pulls up to standing position. Crawls. 'Inspects' objects with index finger. 'Pincer' grasp
10 months	Offers object to carer, but will not release it
11 months	Walks holding on to furniture ('cruising')
1 year	Gives object to carer. 'Walks' on hands and feet. Throws objects down repeatedly ('casting')
13 months	Walks
15 months	Creeps upstairs. Kneels. Takes off shoes. Makes a 2 cube tower
18 months	Jumps with both feet. Stops 'casting'. Throws ball without falling over. Makes a 3–4 cube tower
2 years	Runs. Picks object up off the floor without falling. Turns door knobs. Makes a 6 cube tower
3 years	Rides trike. Dresses and undresses (not shoe laces). Makes a 9 cube tower
4 years	Builds recognisable models with bricks. Draws recognisable pictures. May be able to write name. Can learn to catch a ball
5 years	Has complete control of bowel and bladder

Table 1.1 Development of physical ability (0–5 years)

	Head Control	Ventral Suspension	Sitting	Crawling	Standing
Newborn	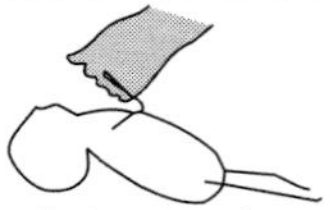 pulled to sit – almost complete head lag.	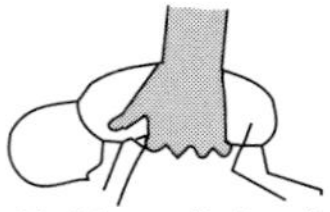 head held up a little, elbows flexed, hips partly extended.	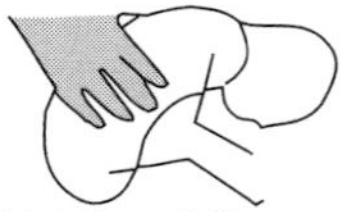 held sitting – fully rounded back.	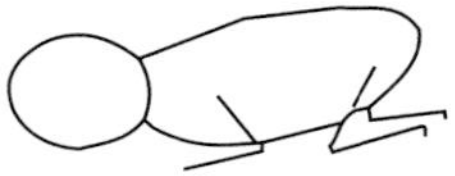 prone – pelvis high, knees under abdomen.	
1 Month			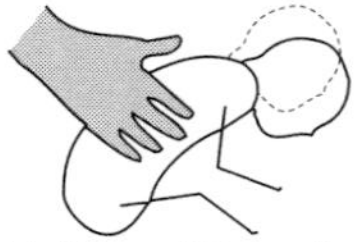 held sitting – lifts head up intermittently.		
6 weeks		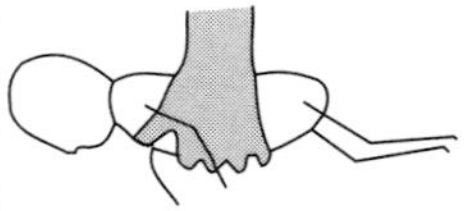 head held up momentarily in same plane as rest of body. Hips extended.		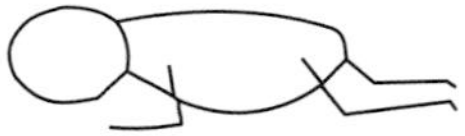 prone – pelvis flat, hips extended.	
2 months	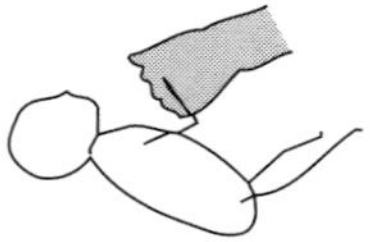 pulled to sit – less head lag.		 held sitting – back straightening; head up.	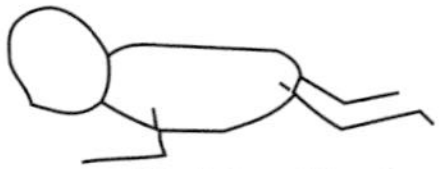 prone – chin intermittently lifted off couch.	
10 weeks		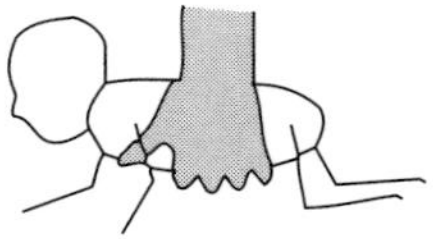 head held up well beyond plane of rest of body.			
3 months				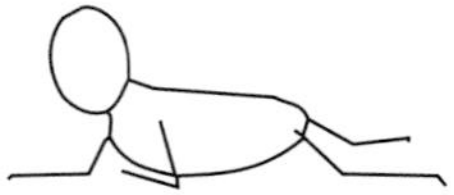 prone – weight on forearms, chest well off couch.	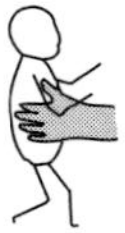 held standing – sags at knees and hips.

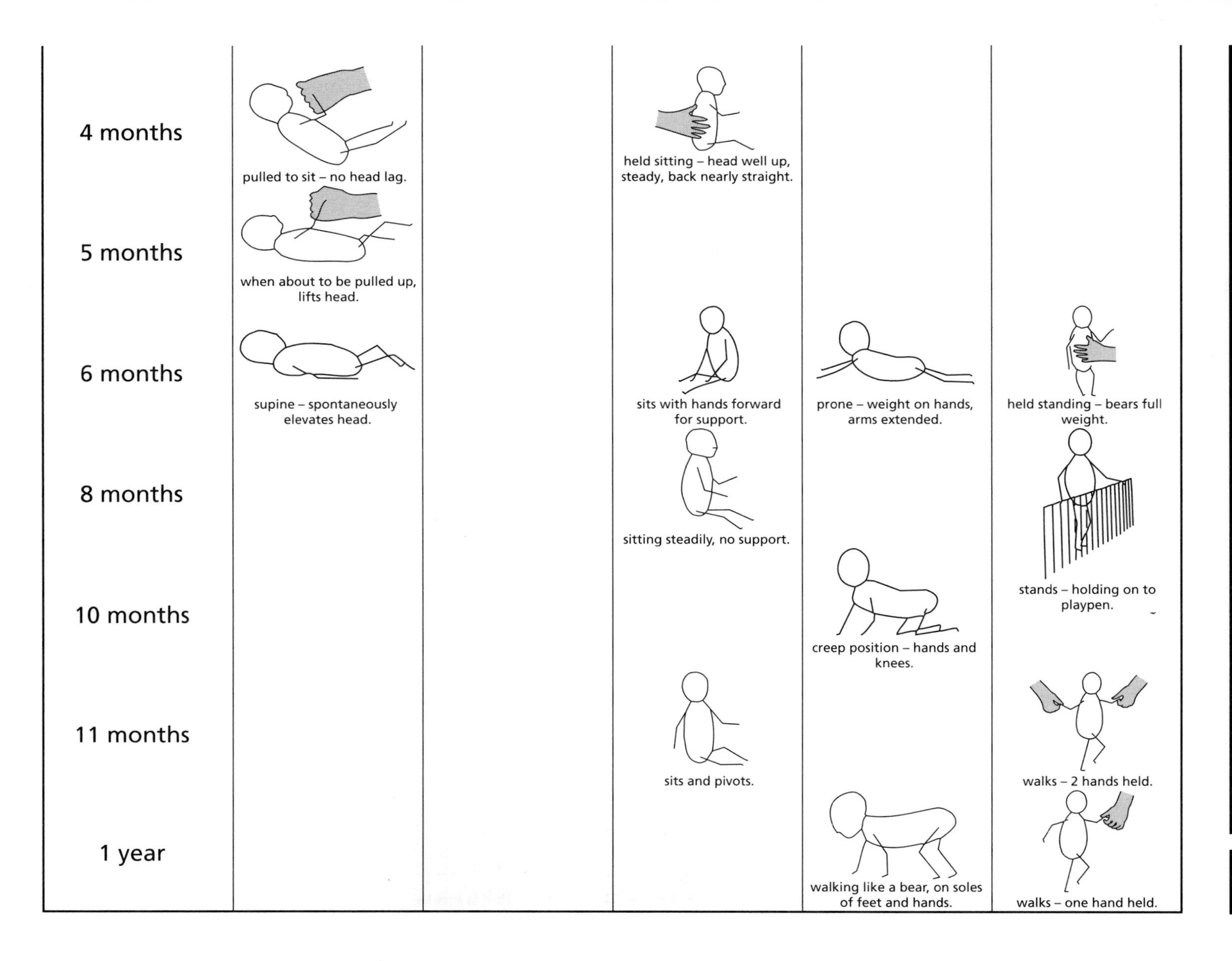

Figure 1.14 Development of posture control during infancy (adapted from Illingworth 1990)

Infancy (0–1 years)

Growth

The newborn baby weighs, on average, 3.5 kg, and its length is about 50 cm. Boys are on average about 100 g heavier than girls, and slightly longer. A baby will usually have doubled its weight by between 4–6 months and have tripled its weight by the time it is 12 months old (see Figure 1.6).

As mentioned above (Figure 1.3), the proportions of body parts are remarkably different from an adult. In particular, at birth the head is very much bigger in relation to the body than in adulthood, while the limbs are shorter. During the first year, the limbs grow at a faster rate, and the head grows at a slower rate than the rest of the body, so that by the time the infant is a year old, the differences in proportion compared with an adult, although still present, are becoming less pronounced.

Newborn infants do not have the ability to shiver. However, they do have deposits of specialised **adipose tissue**, known as 'brown fat', between their shoulder blades. This tissue is metabolically more active than ordinary fat, and can produce large quantities of heat. These fat deposits atrophy with increasing age.

Developmental milestones

Newborn reflexes

Several reflexes (**innate reflexes**) are observed at birth or shortly afterwards.

- A newborn baby will automatically *suck* at objects placed in its mouth
- If a baby's body is supported and its feet touch a solid surface, it will show a characteristic *stepping* action
- A baby's hands *grip* tightly onto objects placed in them
- If the sole of a baby's foot is stroked, its toes will curl as shown in Figure 1.16a (**plantar reflex**)
- The baby will show a **startle reflex** in response to loud noises. The arms and legs are pulled up as shown in Figure 1.16b, with the elbows flexed and the hands closed.
- The baby will also show the **Moro reflex**, which differs from the startle reflex in that the elbow is extended and the hands open

Posture and locomotion

Figure 1.14 shows the main stages in the development of posture and locomotion. The first column shows how a baby gradually becomes able to lift her head, take the weight of her body on her limbs, and become mobile; column 2 shows the increase in the ability of the baby to support herself when held face down (**ventral suspension**); column 3 shows the increase in the ability of the baby to support her head when pulled into a sitting position; column 4 shows the increase in the ability of the baby to support herself when held in the sitting position; and column 5 shows the increase in the ability of the baby to support herself on her legs.

(Don't forget that there are wide variations in development, and that these are only averages. For example, a normal child may sit without support by 5 months, or not until 12 months, and a normal child may walk without support by 7 months, or not until 4 years.)

Tracking, reaching for and manipulating objects

People often imagine that very young babies show little coordination or response. However, careful observation shows that even newborns will turn towards the source of a sound, look at an object and follow a moving object with their eyes (**tracking**), albeit with slower and less smooth movements than an adult. The quality of a newborn baby's sight is poorer than that of an adult, but it is no longer thought that babies can only focus at one distance. Newborn babies are thought to see only primary colours.

Reaching for objects may be seen when the baby is only a few days old. The frequency of this reaching reduces over the first two weeks, and between 4 and 20 weeks it is rarely seen. During this early reaching, the baby does not successfully grasp, or even always make contact with, the object.

By the time the baby is 8 months, they will have learnt how to coordinate reaching with forward leaning when the distance of the object demands this.

By 9 months old, they can adjust the grasp to suit the size of the object.

Even before a baby has reached the stage at which they can successfully reach for an object, if it is presented to them, they will be able to *manipulate* it.

At two months, they will finger the object in the hand holding it.

At four months, they will hold the object in one hand and finger it with the other.

By six months, the baby will pass the object from hand to hand and bang it against a hard surface to make a noise. By this age, they will probably be able to feed themselves a biscuit. Their grasp of an object will be **palmar** (Figure 1.15).

At nine months, the baby can hold an object between the forefinger finger and thumb (**pincer grasp**; Figure 1.15). They approach objects they are interested in with their index finger (Figure 1.15). They may offer an object, such as a block, to a carer, but they will not let go of it until about 11 months old.

a) 6 months: palmer grasp of cube.

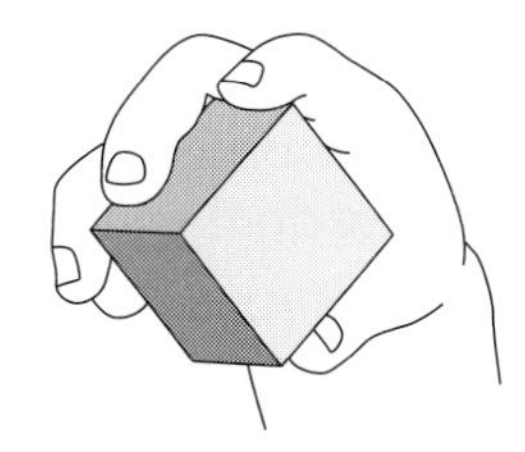

b) 8 months: grasp, intermediate.

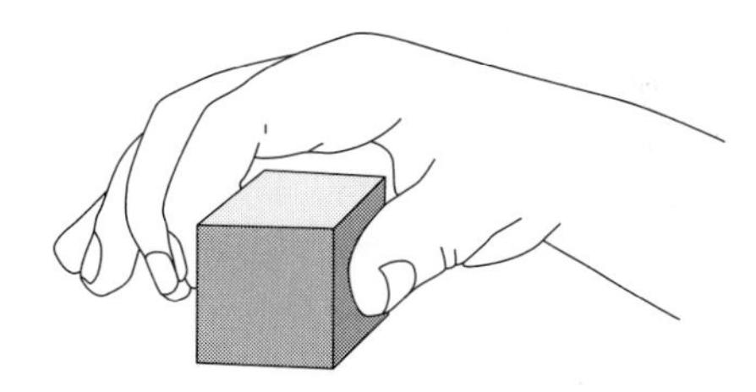

c) 1 year: mature grasp of cube.

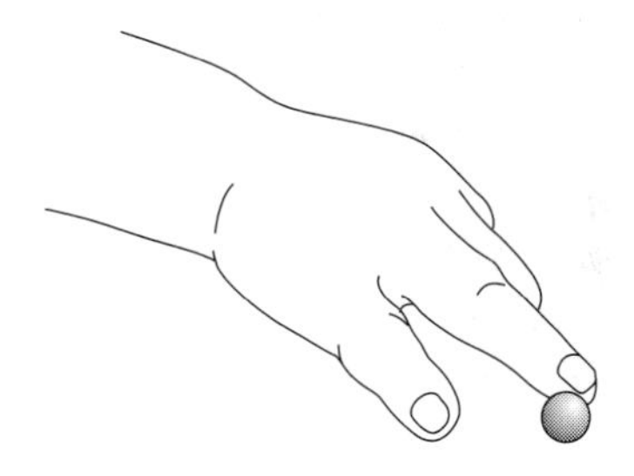

d) 9–10 months: index finger approach to object.

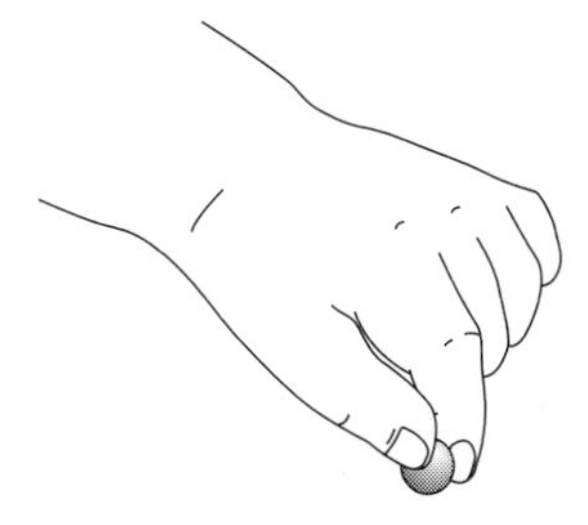

e) 9–10 months: finger–thumb apposition — pellet picked up between tip of forefinger and tip of thumb.

Figure 1.15 Development of manipulation during infancy

activity

1 Growth:
If you have the opportunity to speak to a midwife about her work, ask her about the variations in the birth weight of babies she has delivered.

Find out about the development of the teeth. In what order, and, on average, at what ages, do the teeth appear?

2 Newborn reflexes:
The reflexes listed above are temporary. Find out the average age of disappearance for each of them.

3 Posture and locomotion:
If possible, observe babies at various ages between birth and 1 year (for example, at a nursery) and identify the developmental stages shown in Figure 1.14.

A few babies do not crawl (Figure 1.14). Find out through observation and talking to parents how else babies may move from place to place before they can walk.

What safety precautions should be taken in preparation for the baby becoming mobile?

4 Tracking, reaching for and manipulating objects:
Observe babies at various ages between birth and 1 year and identify the developmental stages illustrated in Figure 1.16.

Use brightly coloured bricks to observe the response of two babies of different ages. Write a comparison, and if possible, illustrate your account with photographs.

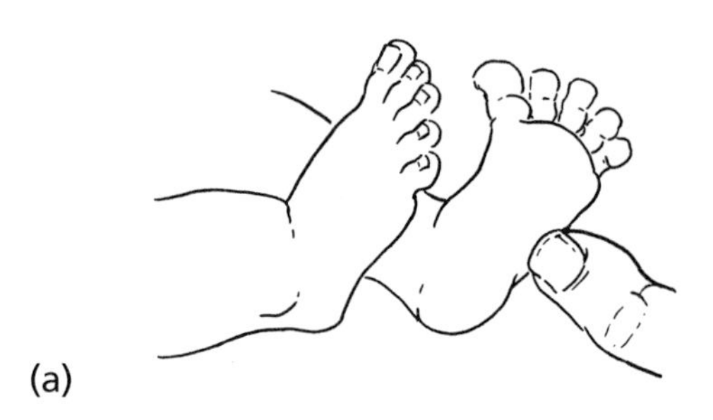

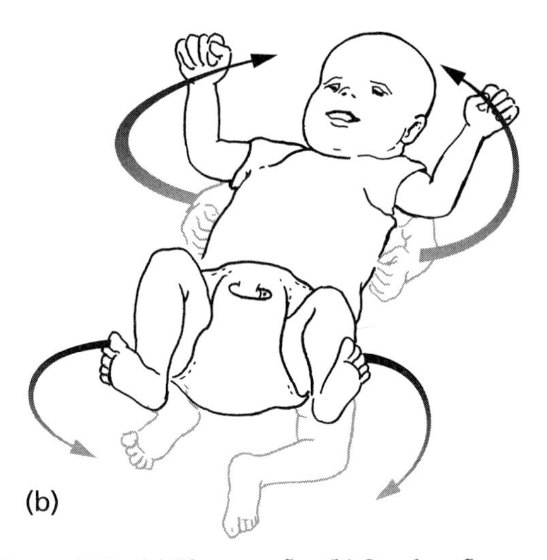

Figure 1.16 (a) Plantar reflex (b) Startle reflex

TODDLER (1–3 YEARS)

Growth

By the time a child is 2 years old, their weight is generally about four times their birth weight (Figure 1.6).

Developmental milestones

Posture and locomotion

By a child's first birthday, they will usually be 'walking' on their hands and feet like a bear (Figure 1.17), and by 13 months

Figure 1.17 'Walking' on hands and feet

they will be taking their first 'proper' steps. At 15 months, they can 'creep' upstairs and kneel. At 18 months, they can jump with both feet, and by two years they will run. At 3 years of age, a child can pedal a trike.

Manipulative skills

When a child is about a year old, they may be seen to repeatedly drop an object when it is given to them. This is known as **casting**, and it will continue until they are about 18 months old.

Once a baby can grasp an object, they will usually put it in their mouth. At about one year, this **mouthing** stops.

By 15 months, a child can make a simple tower using two cubes; by 18 months, 3 or 4 cubes; by 2 years, 6 or 7 cubes; by 3 years, 9 cubes; and by $3\frac{1}{2}$ years, 10 cubes.

Bladder and bowel control

At 18 months, a child will generally be largely dry by day, although complete bladder and bowel control may not be gained until the child is about 5 years old.

activity

1 Posture and locomotion:
A parent will often remember the age at which their child took its first steps. Carry out a survey and plot a graph to show the variation in the ages at which children start walking.
What safety precautions should be taken in preparation for the child standing and walking?
2 Manipulative skills:
Why do babies of less than a year old 'mouth' objects?
From your observations of children (for example, in a nursery), at what age

do children have the ability to do the following:

- take off shoes
- throw a ball
- turn a door knob
- turn the pages of a book?

3 Bladder and bowel control:

What advice are carers given to encourage children to gain bladder and bowel control?

Carry out a survey to find out whether there is a difference in the ages at which boys and girls gain bladder control.

PRE-SCHOOL CHILD (3–5 YEARS)

Growth

Figure 1.18 shows the growth of this age group. The growth rate is constant and slower than the growth of 0–1 year olds.

Developmental milestones

Posture and locomotion

A child will now be becoming more confident in their movements. For example, at 3 years old a child will usually be able to walk downstairs, taking one step at a time.

Manipulative skills

The child will show increasing dexterity. They will be able to draw recognisable pictures and learn to write their name. They will be able to make models with building blocks. With practice, they will also be able to catch a ball.

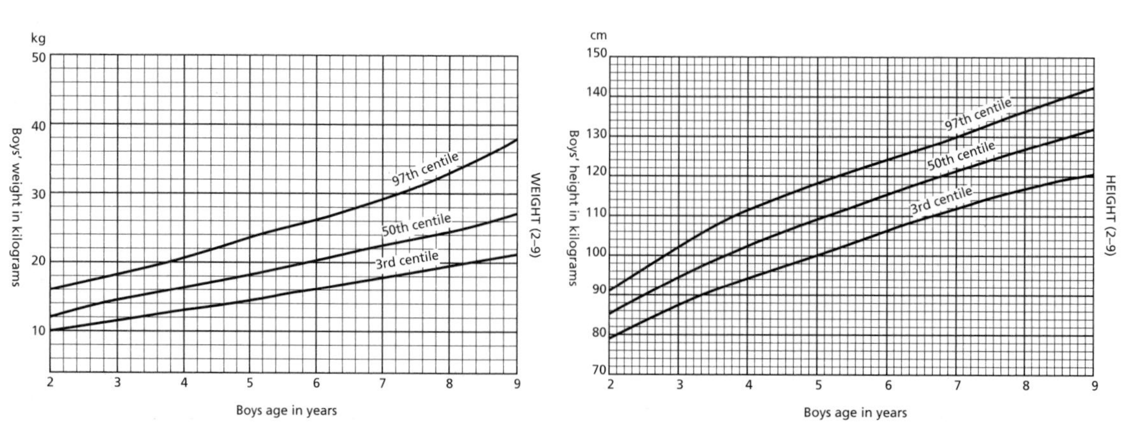

Figure 1.18 Charts showing (a) weights of boys (2–9 years) (b) Heights of boys (2–9 years)

activity

1 What safety precautions will a carer need to consider with a child in the 3–5 age group?
2 Examples are given above of the child becoming increasingly confident in their movements and manipulative skills. Can you give further examples from your observations of children in this age group?

Middle childhood (6 years to adolescence)

Growth

Rapid growth continues throughout this period (Figure 1.18). The skull and brain have usually reached approximately adult size by the time a child is 5, but facial appearance alters as the upper and lower jaw grow rapidly, and the milk teeth are replaced by permanent teeth.

Developmental milestones

As the central nervous system continues to develop, this leads to increased ability to perform complex tasks requiring a high degree of motor skill. For example, children may now become proficient at playing a musical instrument, riding a bike, swimming or gymnastics.

activity

1 Draw a diagram of the milk teeth, and indicate in which order they are generally lost and replaced by permanent teeth.
2 From your observations of this age group, give further examples of activities children may be involved in which require a high degree of motor skill.

Adolescence

It is during adolescence that a sudden spurt in both growth and maturity takes place to produce an adult capable of producing and caring for young.

It starts with **puberty**, during which the **secondary sexual characteristics** develop (see Table 1.2). In developed countries, the average age for the start of puberty is about 10 in girls and 12 in boys. The changes are usually complete by the late teens.

The increase in growth rate in adolescence is known as the **second growth spurt**. This differs significantly in males and females (Figure 1.19). In girls it occurs between 11 and 12 years, whereas in boys it is between 13 and 15 years. Because the growth spurt lasts longer in boys, male adults are generally larger than female adults.

Gender	Secondary sexual characteristics
Males	• The voice 'breaks' (becomes deeper) because of enlargement of the cartilage of the larynx • Growth of characteristic body hair patterns (particularly beard, chest, axillary hair) • Muscular and skeletal development, resulting in wide shoulders and narrow hips • Development of the external genitalia and glands of the reproductive tract (production of sperm begins)
Females	• Menstruation begins. Ovulation usually starts about a year later • The fallopian tubes lengthen • The breasts develop • The pelvis becomes broader • The voice pitch drops (although this is less noticeable in females than males) • Growth of characteristic hair patterns (particularly axillary hair)

Table 1.2 Secondary sexual characteristics

An increase in sex-hormone secretion brings about the changes associated with puberty, although the mechanism which triggers this is unknown. **Testosterone**, produced in the testes, controls the development and maintenance of the secondary sexual characteristics in males. **Oestrogens**, secreted by the ovaries, control the development and maintenance of secondary sexual characteristics in females.

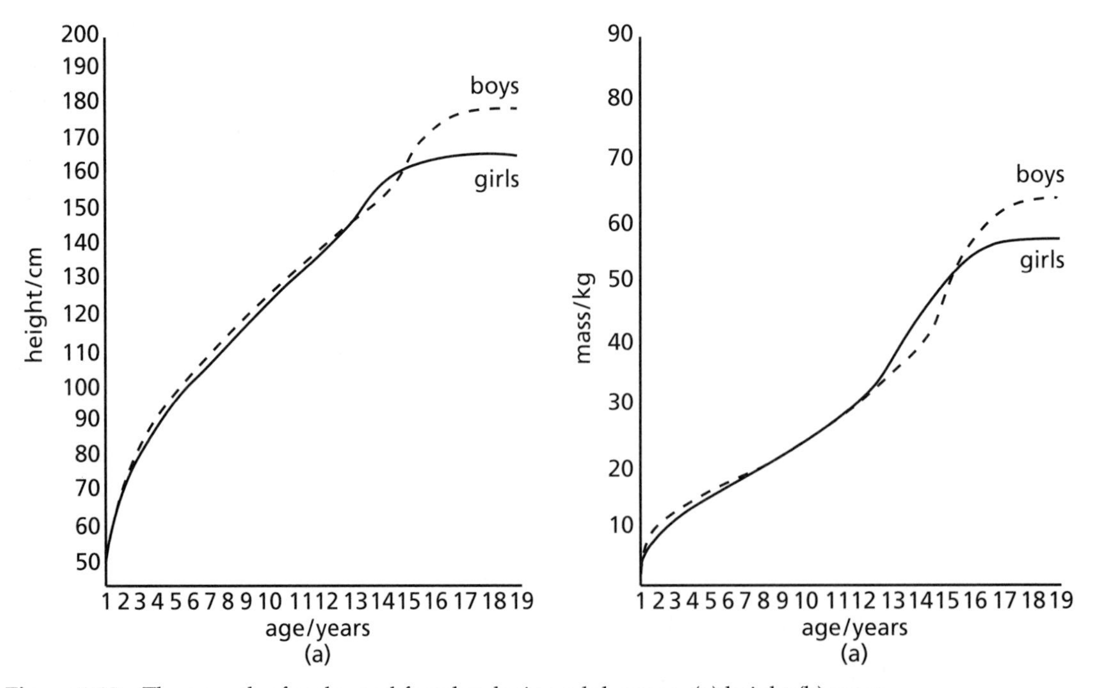

Figure 1.19 The growth of males and females during adolescence (a) height (b) mass

activity

1 Find out about the hormones involved in regulating the production of:

- testosterone
- oestrogens

2 Other hormones are also important in the growth process:

- *somatotrophin* (growth hormone): this is produced throughout life by the **anterior pituitary gland**. More is produced in the growing period. It promotes nitrogen retention and increases protein, fat and carbohydrate metabolism.
- *thyroxine:* this is produced throughout life. It stimulates metabolism, and hence growth.

What conditions are caused by either an excess or a deficit of these hormones? How are these conditions treated?

3 Read the article on p. 26:

What factors affect the age at which a girl has her first period (**menarche**)? What are the benefits mentioned for a delay in the average age of menarche?

ADULTHOOD

Adulthood is the period after adolescence when the body is physically and sexually mature. However, although growth is no longer taking place, cells are still being replaced and physical and physiological changes continue to occur.

For example, the **basal metabolic rate (BMR)** changes throughout adulthood. The BMR is a measure of the rate at which the body breaks down foods, and therefore releases heat, when the person is at rest. The BMR varies, not only with age but also with sex.

At the age of 5, the BMR is around 220 kJ $m^{-2} h^{-1}$ (kilojoules per square metre per hour). After this age, males have a slightly higher BMR than females. There is a fairly steep increase over the years until 20 is reached. At 20, the BMR of females is 150 kJ $m^{-2} h^{-1}$ on average, and 160 kJ $m^{-2} h^{-1}$ for males. Then there is a steady decrease with age. The reasons for this are:

- The proportion of energy used to build and maintain tissue declines with age
- The amount of heat lost decreases as the surface area : volume ratio decreases from birth to adulthood
- The amount of brown fat (metabolically more active than ordinary fat – see the 'Infancy' section on page 11 above) decreases with age

Because the BMR is decreasing, slightly less food will be required. A 'middle-age spread' will result unless the necessary reduction is made!

activity

Find out how a person's BMR can be measured.

Good news girls: the heat is off

The average age of menarche (first period) fell from 16.5 in 1840 to 12.8 last year. But the downward curve, attributed to better health and environmental conditions, is now being reversed, according to research. Declining health and economic conditions are alleged to be responsible.

But the reversed trend may actually be good news – both for the girls of today and the children of tomorrow. Obstetrician Margaret Rees, of The John Radcliffe Hospital, Oxford, says in *The Lancet* medical journal: 'An ever-increasing reproductive span is a daunting prospect, since the age of menopause has not similarly altered, and early menarche is associated with a higher risk of breast cancer.'

Age of menarche is affected by genetic factors, social conditions, general health, nutrition and some types of exercise – such as athletics, gymnastics and ballet. A year of intense pre-menarcheal training can delay a girl's first period by up to five months.

The potential benefits are not restricted to reduced cancer risk. Spontaneous abortions and complications of pregnancy in developed countries are twice as high among girls aged under 15, as among those aged 20 to 24 years. Babies born to American mothers under 15 are more than twice as likely to be of 'low birth weight' than those born to mothers aged 25 to 29.

Marquisa Lavelle, a physical anthropologist at the University of Rhode Island, may have discovered why. Examining pelvic X-rays from healthy girls, Lavelle found that their pelvic inlets – the bony opening of the birth canal – did not reach adult size until the girls reached 17, four or five years after menarche. The implication was as unexpected as it was profound: the adolescent growth spurt does not affect pelvis size . . .

But why should a trait that can impede childbirth in teenage girls have evolved at all? Writing in *New Scientist*, Bogin says that the answer may lie with the need to learn social skills. He says: 'A mother-to-be must acquire information about pregnancy and experience in adult socio-sexual relations and child care. This is where adolescence comes into play.'

His intriguing theory is that the dramatic physical changes of adolescence are designed to advertise sexual and social maturation. This encourages adults to draw adolescent girls into their social circles. They then become acquainted with male–female bonding and 'aunt-like' caring for children.

(The Guardian, 4 January 1994)

The **menopause** occurs in women, usually between the ages of 45 and 55. The woman no longer ovulates and therefore can no longer become pregnant. As a result of the drop in hormone levels of **progesterone** and **oestrogens**:

- the ovaries, uterus and cervix shrink
- the Fallopian tube shortens
- the walls of the vagina lose elasticity
- mucus production decreases and becomes alkaline

From their 40s onwards, men can still play a reproductive role, but certain changes occur in their reproductive system:

- Sperm production takes longer
- Sexual arousal takes longer
- Erections are less frequent and do not last as long
- Ejaculations are less powerful and less frequent

The onset of all changes in the male and female reproductive system is gradual and can be accommodated as long as psychological factors do not interfere.

Research the causes, signs and possible symptoms of the menopause. Use the following list as a guide:

- **climacteric** (define this)
- possible emotional effects on the woman and her family
- hormone replacement therapy (HRT)

Old age

The ageing process begins in adulthood (see above). After the age of 30, the efficiency of our systems declines by nearly 1% a year, and the probability of dying doubles every 7 years.

The skeletal system

- Bones become lighter and more brittle, a process known as **osteoporosis**. This means that bones are more likely to break if there is a sudden stress, or to deform if there is a continuous slight stress. Even turning over in bed may cause enough stress to break affected bones. Osteoporosis affects one in four women and far fewer men. The bones most commonly affected are those of the wrist and lower arm, the vertebrae and the hips.

  Throughout life, bone is being built and lost. Gradually, the process of bone loss becomes faster than the process of bone production. Between the age of 40 and death, men lose 20% of the protein and mineral material that makes up their bones, while women lose 35%.

  There are practical ways in which the likelihood of osteoporosis can be reduced:

  - Keep your diet rich in calcium (whatever your age!)
  - Adults, especially those over 50, should keep active
  - Hormone replacement therapy may be an option for post-menopausal women
- The discs of **cartilage** between the spinal vertebrae become thinner and harder, leading to loss of height and sometimes hunching of the back
- The **ligaments** lose elasticity, and the **articular cartilage** (which covers the ends of bones at joints to allow smooth movements) becomes less efficient. This leads to stiffening of the joints

The muscular system

Muscle fibres are replaced with connective tissue, and so become weaker and less flexible.

The skin

The **collagen** fibres in the skin become shorter, which means the skin becomes less elastic and therefore wrinkles. The **epidermis** (the thin outer layer of the skin) becomes thinner, which may make the skin appear 'papery', and abnormal **pigmentation** may develop.

The senses

Generally, the senses become less accurate as we get older.

- The lens of the eye loses elasticity. The eyes tend to become longsighted and focusing is difficult. The 'arcus senilis', an opaque ring at the outer edge of the iris, is of no significance
- Hearing may be impaired, particularly for high-pitched sounds. The most common cause of hearing loss in the elderly is wax in the ear
- Touch may become less sensitive. The receptors in the skin deteriorate and the skin becomes less elastic. These receptors are sensitive to pain, pressure and temperature and provide a measure of safety enabling a rapid response to avoid things which are too hot or cold
- There is a marked reduction in the number of taste buds in the elderly, and the sense of smell also deteriorates

The endocrine system

Many of the body's metabolic functions are regulated by the production of **thyroxine** in the thyroid gland. In the elderly person:

- less thyroxine is produced, causing the metabolic rate to slow down, resulting in less energy and stamina
- temperature control is also partly governed by thyroxine, which could account for an increasing ability to deal with temperature changes in old age

The cardiovascular system

- The heart becomes less efficient at pumping blood around the body. As a result, less blood flows through the kidneys and **filtration** is not as efficient
- The tissue walls of the blood vessels lose elasticity and become rigid. Blood flow is impaired by this rigidity and by the build-up of fatty deposits on the vessel walls

The respiratory system

- The muscles of the diaphragm become weaker, resulting in shallower breathing
- The walls of the **alveoli** lose elasticity and thicken, affecting gaseous exchange in the lungs
- Certain disorders, e.g. bronchitis, may also affect the ability to inhale effectively

The digestive system

- The muscles of the alimentary canal become weaker, which causes the digestive process to be less efficient
- Peristalsis slows down, which may cause constipation
- The breaking-down of food into small particles is less efficient, and as a result fewer valuable nutrients are absorbed

Despite the degenerative physical changes

described above, it is important that the ageing process be approached with a positive attitude. Improved health care in developed countries has increased life expectancy and the quality of life in recent years. Support and practical help should be given to encourage elders to realise their self-potential, and they should be given the opportunity, wherever possible, to make contributions which utilise their wealth of experience.

activity

1. Read pages 148–150 in Thomson and Manuel (1996) *Further Studies for Health*. This will give you information on **degenerative diseases** such as Alzheimer's.
2. Look for advertisements for 'anti-ageing' skin creams. Find out how these work and how effective they are.
3. Find out what you can about what is known of the causes of ageing.
4. What evidence is there of **ageism** in the workplace, and what steps are being taken to prevent it?
5. Discuss examples of positive and negative depictions of the elderly in the media.
6. Read the newspaper article on p. 30.

   Find out the average age attained by:

   - males
   - females
7. List the potential hazards resulting from:

   - a raised pain threshold
   - failing eyesight and hearing
   - a reduced sense of smell and taste
   - weakening bones
   - wasting of the muscles

Male brains lose battle of sexes

Professor explains why men fail the test of time

As men age they lose brain tissue three times as fast as women, says Ruben Gur, a psychologist at the University of Pennsylvania Medical Centre . . .

Men lost brain tissue but metabolised glucose more vigorously – in effect, burned fuel faster – in an attempt apparently to sustain their mental abilities. Women's brain activity slowed gradually. 'That suggests women have a sort of mechanism we are not even beginning to understand, whereby they are able to reduce the rate of activity proportionate to their loss of tissue. Males seem to be continuing to burn their cells at the rate they used to when they had all their marbles,' he said . . .

The difference in brain activity might be part of the reason why women tend to survive for at least a decade longer than men. 'It is quite well understood that men are more dispensable as they grow older, and maybe this is a built-in mechanism to make sure unneeded parents aren't staying around.'

(The Guardian, 12 February 1996)

CHAPTER 2

Factors Affecting Physical Development

Various factors affect growth and development. From pre-conception to birth, these include diet, the use of drugs, diseases suffered by the mother, and premature birth.

Throughout childhood, the factors affecting growth and development include genetics; economic factors such as diet and housing; social factors such as education, group membership, and culture; environmental factors such as water pollution, air pollution, and noise pollution; and disease and illness.

Factors affecting physical development from pre-conception to birth

The baby is virtually fully formed by 12 weeks after conception (see Chapter 1). It is, therefore, during this time of rapid development that the foetus can be most severely damaged. By the 16th week, the placenta is fully formed and functioning, and harm to the baby is much less likely.

Because a woman will probably not know that she is pregnant for many of the first crucial weeks of development, it is important that she prepare in advance for pregnancy.

DIET

Because the baby is, in effect, a parasite, it is very efficient at taking the nutrients it requires from the mother. It is very unlikely, therefore, that the amount of food the mother consumes will have any influence on the birth weight of the baby. Even if the mother's diet is lacking in some way, this is more likely to have an adverse effect on her than on her baby. For example, if the mother's diet lacks iron, the mother will become severely anaemic, but the baby will not. If her diet lacks calcium, the baby's bones will develop normally, but this will deplete the calcium reserves in the mother's bones, leaving them softer, or even bent.

A woman should gain only 9–13 kg during the whole of her pregnancy. This means that while pregnant it is not necessary for her to eat more than usual. What is important is that she take care to eat a normal balanced diet. The components of a balanced diet are shown in Figure 2.1. A balanced meal consists of about one part protein, one part fat and four or five parts carbohydrate. It should include mineral- and vitamin-rich foods.

Normally, 50–60% of **protein** would come

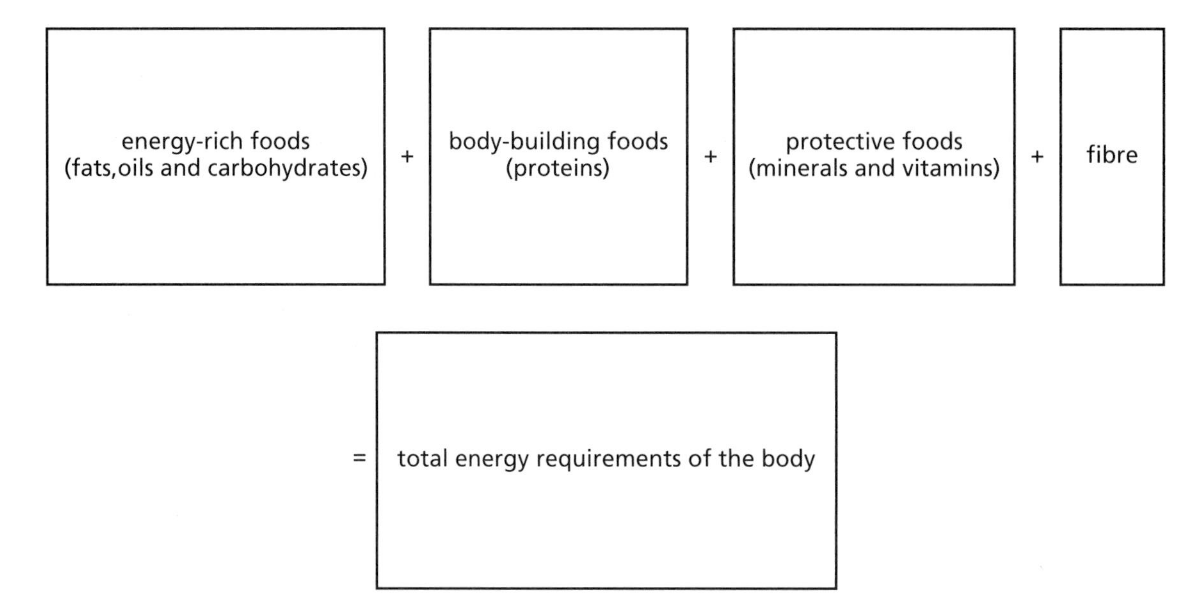

Figure 2.1 The components of a healthy diet

from meat, and the rest from vegetable sources. In vegetarian diets, a wide range of vegetables should be eaten to ensure that all essential amino acids are included.

A small amount of **fat** is required to supply the fat-soluble vitamins A, D and E and essential fatty acids. Fat can supply energy needs, but too much fat in the diet can cause atherosclerosis of the blood vessels.

Carbohydrates are the primary source of energy.

It is important for pregnant women to have adequate **fibre** in their diet. The increased levels of **progesterone** cause relaxation of the intestine, which can lead to constipation. Fibre, which consists of cellulose that is found in plant foods, cannot be broken down in the intestinal tract since humans do not possess the enzymes that carry out the breakdown. Because it remains undigested, it adds bulk to the contents of the colon and helps to retain water which softens the faeces. Both of these effects help to prevent constipation.

Vitamins are essential in small amounts in the diet, for the baby's growth as well as for the mother's health.

- *Vitamin A.* Keeps skin and bones healthy, helps prevent infection of the nose and throat, and is necessary for vision in dim light. Lack of Vitamin A causes poor night vision and increases the chances of infection of the nose and throat. Vitamin A is found in carrots, fish liver oils and green vegetables. Recent research has shown that high levels of Vitamin A could be harmful to the foetus in the early months of pregnancy. For this reason, women are now advised to avoid liver, which has very high levels of this vitamin
- *Vitamin B1.* Helps the body obtain energy from food. Lack of it reduces growth and causes **beri-beri**, when the limbs become paralysed. Vitamin B1 is found in yeast, wholemeal bread, nuts, peas and beans
- *Vitamin B2.* Enables the body to obtain energy from food. Lack of it causes stunted growth, cracks in the skin around the mouth, an inflamed tongue, and damage to the cornea of the eye. Vitamin B2 is found in green vegetables, cheese, yeast, eggs, milk and liver

- *Vitamin B12.* Enables the body to form protein and fat and to store carbohydrate. Lack of it causes **pernicious anaemia**, a disease in which haemoglobin is not produced for red blood cells. This vitamin is found in liver, meat, eggs, milk and fish
- *Vitamin C.* Helps to heal wounds and is needed for healthy gums and teeth. A lack of it causes **scurvy**, a disease where gums become soft and the teeth loose, and wounds fail to heal properly. Vitamin C is found in oranges, lemons, blackcurrants, green vegetables, tomatoes and potatoes. It is destroyed by cooking food
- *Vitamin D.* Enables the body to absorb calcium and phosphorus for bone building. It is found in liver, butter, cheese, eggs and fish and formed by the action of ultraviolet light on the skin
- *Vitamin K.* Needed for blood to clot in wounds. Lack of it causes **haemorrhage** when the skin is broken. It is found in cabbage and cereals, and is made by bacteria in the digestive system
- *Folic acid.* Recently, it has been discovered that folic acid plays a crucial part in the healthy development of the foetus. Research has shown that an inadequate intake of folic acid makes it more likely that a woman will have a baby with **neural tube defects** (**NTDs**). These defects are rare, but can be very serious. NTDs affect the normal development of the spine and brain in the foetus. The two most common forms are **spina bifida** and **anencephaly**.

In spina bifida, one or more of the vertebrae of the backbone fail to form. As a result, the spinal cord may be damaged. Sometimes the condition is mild, but in its severest form it can cause serious paralysis and a wide range of physical disabilities.

Anencephaly means that most of the brain and skull have failed to develop. Babies with this condition are usually stillborn or die shortly after birth.

Since 1992, the UK Department of Health has advised women who are planning a pregnancy, and those who are less than 12 weeks into their pregnancy, to increase their levels of folic acid by:

- eating plenty of foods that naturally contain folic acid (e.g. green vegetables, beans and pulses, milk and yogurt, yeast or malt extracts)
- choosing foods that have folic acid added to them (e.g. some breads, breakfast cereals and milk drinks)
- taking a daily supplement in the form of a 400 µg folic acid tablet.

activity

Look at the labelling on foods with added folic acid, and calculate how much you would need to consume daily to obtain the recommended 400 µg of folic acid.

Fifteen **minerals** are needed in the diet. Most of these are supplied by meat, eggs, milk, vegetables and fruit.

The following are some of these minerals:

	Daily requirement (mg)
Sodium chloride	5–10
Potassium	2
Magnesium	0.3
Phosphorus	1.5
Calcium	0.8
Iron	0.01
Iodine	0.00003

In the past, **iron** and **vitamin tablets** were routinely given to pregnant women. Nowadays, this depends on the results of their blood tests. If **haemoglobin** is low, iron tablets will be prescribed.

activity

1 What other minerals are required in the diet in addition to those listed in the text?

2 Find out the functions of each of these minerals in the mother's body and that of the developing foetus.

Because of the risk of the disease **listeria**, women are advised *not* to eat or drink unpasteurised milk or milk products, and because of the risk of **salmonella**, women are advised *not* to eat soft or uncooked egg yolks.

activity

1 Carry out an investigation based on one of the following topics:
   - food cravings during pregnancy
   - using diet to control sickness in pregnancy

2 If you have access to a computer diet programme, record your diet for a week and check if it is balanced.

DRUGS

Most drugs taken by the mother will diffuse across the placenta to the foetal circulation. Some of these may cause harm, particularly during the 12 weeks after conception. Drugs which adversely affect the development of the foetus are known as **teratogenic**. It is important, therefore, that the mother takes the correct dose of any prescribed medicines, and checks carefully whether non-prescribed drugs she may require are safe to be taken during pregnancy. Examples of the latter include **aspirin** and **alkali** for indigestion.

In some cases, drugs may be used to treat the foetus – for example, **antibiotics**, which are administered to the mother and which rapidly cross the placental barrier.

Women who smoke during pregnancy are more likely to produce a premature or stillborn baby. There is also evidence that smoking in pregnancy causes mental and physical retardation later in the child's life. Even 'passive smoking' can harm the baby's development, so women planning a pregnancy should not only give up smoking but also encourage their partner to do likewise.

Alcohol is teratogenic if taken in excess. Babies born to mothers who drank large amounts of alcohol throughout the pregnancy may be born with **foetal alcohol syndrome**. These children have characteristic facial deformities, stunted growth and mental retardation. More moderate drinking may increase the risk of miscarriage, but many women continue to drink small amounts of alcohol throughout their pregnancy with no ill effects.

Illegal drugs, such as **LSD**, are teratogenic and may cause the foetus to grow more slowly. Babies born to **heroin** addicts are addicted themselves and suffer withdrawal symptoms. They are likely to be underweight and may even die. If necessary, women should seek professional help to enable them to stop taking these drugs before conception.

— activity —

1 Find information on the **Thalidomide** tragedy and how this contributed to the tightening up of regulations on the testing of the effect of drugs on the unborn baby.
2 Some women report that as soon as they become pregnant, they develop an aversion to harmful substances such as **caffeine**, **nicotine** or alcohol. Conduct a survey to find out how common this is and how long the aversion lasts for.
3 Look at Figure 2.2, and then design your own advertisement to encourage pregnant women to give up smoking. What practical advice would you give to enable them to do this?

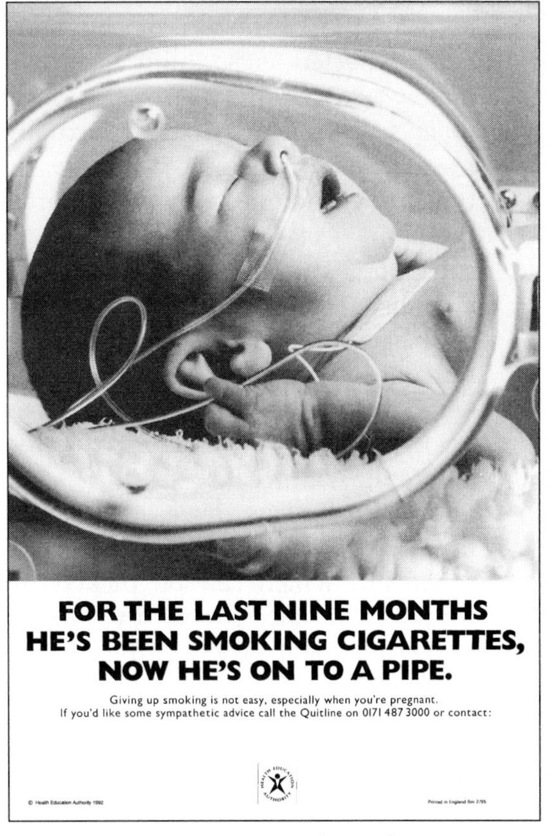

Figure 2.2 A recent anti-smoking advertisement aimed at pregnant women

Diseases

The foetus can be affected by infections in two ways:

1 by diseases of the mother which in some way affect the development of the baby. (For example, raised blood pressure or kidney disease retards the growth of the placenta, which leads to a small baby.)
2 by viruses or small bacteria crossing the

placenta from the mother to the foetus. For example:

- *rubella (German measles).* This is caused by a **virus** (see page 89 below). The symptoms are mild, and once a person has the disease they will not have it again. Young girls are routinely inoculated against the disease because of the danger it poses to the unborn baby if the mother becomes infected in the first 12 weeks of her pregnancy. Rubella can cause congenital defects such as deafness, blindness or heart disease. If a pregnant woman does have the disease, she will be offered a termination because the likelihood of the baby being affected is so high (approximately 12%)
- *syphilis.* This is a bacterial sexually transmitted disease. It can only be transmitted across the placenta after the 20th week of pregnancy. It will cause the baby to develop congenital syphilis, or can even lead to the death of the foetus. If the woman is diagnosed as having the disease at the beginning of the pregnancy (see below), it can be satisfactorily treated before the 20th week
- *toxoplasmosis.* This disease is caused by a **protozoan** (a single-celled organism) which can be picked up from cats' faeces or by eating uncooked meat. The symptoms are mild, but if a pregnant woman has the infection during the first 12 weeks of her pregnancy, it may pass to the foetus and cause blindness or mental retardation in the newborn baby

Premature birth

A **premature birth** is one that takes place before 37 weeks of complete **gestation**. Since the date of conception is often not precisely known, a premature baby was previously defined as one weighing less than 2.5 kg.

The main problem facing premature babies is the immaturity of the lungs. Until they develop sufficiently to be coated with **surfactant** (see the 'Development of the foetus' section, weeks 21–25, on page 12 above), the lungs will collapse when the baby breathes out. Recently, it has become possible to inject surfactant into the lungs, which improves a baby's chance of survival considerably.

Most premature babies progress normally, and after a few weeks there will be no differences between a premature and a full-term baby. However, during developmental tests (see pages 66–70 below), allowances must be made for the pre-term baby. For example, when it is 6 months old, a baby born 2 months early should be compared to a baby of 4 months old. **Immunisations** (see below) should be given according to their actual age from birth.

activity

1 There have been such improvements in neonatal intensive-care units that a few babies born below the legal abortion limit of 24 weeks are now surviving. However, because of the cost of looking after these babies, and the likelihood that they will not survive or may suffer brain damage, some people have sug-

gested that only babies born after 25 weeks should be treated. Discuss this dilemma.

2 If possible, talk to a professional from your local neonatal intensive-care unit and find out about the problems faced in caring for premature babies, and the ways in which these problems may be overcome.

3 Poor pre-natal care (for example, if the mother continues to smoke) and the mother's age being below 16 or above 35 increase the risk of a premature delivery. Can you find examples of other causes of premature labour, and how this may be prevented?

Factors affecting physical development throughout childhood

There are very many factors which affect growth and development. Because these factors act in combination, it is often difficult to determine the actual impact of any one factor.

GENETICS

(NB: for a more detailed consideration of this topic, refer to Carter 1992 and Gregory 1995 – see the 'References and resources' section at the end of Part I of this book.)

The genes an individual inherits from their parents will obviously affect that person's growth and development. For example, Figure 2.3 shows how a person's height can be predicted from the heights of the parents.

All the cells of the body, except for the eggs and sperm (**gametes**), contain 23 pairs of **chromosomes**. One of each pair has come from the father, and one from the mother. (See the information on 'Meiosis' on page 40 below). The chromosomes contain **deoxyribonucleic acid (DNA)** which codes for all the **polypeptides** (sub-units of proteins) the body makes. The length of DNA which codes for one polypeptide is known as a **gene**. All biochemical reactions in the body are catalysed by **enzymes**, which are proteins. In this way, the genes control the body's metabolism and, therefore, growth and development. Figure 2.5 summarises this information.

A person's **genotype** refers to the genes they possess. The term **phenotype** describes the physical characteristics determined by the genes.

Each characteristic is determined by one or more pairs of genes; one of each pair is on the chromosome inherited from the mother, and one of each pair is on the chromosome inherited from the father (see again the 'Meiosis' information below). Genes exist in alternative forms known as **alleles**. For example, brown and blue are alternative forms (alleles) of the gene for eye colour. One allele is usually **dominant** over the other **recessive** allele.

For example, the ability to roll one's tongue (Figure 2.4) is genetically determined. The 'rolling' allele, R, is dominant over the recessive, 'non-rolling' allele, r. (It is customary to abbreviate the dominant allele to the initial capital letter, and the recessive allele to the corresponding lower-case letter.) A person who cannot roll their tongue will have the alleles rr. A person who *can* roll their tongue will have either the alleles RR or Rr. In the latter case, the dominant, 'rolling' allele masks

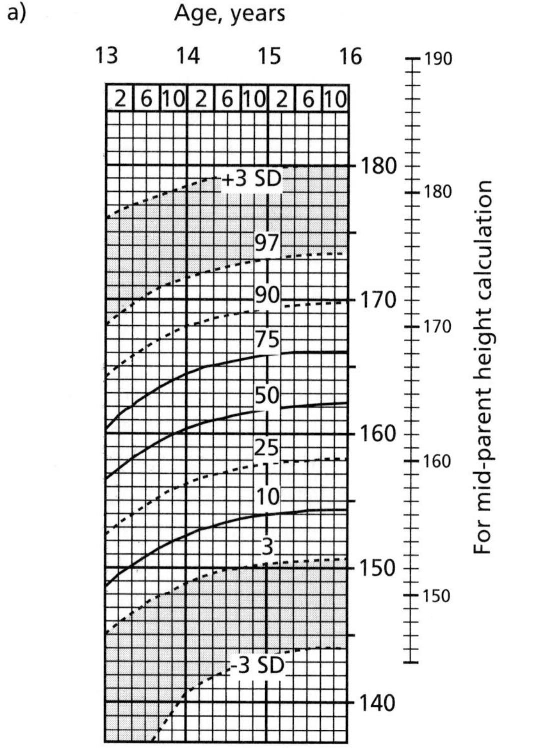

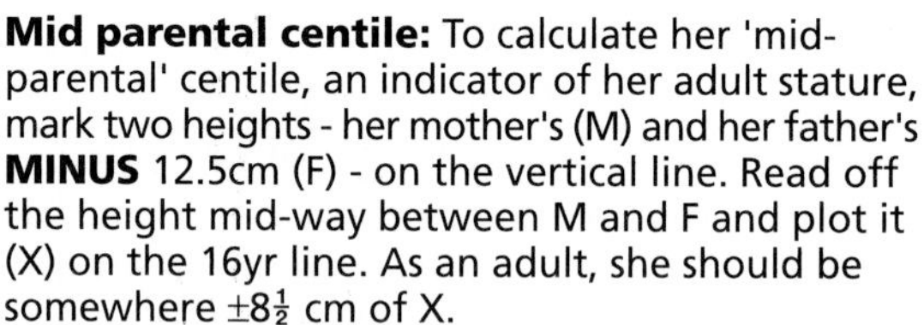

Mid parental centile: To calculate her 'mid-parental' centile, an indicator of her adult stature, mark two heights - her mother's (M) and her father's **MINUS** 12.5cm (F) - on the vertical line. Read off the height mid-way between M and F and plot it (X) on the 16yr line. As an adult, she should be somewhere $\pm 8\frac{1}{2}$ cm of X.

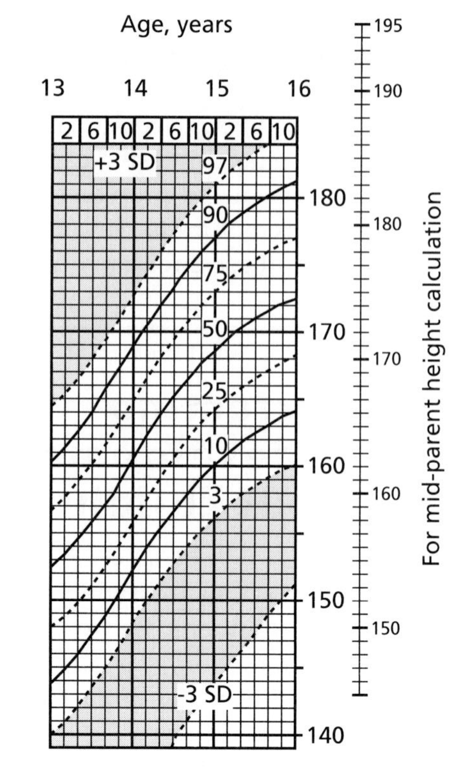

Mid parental centile: To calculate his 'mid-parental' centile, an indicator of his adult stature, mark two heights - his father's (F) and his mother's PLUS 12.5cm (M) - on the vertical line. Read off the height mid-way between F and M and plot it (X) on the 16yr line. As an adult, he should be somewhere $\pm 8\frac{1}{2}$cm of X.

Figure 2.3 Charts to estimate (a) girls' and (b) boys' adult height

the effect of the recessive, 'non-rolling' allele. A person with identical alleles for a characteristic (e.g. RR or rr) is known as **homozygous**, whereas a person with different alleles for a characteristic (e.g. Rr) is known as **heterozygous**. Figure 2.6 illustrates how alleles may be passed to the offspring.

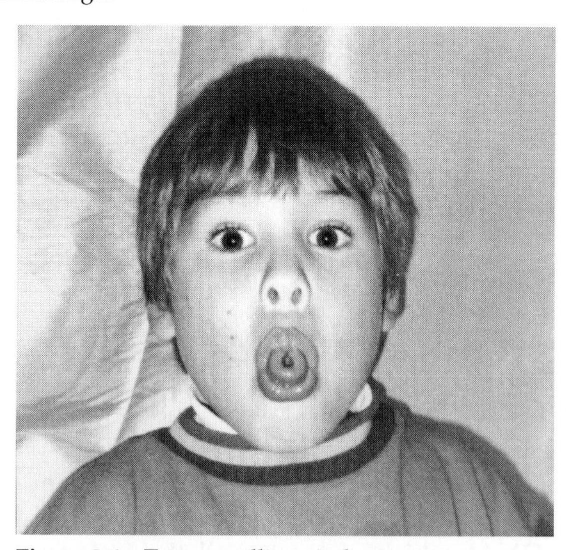

Figure 2.4 Tongue rolling. A characteristic determined by a dominant allele

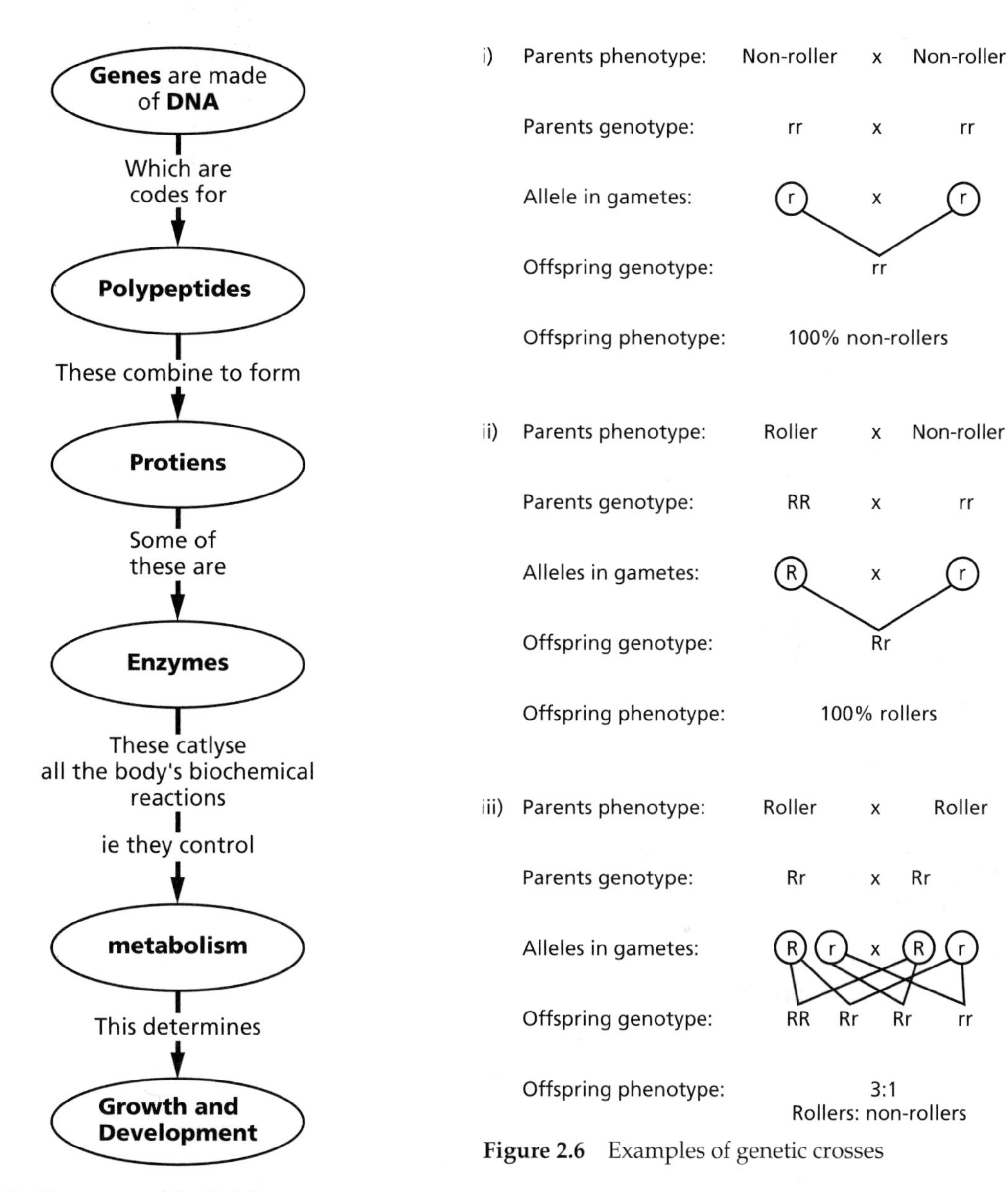

Figure 2.5 Summary of the link between genes and growth and development

Figure 2.6 Examples of genetic crosses

Meiosis and Variation

All gametes (i.e., eggs and sperm) are formed by **meiosis**. Figure 2.7 shows the main stages in this process.

There are two functions of meiosis:

1 to halve the number of chromosomes in the gametes, leading to the restoration of the **diploid** number (46) in the zygote (Figure 2.8).

2 to bring about **variation** (observable differences between individuals). Meiosis does this in the following ways:

- *independent assortment:* Figure 2.7D shows the separation of matching (**homologous**) chromosomes. One chromosome of each pair will have been inherited from the father (paternal) and one from the mother (maternal). When the homologous chromosomes draw apart in **anaphase I**, a mixture of maternal and paternal chromosomes (and therefore genes) will end up in the gametes
- *crossing over (or genetic recombination):* during **prophase I**, a process known as **crossing over** occurs. Homologous chromosomes become joined at a number of points (**chiasmata**). There is then a breakage at these points which leads to the crossing over of genes (Figure 2.9)

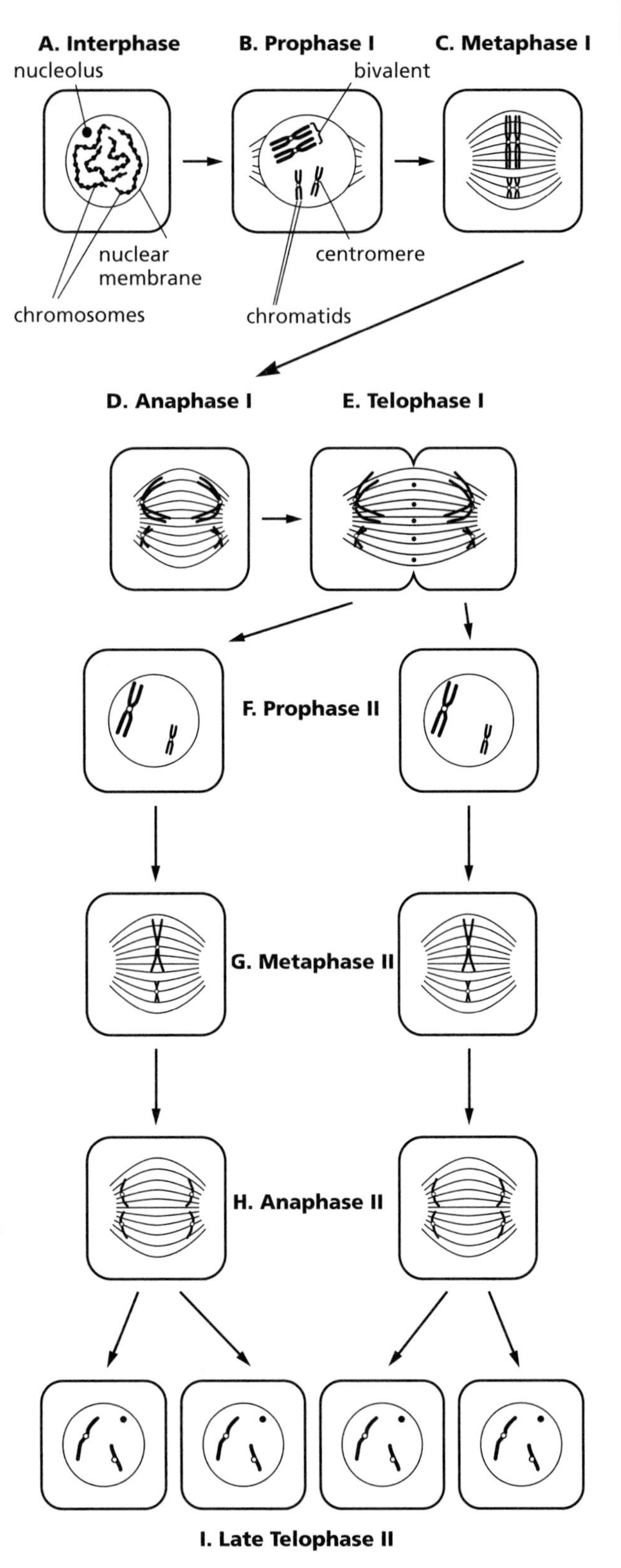

Figure 2.7 The stages of meiosis

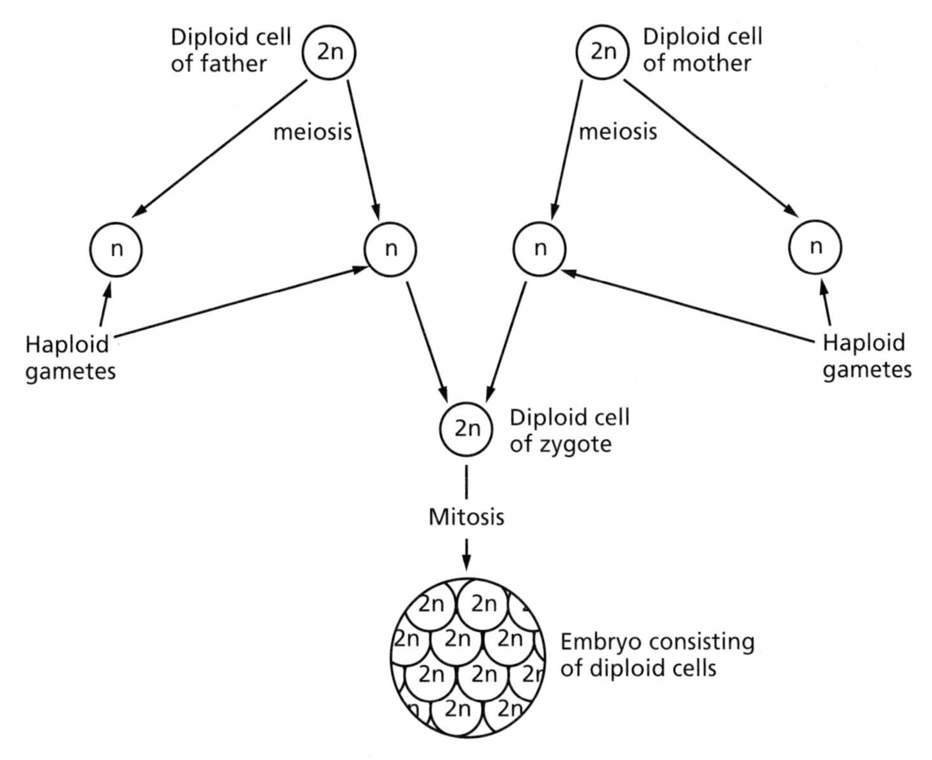

Figure 2.8 Maintenance of the diploid number of chromosomes

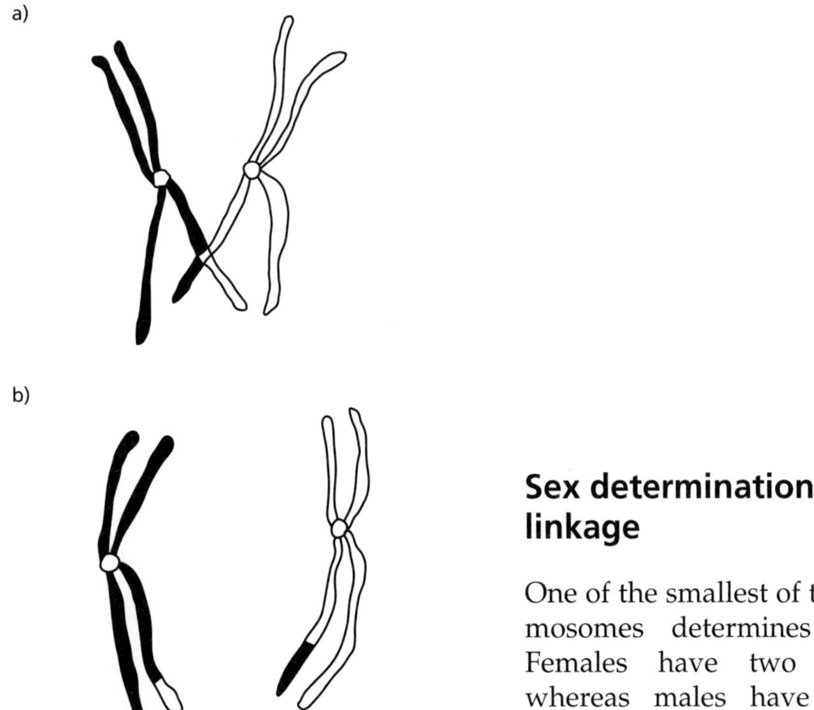

Figure 2.9 Crossing over (a) prophase I (b) anaphase I

Sex determination and sex linkage

One of the smallest of the 23 pairs of chromosomes determines a person's sex. Females have two **X chromosomes**, whereas males have one X and one smaller **Y chromosome**. The genes for certain characteristics are carried on the sex chromosomes (usually the X chromosome because it is longer than the Y chromosome), and we say that these characteristics are **sex-linked**. Examples of human diseases that are determined by sex-linked genes include **Duchene muscular dystrophy (DMD)** and **haemophilia A**. These diseases are more common in males than in females. This is because males only have one X chromosome, and, therefore, only one allele. If they have the harmful recessive allele which causes the disease, it will not be masked by a 'normal' allele. Females who have the disease-causing recessive allele are only likely to be **carriers** and not suffer the disease themselves. This is because on their second chromosome they will carry the dominant 'normal' allele which will mask the effect of the disease-causing allele. These carriers can, of course, pass the harmful allele onto their offspring.

Chromosomal abnormalities

Occasionally, there are 'mistakes' in meiosis which result in the production of gametes with either an alteration in the number of chromosomes, or an alteration in the structure of one or more chromosomes. All the cells of an individual produced from such a gamete will carry the same mistake, or **mutation**, and will be unable to code for the correct proteins.

There are about 5,000 diseases that are caused by mutations. About one child in 30 born in the UK has an inborn error of some kind; and about a third of all hospital admissions involve a genetic disease. Some of the damaged genes descend from mutations that happened generations ago, but others are mistakes in the eggs or sperm of the parents themselves.

Genetic counselling

Genetic counsellers give advice to couples planning to have a child on the probability of their producing a child with a genetic disease. They may use any of the following sources of information:

- If the parents already have an affected child, it is easier for them to predict the likelihood of the next child being affected. For example, if an unaffected couple have a child with cystic fibrosis, there is a one in four chance that their next child will be affected
- **Pedigree analysis** involves the examination of a family tree showing affected members of the family (see Figure 2.10)
- The frequency of the gene in the population as a whole indicates the likely genotype of the spouse
- If the prospective parents are related to each other, they are more likely to have inherited the same gene
- For some genetic diseases, a sample of blood or cheek cells can be tested with a **DNA probe** to test for the presence of the harmful allele. In this way, carriers of the disease can be identified

Genetic counsellers will also give advice to parents prior to screening of the foetus (see the 'amniocentesis' and 'chorionic villus sampling' sections on pages 64–65 below).

Once any risks have been identified, the genetic counseller will discuss the options available to a couple, to enable them to make an informed decision. These options will be influenced by the moral and religious beliefs of the couple and their cultural background. They may include:

- not having children
- using in vitro fertilisation (**test-tube baby**) so that the cells of the embryo can be screened for genetic abnormalities before implantation. With sex-

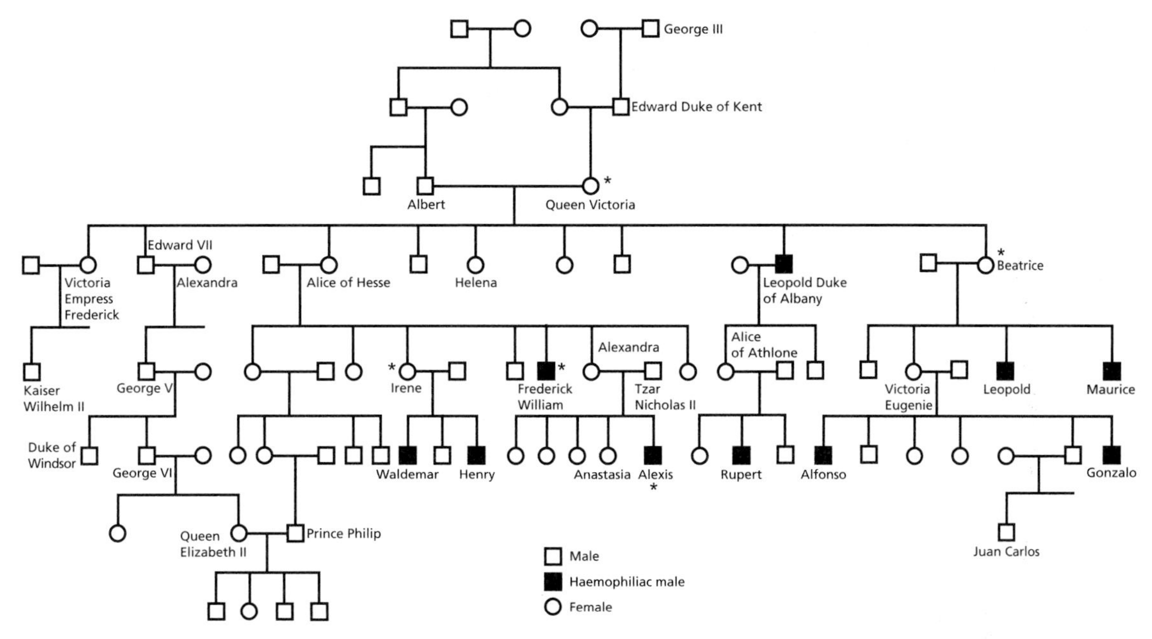

Figure 2.10 Family tree showing the inheritance of haemophilia in the royal family

linked diseases (see pages 40–42 above), a female embryo may be selected for implantation

- using egg, sperm or embryo donation
- terminating the pregnancy if foetal screening shows abnormalities

activity

(See Appendix A for answers to questions 1, 3, 4, 5.)

1 Look at Figure 2.5 and explain the following terms:

- gene
- DNA
- polypeptide
- protein
- enzyme
- metabolism

2 Find an account of **protein synthesis** in an A Level textbook. Use diagrams to show how DNA codes for a polypeptide.

3 Look at Figure 2.6. What would be the possible phenotypes of the offspring from a mother who was a heterozygous tongue-roller, and a father who could not roll his tongue?

4 Draw a diagram similar to Figure 2.6 to show the inheritance of X and Y chromosomes. This will illustrate that there is a 50% chance of a baby being male or female.

5 Look at Figure 2.10 which shows the inheritance of haemophilia in the Royal Family. Work out the genotypes of the marked (*) individuals. (Remember, because the allele is carried on the X chromosome, males only carry one allele, and haemophilia is a recessive condition.)

6 The following diseases are all caused by **gene** or **chromosome abnormalities**.

Select one disease and then find out about the genetic causes; the symptoms; prognosis and treatment:

- Duchenne muscular dystrophy
- haemophilia A
- Turner's syndrome
- Klinefelter's syndrome
- Down's syndrome
- cystic fibrosis
- sickle cell anaemia
- Huntingdon's chorea
- achondroplasia

7 Read through the list of options a genetic counseller may guide a couple through. Discuss the ethical implications of each option.

8 **Gene therapy** is the treatment of a genetic disease by altering a patient's genotype. Although it is technically possible to manipulate genes in the gametes, this is not done because it would mean the inserted genes would be passed down the generations with unknown effects in any offspring. For this reason, genes have only been added to body cells where they will make proteins but will not be passed on to the offspring. This type of gene therapy has been used to treat cystic fibrosis. Find out exactly how this is done and how successful it is.

Discuss the ethical issues involved in manipulating genes in the gametes.

9 To simulate **independent assortment**, join two different coloured beads to make 23 pairs. Put these in a jar. These represent the 23 pairs of homologous chromosomes, one colour representing the maternal chromosomes and the other colour the paternal chromosomes. With your eyes shut, take a pair and split it, putting the single beads in two containers. Repeat this with the remaining 22 pairs. This represents the independent assortment of chromosomes in meiosis.

ECONOMIC FACTORS

There is no official definition of **poverty**, but two that are often used are:

- Income Support level
- 50% of average income after housing costs

Children are more at risk of poverty than the rest of society, and in recent years the number has been increasing. For example, in 1985, there were 1 million children living on Income Support; in 1995, there were 3 million.

Social class is the most widely used indicator of the economic and social circumstances of individuals. Table 2.1 gives the Registrar-General's classification of social class. According to this classification:

Table 2.1 Registrar-General's classification of social class

Social class		Examples of occupations
I	Professional	Lawyer, doctor
II	Intermediate	Teacher, nurse, manager
III(NM)	Skilled non-manual	Typist, shop assistant
III(M)	Skilled manual	Miner, cook, electrician
IV	Semi-skilled manual	Farm worker, packer
V	Unskilled manual	Cleaner, labourer

- men are allocated a social class according to their own occupation
- married women are ascribed the social class of their husband
- children in two-parent families are ascribed the social class of their father
- single women living alone, or with their children, are allocated a social class according to their own occupation

The following list from Blackburn (1991) shows trends in class and child growth, health and development:

- In 1986, babies born to social class IV and V families were 148% more likely to die in the perinatal period than babies born to social class I and II families
- In 1986, babies born to parents in social classes IV and V had a 178% greater chance of dying in the post-neonatal period than babies of social class I and II parents
- Two-thirds of all low birth-weight babies are born to working-class mothers
- The mortality rate for all causes of death tells us that children aged one to five, from social classes IV and V, are twice as likely to die as their counterparts from social classes I and II
- Large-scale longitudinal studies show that children from manual classes suffer more respiratory infections and diseases, ear infections and squints, and are likely to be of shorter stature than their counterparts in non-manual classes

Diet

In June 1991, the National Children's Home charity commissioned a survey on the eating habits of low-income families in the UK. The results suggested that 1 in 5 parents regularly denied themselves food through lack of money, and 1 in 10 children under the age of 5 went without enough to eat at least once a month. The report claimed to have found a direct relationship between those on the lowest income and those with the poorest diet.

It is, therefore, likely that nutrition is one of the most important factors in the trends in class and child health, growth and development described above. In 1750, the average young male height was about 160 cm, and in 1980 it was 176 cm. It is thought that increased income leading to an improved diet is the main reason for this increase in height, and that inequalities in income and diet are responsible for variations in height between children from different social classes. In richer countries than the UK, adults are taller on average. For example, in the Netherlands, young males average over 180 cm.

Because diet affects immunity, and children on poor diets may not have adequate vitamins and minerals, children with an inadequate diet are more susceptible to disease.

activity

1 Table 2.1 gives a classification of social class based on a hierarchy that reflects the traditional status of male occupations. Why does this not accurately reflect the status of children, and can you suggest improvements? (See Appendix A for answers.)
2 There are an increasing number of co-operative organisations bringing cheap fresh food and vegetables into areas where there is no access to good shops. Find out if there is such a scheme in your locality and if there is how it is funded. If there is no such scheme, evaluate the necessity for one and list the practicalities to be considered when setting it up.
3 Read the article below.
   - Use a table of calorific values of foods and go around your local supermarket to find healthy foods that cost no more than 7p for 100 calories
   - In a group in your school or college, try to design a healthy diet to feed an

adult and two children on the amount of money they would have if they were on Income Support

4 The World Health Organisation estimates that almost a third of the world's children are undernourished. Find out why this should be when food supplies are sufficient to meet the world's aggregate minimum requirements.

Under-fives get too much salt and sugar

Parents are feeding pre-school children twice the recommended levels of sugar and salt, according to the biggest study of its kind for nearly 30 years.

Chocolate bars, sweet drinks and biscuits, and salty crisps were the biggest contributors to the imbalance in the diets of 1,700 children aged between 1½ and 4½ years monitored over a four-day period.

Yet most appeared to be thriving and were taller and heavier than when the Government last conducted a similar exercise in 1967 . . .

But the study reveals that children raised by single parents, who are more likely to be poor, receive significantly less vitamin C and carotene – found mainly in fruit and vegetables – than children raised by married or cohabiting couples. Single parents were also likely to feed their children more fat, often the cheapest source of energy.

Parents on income support must find food for their children costing no more than 7p on average for 100 calories just to make sure they don't lose weight, according to Suzi Leather, a member of the low income panel of the Department of Health's Nutritional Task Force.

On this basis custard cream biscuits cost 2p, frozen chips 4p, and chocolate bars 8p. But oranges cost 30p, frozen cod fillet 95p and celery £1.03.

The study also revealed that children given vitamin and mineral supplements are least likely to need them because they already receive wholesome foods . . .

A surprising finding is that most pre-school children eat less fat (36 per cent of total calories) than adults (41 per cent).

But Dr Metters said the trend was for children to increase fat intake when they were old enough to buy crisps and other take-away food from shops.

National Diet and Nutrition Survey: children aged 1½ to 4½ years. Vol 1, Diet and nutrition; Vol 2, Dental survey.

(The Guardian, 23 March 1995)

Housing

People who live in unhealthy homes usually suffer from other forms of social and economic disadvantage, so it becomes difficult to disentangle the effect of housing conditions on health from other factors. Moreover, there may be links between housing conditions and health not necessarily connected to poverty. For example, it has been suggested that the trend towards centrally heated homes with fitted carpets has increased the likelihood of allergies resulting from 'dust mites'.

Nevertheless, the strong relationship between health and housing can be related to four aspects of that housing:

1 the geographical location – where people live
2 patterns of tenure
3 the poor layout and design of homes
4 the costs of fuel and other essential services.

1 *The geographical location – where people live.* Low-income families are much more likely to be housed in neighbourhoods that are unattractive, densely populated, with poorly maintained houses and few communal areas and amenities. This gives rise to a number of disadvantages for children:
   - Children living in these areas are susceptible to the effects of pollution, such as lead poisoning (see below)
   - Because of the difficulties of supervising children in these environmentally poor areas, child accident rates are higher. The Child Accident Prevention Trust estimates that 250,000 childhood accidents a year can be attributed to bad housing design
   - If children do not have access to a garden or play area, their development may be affected

2 *Patterns of tenure.* Rented accommodation is particularly likely to be damp. This is a serious health hazard as spores from fungi lead to a high frequency of respiratory diseases. If children are adversely affected, their progress and development at school may be impeded by frequent absences.

3 *Poor layout and design of homes.* Children who live in flats have higher incidences of respiratory infections than children who live in houses, leading to the problems mentioned above.

4 *The costs of fuel and other essential services.* If people fail to pay for essential services, they may be disconnected. As the article 'Slum diseases rise as water supply is cut' (page 49), shows, this may have serious health implications.

Homelessness may be considered under this heading. Families living in hotels are often overcrowded, with poor access to cooking facilities. If they have to move from one bed and breakfast establishment to another, the children will be disadvantaged as their education will be disrupted as they move from school to school.

Every year, as many as 40,000 children run away from home or care. Research by National Children's Home Action for Children has found that between 5% and 10% of these are likely to be harmed by being involved in activities such as drugs and sexual abuse and prostitution.

activity

Read the article 'Not home, not alone', below.

What harmful effects does homelessness have on children, and how can their needs be met?

No home, not alone

Each year, 180,000 British children become homeless. Stuart Cumella and Panos Vostanis report

Even by the narrow official definition of 'homelessness', about 180,000 children become homeless in England each year – making them the largest single group in the homeless population. Little is known about how it happened, when and if they are rehoused, and the long-term impact on their development and mental health.

We have just completed the first part of a research project to fill in these gaps and identify the most effective means of meeting the mental health needs of such children . . .

We were not surprised to find that 90 per cent were single-parent families, with limited supporting resources, both in family and finance. But we were surprised that over four-fifths had become homeless to escape from violence from a male partner or ex-partner, or from neighbours. They had fled repeated life-threatening assaults, abandoning home and possessions, becoming refugees in their own country.

This experience, with the loss of home, breakdown of family relationships, and disruption to social relationships, had a devastating effect on the mental health of adults and children. Half the parents had clinically-significant mental health problems; over two-thirds of the children had either a problem severe enough to require treatment, a behavioural problem, and/or significant delays in social or language development. That's three times higher than those in a comparison sample of children of the same age who were not homeless but lived in deprived city areas.

It is well-known that mental health problems are much more common among children who have physically or mentally ill parents, or whose families experience marital conflict and domestic violence. But previous research has also shown the importance of 'protective factors' such as friendships and school in preventing problem development.

We found that for homeless children these protective factors are often weakened by the inability or reluctance of some schools and nursery schools to admit them, and by their loss of contact with friends. Other services were often slow to meet their needs. Less than a third of the children were still attending school or nursery, while only 3 per cent had seen a psychiatrist or psychologist in the last 12 months.

Yet early and effective help can play a major part in improving educational and life opportunities, and preventing mental illness or criminality in adult life . . .

Our main conclusion is that homeless children have many mental health needs, and also urgently require concerted action from central government in partnership with local authorities, health commissions and the criminal justice system, to facilitate: rapid re-housing into permanent accommodation; effective social support and health-care; and protection from violence and intimidation.

Homeless centres are essential for families who need emergency accommodation. And schools and nursery schools near them should have additional funding to maintain a minimum number of places for such children in order to minimise delays in admission and loss of schooling. Social services departments should designate workers to be attached to each centre, to help arrange appropriate and rapid access to health, education, and services for such families.

Finally, local health commissions and NHS trusts should collaborate in arranging sessions for psychiatrists, health visitors and community psychiatric nurses to specialise in work with the homeless.

(The Guardian, 12 June 1996)

Slum diseases rise as water supply is cut

Hepatitis and dysentery, diseases of Victorian slums, are spreading in Britain's inner cities as a direct result of privatised water companies disconnecting supplies . . .

The principal anti-poverty officer at Birmingham City Council said: 'Outbreaks of hepatitis A occur when sewage cannot be washed away, when people cannot wash their hands after going to the toilet, and especially when there are children in the home. Disconnecting the water supply takes us back to the nineteenth century.'

Experts at the Department of Health are worried by the huge rise in dysentery and hepatitis cases since water privatisation . . .

Last year, 21,000 households in England and Wales were disconnected, an increase of 177 per cent on 1991. Among the worst cities were Birmingham, Bristol, Liverpool and Sheffield, where densely populated communities were cut off for more than two weeks.

Since 1988, there has been a threefold increase in the number of dysentery cases in England and Wales, from 3,692 to 9,935 in 1992. Hepatitis has increased from 3,379 cases in 1987 to 9,020 in 1992.

Water prices throughout Britain have risen by an average of nearly 50 per cent in the past five years, but this has not been matched by increases in housing benefit or income support . . .

The director of public health at Sandwell Health Authority has completed a study relating disconnections to hepatitis and dysentery outbreaks in his area, which covers about 300,000 people. He compared the postcodes of the people whose water was cut off with those of the dysentery and hepatitis victims. The result was statistically 'very significant'.

'There is less than a one in a thousand possibility of us arriving at that correlation by chance,' he said.

There is no sign of a general change in policy by water companies, although some, including North West Water, have become less 'trigger happy', resulting in fewer disconnections over the past few months.

(The Observer, 1993)

activity

Find out about any schemes operated by, or advice given by, the companies supplying essential services, to help their customers pay their bills. Under what circumstances will services be cut off, and is this influenced by there being children in the family?

SOCIAL FACTORS

Education

In formal education, children spend a lot more time learning through talking and listening than they do through doing. They are in formal education from at least age 5 to age 16, and this period of education will therefore have a significant effect on their development in middle childhood and later. Although Piaget's work (see Chapter 3) shows that children develop certain abilities at certain ages regardless of special instruction, evidence shows that schooling is important in promoting a variety of specific cognitive abilities, such as mental arithmetic.

The performance of children in memory tests is better for those who have received schooling compared with those who have not. These children are also better at explaining how they arrived at an answer to a problem.

Although there are exceptions, for many people their schooling affects their future economic power and social status. There is a strong positive correlation between the number of years a person spends in education and their income.

activity

1 There is controversy over how children learn to read and how reading should be taught. Find out about the different theories and visit a school to watch, and perhaps help with, techniques used to help young children read.
2 Discuss, using your own school experiences, the factors which affect a child's progress at school. From this discussion, produce a list of the characteristics of a good school, classroom and teacher.

Group membership

The development of a child will be influenced by their group membership. This will include their membership of a **peer group** and their membership of a **family group**.

Family group

The family is the main support system for a child. Inadequate support from the family leads to developmental problems. In a study of children born on an Hawaiian island, Werner and Smith (1982) found that the following family circumstances reduced the risk of developmental difficulties:

- The family had no more than four children
- More than 2 years separated the child studied and the next younger or older sibling
- Alternate caregivers were available to the mother within the household (father, grandparents or older siblings)
- The workload of the mother, even when she was employed outside the home, was not excessive
- The child had a substantial amount of attention by caregivers during infancy
- A sibling was available as a caregiver or confidant during childhood
- The family provided structure and rules during the child's adolescence
- The family was cohesive
- The child had an informal, multigenerational network of kin and friends during adolescence
- The cumulative number of chronic stressful life events experienced during childhood and adolescence was not great

The *structure* of the family group can vary widely. For example, the child may be living with a **lone parent** or **two parents** (in 1992, a fifth of mothers with dependent children were lone mothers, and this figure continues to increase); the parents may be **biological**, **adoptive** or **foster** parents. Alternatively, the child may be living in a **residential home**. For many children, the structure of their family group will change over time.

Single-parent families

Children may be brought up by a lone parent because their mother never lived with their father; because of divorce and separation; or because of the death of one-parent. In most cases, children in a single-parent family are living with their mother.

Many single women who are raising children are teenagers, and it has been shown that these children are at a developmental disadvantage. For example, pre-school children of single teenage mothers have been found to be more aggressive and less cognitively advanced than the children of older, married mothers. Suggested explanations for these findings are that young mothers are less well equipped emotionally; they may be less prepared to bring up children and less interested in doing so, and therefore they talk less to their infants; and they are likely to have very limited financial resources (in 1990–91, 68% received social security benefits).

A number of studies have shown that divorce has a negative effect on children's academic achievement and social development. This may be because many of the problems associated with divorce are of the same kind as those faced by unmarried single women. For example, it is likely that a divorced parent will face financial problems; they may be trying to accomplish by themselves what is usually a demanding job for two adults; and they may be socially isolated and lonely.

However, many researchers have concluded that it is not the divorce itself which causes problems the children may have, but the conflict between the parents that brings about and accompanies the divorce.

Children whose parents remarry following divorce are more likely to show damaging effects than those whose parents stay single. Step-children are more likely than those living with a divorced mother: to leave school at 16; to leave home due to friction; and to marry by the age of 20.

Adoption and fostering

Research has shown that children who

have spent time in residential care are likely to fare better if they are subsequently adopted than if they are returned to their biological family. In one piece of research (Tizard and Hodges, 1978), in which children from residential care were either adopted or returned to their biological families, adopted children scored better on tests of intellectual achievement; were able to read at a more advanced level; and were more likely to form mutual attachments to their adoptive parents than the other children were to their biological parents. A number of different explanations for these findings have been suggested. In some cases, children were returned to their biological family where there were other children who required their mother's attention, or where there was a step-father who was not interested in them. Also, most of the adoptive families were financially better off than the biological families. (See the 'Economic factors' section on page 44 above.)

Residential care

The impact of residential care on a child's development depends largely on the quality of care received. Extended residence in a poorly staffed institution retards both mental and social development. Residence in a well-staffed institution produces less pronounced developmental difficulties. Even in good-quality institutions, although children are fed well, staff are well trained and toys and books are plentiful, the turnover and scheduling of staff is likely to discourage the formation of close personal relationships between adults and children. The degree to which children recover depends on their subsequent environments and the age at which they leave the institution.

Domestic violence

In some cases, there will be particular factors within the family group which affect

DEAR DR

I read the report in the Oct. 30 issue of ______ __ about your study of only children. I am an only child, now 57 years old and I want to tell you some things about my life. Not only was I an only child but I grew up in the country where there were no nearby children to play with. My mother did not want children around. She used to say 'I don't want my kid to bother anybody and I don't want nobody's kids bothering me.'

... From the first year of school I was teased and made fun of. For example, in about third or fourth grade I dreaded to get on the school bus to go to school because the other children on the bus called me 'Mommy's baby.' In about the second grade I heard the boys use a vulgar word. I asked what it meant and they made fun of me. So I learned a lesson — don't ask questions. This can lead to a lot of confusion to hear talk one doesn't understand and not be able to learn what it means ...

I never went out with a girl while I was in school — in fact I hardly talked to them. In our school the boys and girls did not play together. Boys were sent to one part of the playground and girls to another. So, I didn't learn anything about girls. When we got into high school and the boys and girls started dating I could only listen to their stories about their experiences.

I could tell you a lot more but the important thing is I have never married or had any children. I have not been very successful in an occupation or vocation. I believe my troubles are not all due to being an only child, but I do believe you are right in recommending playmates for preschool children and I will add playmates for the school agers and not have them strictly supervised by adults. I believe I confirm the experiments with monkeys in being overly timid sometimes and overly aggressive sometimes. Parents of only children should make special efforts to provide playmates for [their children].

Sincerely yours,

Figure 2.11 Letter from a friendless man giving his account of the importance of childhood friendships for development

a child's development. For example, children are often involved in **domestic violence**. A report by National Childrens' Homes (NCH) Action for Children and the NSPCC found that the short-term effects of this include fear, nervousness and confusion, and that longer-term problems include an inability to make and keep close friends, aggressiveness, lack of concentration and hyperactivity, depression, low self-esteem and eating disorders. Education may also be seriously disrupted.

Peer group

Peers can have either a positive or a negative effect on a child's progress at school. For example, working with peers improves a child's problem-solving ability, but research has shown that a child who is a member of a 'gang' progresses more slowly than a non-member. Participation in peer-group activities outside school promotes social competence and provides a kind of preparation for adult life that is quite different from that organised by adults in the classroom and home (see Figure 2.11 above).

activity

1 'The costs and responsibilities of having children are the same for couples as they are for single people', the Chancellor asserted in his 1995 Budget speech as a precursor to cuts in benefit for lone parents. With reference to household overheads, such as gas and electricity bills, and childcare expenses, explain whether you think this assertion is correct.

2 Read the description below of an experiment (Overmier and Seligman 1967 – refer to Cole and Cole 1993) which demonstrates 'learned helplessness'. How can these findings be related to the care of infants?

> A number of shocks were given to the paws of a group of dogs. These dogs received shocks no matter what they did. Then these dogs and a comparison group of dogs that had no experience with unavoidable shocks were placed in a large box with a metal grid floor to which shocks could be delivered. If the animal crossed over to the other side of the box quickly enough it could avoid receiving a shock. Dogs in the group which had not previously received unavoidable shocks, soon learned to move across the box without receiving shocks. However, dogs in the group that had been previously subjected to unavoidable shocks did not learn to avoid shocks; they just laid down and whined.
>
> *(Overmier and Seligman 1967)*

3
- Most young people who have been in residential care leave with no educational qualifications
- 80% of care-leavers are unemployed two years after leaving care
- 40% of young homeless people have a care background
- Women who have spent significant parts of their infancy and childhood in care are more likely to experience

problems in caring for their children than women who were not in 'care'

What measures do you think could be taken to improve these statistics?

4 Experts disagree on the consequences of day-care during the first year of life. Visit a nursery offering this type of care and observe the precautions taken to attempt to overcome any potential problems.
5 Discuss how the following factors could influence a child's development:
   - the number of children in the family
   - the position of a child in the family (e.g. oldest or youngest)
   - having a sibling who has a disability
   - being brought up in an extended family (i.e. with a number of adults)

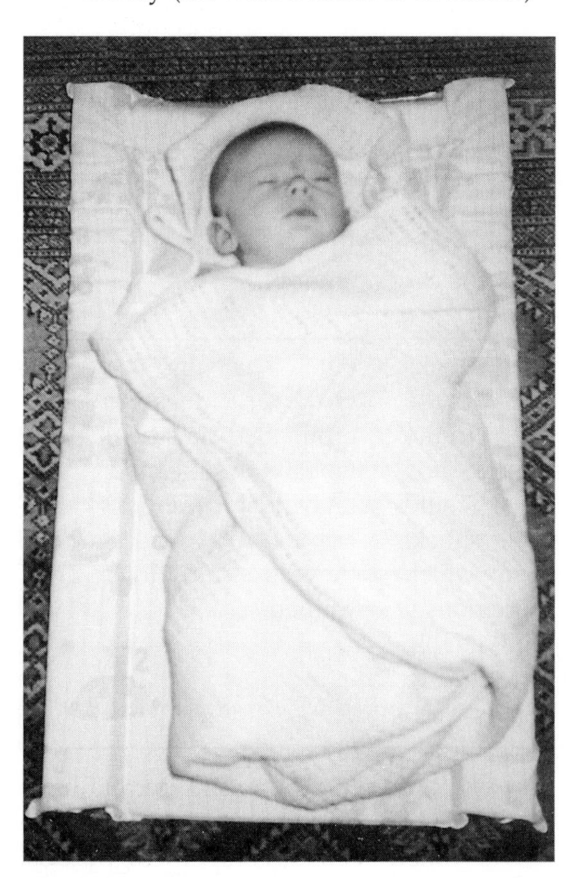

Figure 2.12 Swaddling a baby keeps her safe but may restrict her development

6 Research has found a strong correlation between parental neglect and obesity in children. Can you suggest reasons to explain this relationship?
7 A great deal is written about the impact of television viewing on children. Debate the following statement: 'Violence depicted on television increases aggressiveness in children.'
8 From your personal experiences, how do you think peer group membership can affect development? At what age(s) do you think young people are particularly influenced by their peers?
9 There have been a number of infamous cases of children being raised in virtually complete isolation (see pages 151–52 below). Read an account of one of these cases to find out how the child's development was affected and to what extent the child recovered once the period of isolation was ended.

Culture

Although physical development follows a sequential pattern, different cultural methods of child-rearing can sometimes affect physical development. For example, in some cultures it is traditional to **swaddle** babies. This involves wrapping the baby tightly in a length of cloth (Figure 2.12). Because this inhibits the ability of a baby to roll, its exploration of the environment is limited, which means its development may be affected.

Different expectations in relation to promoting independence can affect the rate of physical achievement. Parents in every culture have their own ideas of when their children should be able to do certain things. For example, children in some cultures are encouraged to assist with the care of younger children or with agricultural activities (Figure 2.13), which means that they will develop certain abilities earlier than children from other cultures. It will also have an impact on their personality development.

– activity –

1 Read the article on p. 56 describing foot-binding in China. Can you find other examples of ways in which different cultures may alter the appearance of the body?
2 Talk to your parents and grandparents about the age at which they were allowed to do certain things. For example, to travel to school or go out with friends without being accompanied by an adult. How and why do their experiences differ from yours and from young children nowadays? How has the promotion of independence changed and has this affected the rate of physical achievement in children?

Figure 2.13 Children in some cultures are responsible for childcare/involved in agricultural work

ENVIRONMENT

Pollution of the environment can have a marked effect on a child's growth and development.

Water pollution

Humans need water for a wide variety of uses. It must be clean and not contaminated with pollutants, in order to prevent infectious diseases and poisoning. Waterborne disease-causing organisms include various parasitic worms and also **protozoa** like ***Entamoeba histolytica***, which causes

The Art of Confinement

'A person is unfortunate in being born a woman, but still more unfortunate if born a Chinese woman,' said the Chinese women's campaigner Cheng Kuan-ying in 1892. In those days, liberal reformers in Britain were campaigning for the right of women to vote; in China, activists like Cheng were concerned with something more basic: a woman's right to move around with constant, agonising pain.

By the end of the 19th century, there were around 100 million women in China whose feet had been bound. Foot-binding kept them in their place – literally. Unable to go outdoors unaided, they were in no danger of running away from their husbands. Instead, they languished at home, prevented from developing any skills apart from making the ornamental shoes which symbolised their mutilation ...

But it was the binding, not the shoes, that did the damage. This process could take up to three years and often began when the victims were as young as two years old. The four little toes were bent under the foot and bound in place with bandages, leaving the big toe pointing forward. The bandage forced the toes and heel together, grossly exaggerating the foot's arch, often breaking the toes and forcing the toenails to grow into the soles of the feet. By the end of it, the feet were irretrievably deformed. The gruesome task was usually undertaken by mothers, who ignored the girls' screams because they knew the alternative: no husband.

The practice originated in the 11th century, when – as one theory goes – the Chinese upper classes decided to copy the tiny shoes of the imperial dancers. Soon, for middle- and upper-class girls all over the country, tiny feet became synonymous with wealth and status ...

By the turn of the century, international criticism of the practice had grown clamorous. But an imperial decree outlawing it had little effect: it took a revolution to end foot-binding. The Nationalists, recognising that the practice effectively crippled half the potential workforce, made it a penal offence in 1911. Perhaps the most tragic victims of all were those girls born into imperial China who had their feet bound, only to learn in 1911 that their suffering had been in vain ...

(Independent on Sunday, 24 March 1996)

amoebic dysentery. **Pathogenic bacteria** carried in water may cause intestinal infections, and more serious diseases such as cholera and typhoid. Many pathogenic viruses are carried in water, e.g., the **poliomyelitis** virus. In the Third World, over 4 million children die a year from drinking unclean water, mainly because it is contaminated with pathogens.

Toxic chemicals in industrial, agricultural and domestic waste are common pollutants of water. Purification is carried out before water is used, but although the treatment can remove organic waste and some bacterial contamination, it cannot cope with heavy chemical pollution. Examples of chemical pollutants in water which affect children include the following:

- **Lead** is taken into humans via air, food and water. It concentrates in the liver, kidney and bones. There is evidence that in children it can cause mental retardation. (See 'Lead poisoning' in the 'Childhood Diseases' section in Chapter 3, page 92 below.)

- **Nitrates** enter water from fertilisers which are leached out of soil.

activity

Read the article below. What recommendations would you make to the mother of a newborn baby in an area where nitrates in the tap water are high?

Blue-baby syndrome

Too much nitrate in drinking water can cause a blood disorder in babies younger than three months. The disorder is called blue-baby syndrome. The infant's lips and body take on a marked blue hue. The cause is that bacteria, either in an unsterilised feeding bottle, or within the child's gut, convert nitrate into nitrite ... The haemoglobin in the baby's blood makes up the nitrite instead of oxygen: the result is that the baby suffers severe respiratory failure.

In Britain, the last reported case of blue-baby syndrome was in 1972, but the World Health Organization reported 2,000 cases between 1945 and 1986. One hundred and sixty of these babies died. In most cases the babies had drunk water with more than 25 milligrams of nitrate per litre from private water sources. Of far greater significance was that their mothers had not sterilised the feeding bottles.

(The New Scientist, 15 September 1990)

Air pollution

Children are particularly susceptible to air pollution, partly because of their large lung surface area : body volume ratio, which is a factor of their small size.

Asthma is a condition resulting largely from air pollution, particularly traffic emissions (see 'Asthma' in the 'Childhood Diseases' section in Chapter 3 on page 92 below).

Some asthma facts:

- Asthma affects 1 in 7 children
- It is the most important cause of emergency hospital admissions
- Respiratory diseases account for a third of children's GP visits
- Asthma accounts for 1 in 20 childhood deaths
- Hospital admissions for childhood asthma have increased 13-fold since the early 1960s

Lead poisoning is another condition which particularly affects children and which is caused by air pollution. (See 'Lead poisoning' in the 'Childhood Diseases' section in Chapter 3 below.)

Table 2.2 summarises the health effects of vehicle pollution.

Pollutant	Source	Health effect
Nitrogen dioxide (NO2)	One of the nitrogen oxides emitted in vehicle exhaust	May exacerbate asthma and possibly increase susceptibility to infections
Sulphur dioxide (SO_2)	Mostly produced by burning coal. Some SO_2 is emitted by diesel vehicles	May provoke wheezing and exacerbate asthma. It is also associated with chronic bronchitis
Particulates PM10, total suspended particulates, black smoke	Includes a wide range of solid and liquid particles in air. Those less than 10 μm in diameter (PM10) penetrate the lung fairly efficiently and are most hazardous to health. Diesel vehicles produce proportionally more particulates than petrol vehicles	Associated with a wide range of respiratory symptoms. Long-term exposure is associated with an increased risk of death from heart and lung disease. Particulates can carry carcinogenic materials into the lungs
Acid aerosols	Airborne acid formed from common pollutants including sulphur and nitrogen oxides	May exacerbate asthma and increase susceptibility to respiratory infection. May reduce lung function in those with asthma
Carbon monoxide (CO)	Comes mainly from petrol car exhaust	Lethal at high doses. At low doses, can impair concentration and neuro-behavioural function. Increases the likelihood of exercise-related heart pain in people with coronary heart disease. May present a risk to the foetus
Ozone (O_3)	Secondary pollutant produced from nitrogen oxides and volatile organic compounds in the air	Irritates the eyes and air passages. Increases the sensitivity of the airways to allergic triggers in people with asthma. May increase susceptibility to infection
Lead	Compound present in leaded petrol to help the engine run smoothly	Impairs the normal intellectual development and learning ability of children
Volatile organic compounds (VOCs)	A group of chemicals emitted from the evaporation of solvents and distribution of petrol fuel. Also present in vehicle exhaust	Benzene has given most cause for concern in this group of chemicals. It is a cancer-causing agent which can cause leukaemia at higher doses than are present in the normal environment
Polycyclic aromatic hydrocarbons (PAHs)	Produced by the incomplete combustion of fuel. PAHs become attached to particulates	Includes a complex range of chemicals, some of which are carcinogens. It is likely that exposure to PAHs in traffic exhaust poses a low cancer risk to the general population
Asbestos	May be present in brake pads and clutch linings, especially in heavy-duty vehicles. Asbestos fibres and dust are released into the atmosphere when vehicles brake	Asbestos can cause lung cancer and mesothelioma, cancer of the lung lining. The consequences of the low levels of exposure from braking vehicles are not known

Table 2.2 The health effects of vehicle pollution
Source: 'How vehicle pollution affects our health', Dr C. Read (ed). London Symposium of 20 May 1994, supported by the Ashden Trust

Noise pollution

Noise is defined as unwanted sound. Because it can be a health hazard, it can be considered as a form of pollution. Noise maps produced by the Council for the Protection of Rural England show that there are very few tranquil areas remaining in England. With forecasts of huge traffic increases in the next 20 years, the noise levels are set to increase further.

Sounds above about 90 dB can damage hearing. If exposure is over a long period, this damage can be permanent.

There is much evidence for higher levels of noise being responsible for social and medical problems. For example, it has been found that children living on noisy main roads had far fewer friends than those in quiet suburbs, and that traffic noise adversely affects children's progress at school.

activity

1. Occasionally, a number of children in the same locality are diagnosed as suffering from leukaemia. What factors are suggested by scientists as possible causes for these 'clusters'?
2. What are the sources of air pollution other than vehicle emissions? Try to find out how the cleanliness of the air in your locality compares with the rest of the country. Is this reflected in the numbers of children affected by respiratory diseases?
3. Traffic was mentioned above as one source of noise pollution. What other sources are children affected by?

Disease and illness

Diseases or illnesses suffered in childhood can affect growth and development. The following are examples of conditions which can affect a child's development.

Autism

Autistic children show abnormal social behaviour. They lack interest in people and fail to show the normal attachment to adults. There is a spectrum of severity, and the degree of severity can change as the child gets older. Mild forms of **autism** are sometimes known as **Asperger's syndrome** and **semantic–pragmatic disorder** and affect about 15–20 children in 10,000. 4 in 10,000 and four times as many boys as girls are affected by the more severe, classic type of autism. It is thought that the cause of autism may be related to abnormal levels of essential fatty acids in the blood, or to an abnormal blood flow through the brain.

Mild degrees of autism are difficult to diagnose, and it can be difficult to know if a child suffers from the condition or is just extremely shy. Signs that the child is autistic rather than shy include the following:

- The parents feel the child does not relate to them in a normal way
- The child appears not to enjoy any form of communication
- The child shows no awareness of other peoples' feelings
- The child does not pretend or play, or does so in a very repetitive way

- The child has meaningless repetitive routines

Because an autistic child is not communicating with other people, or shows limited communication, and because learning through play (see pages 134–6) is restricted, the child's pattern of development will be affected. It is not the case that an autistic child reaches the same developmental milestones in the same order but at a slower rate as the 'normal' child. In an autistic child, the overall level of development is low, but often with 'islands' of brilliance. For example, an autistic child may show a very limited ability to communicate with other children, but may show considerably better powers of memory or drawing skills. Extreme examples include a 1½ year old who could sing an entire opera, and a 2 year old who can read. Such individuals are known as **idiots-savants**.

Deafness and hearing loss

A deaf child of normal intelligence can rely on sight to gain experience of the surroundings to such an extent that both parents and health professionals may not diagnose the condition. Interestingly, the area of the brain that normally receives the auditory input from spoken language may get taken over by the visual input of sign language. Babies born deaf babble at first just like babies who can hear. Once deaf babies start to learn the manual gestures of sign language, this vocal babbling stops and they will start 'babbling' with their hands, making the movements that will become the elements of sign language. Because of lack of stimulation, by the time a deaf child is between 2 and 5 years old they may show problems in language acquisition, comprehension or behavioural disorders. It should be noted, however, that deaf children born to deaf parents who communicate in sign language acquire language at least as rapidly and fully as hearing children born into hearing households.

Blindness and visual defects

Partial sight means that there is some vision which can be used for education; **blind** means that the child can only use methods for education which do not require the use of any vision. These conditions can be caused by defects of the eye, the optic nerve or the brain.

A **congenitally blind** baby will develop a more sophisticated sense of touch than a sighted baby. The area of the brain concerned with sight will decrease, and the area concerned with touch will increase. Severe visual defects can reduce the rate of early development. For example, smiling, reaching, grasping, sitting, crawling and walking may all be delayed. Even language development may be delayed because it is difficult for a baby to link an object they touch with their name. Older children with impaired vision may continuously 'babble' to maintain social contact.

If the parents feel that the baby is unresponsive, they may reduce the amount of attention they give. This lack of social contact can lead to behavioural problems such as rocking or head-banging.

activity

1 Find out about the different therapies developed to help autistic children. How widely available are these to children in your area?
2 Find out about the world's sign languages. What are their similarities, and what are their differences?
3 Find out what help and resources are available in your area to help children with visual and hearing defects.

CHAPTER 3

Ways *of* Promoting *and* Maintaining Good Health

Ways of promoting and maintaining good health include regular health checks on the pregnant woman, the developing foetus, the newborn baby, the infant, the pre-school child, and the school child. Other ways include immunisation; healthy living practices, such as adequate sleep and exercise, good nutrition and personal hygiene; and accident prevention. Finally there is environmental health, which includes the control of water, air and noise pollution.

Many diseases are more common in the early years of life. These include those caused by bacteria, including gum disease and tooth decay, and whooping cough (pertussis). Then there are those caused by viruses including German measles (rubella), measles, mumps, chicken pox, and the common cold. Common parasites are thread worms and headlice. Two environmental diseases which affect children in particular are asthma and lead poisoning.

Health checks (screening and diagnostic testing)

From conception onwards, every child in the UK is given regular tests to diagnose any problems associated with growth or development. This gives the opportunity for:

- early remedial action
- support for the parents
- safeguarding of the child

HEALTH CHECKS FROM CONCEPTION TO BIRTH

Tests to check for the healthy development of the foetus form an important part of the antenatal care a woman receives. Doctors or midwives will arrange for the following tests to be carried out as necessary:

Blood tests

Blood samples will be taken from a woman at intervals throughout her pregnancy. A number of tests will then be made.

Rhesus factor

The mother's blood will be tested to find out whether she is **Rhesus positive** or **Rhesus negative**. People who are Rhesus positive have **antigens** on the surface of their red blood cells. These cause the red blood cells from people who are Rhesus negative to produce the corresponding **Rhesus antibodies**. The antibodies bind the antigens together and so cause the clumping together of the Rhesus-positive blood cells. Sometimes, in the last few months of the pregnancy, a few fragments of the foetal red blood cells will cross the placenta into the mother's bloodstream. If the father is Rhesus positive and the baby inherits this condition, and the mother is Rhesus negative, the cells of the baby will cause the mother to produce Rhesus antibodies. Some of these antibodies will move back across the placenta to the foetal circulation. With a first baby, the antibodies do not usually form quickly enough to reach a level which could cause harm. However, because the antibodies will already be in the mother's blood, subsequent Rhesus-positive children may be affected with potentially fatal results. When the foetal red blood cells clump together, they become stuck in the **capillaries** and eventually burst, releasing their **haemoglobin**. This is known as **haemolysis**. (See Figure 3.1 for a summary.)

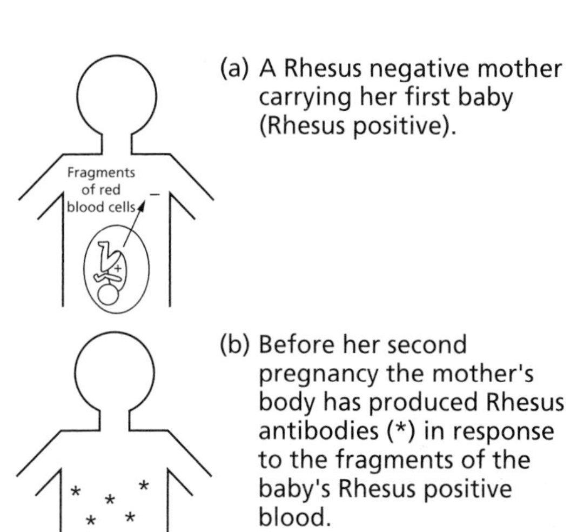

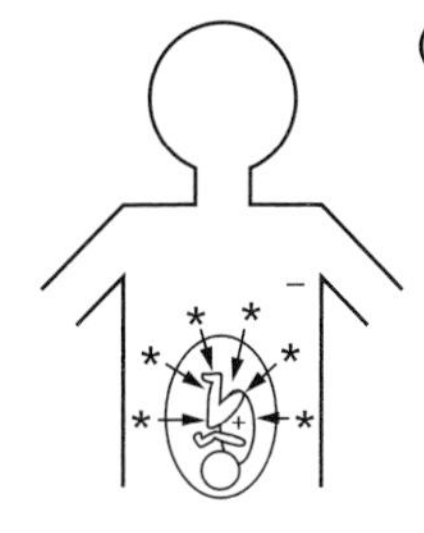

(c) During the second pregnancy with a Rhesus positive baby, antibodies move across the placenta to the foetal circulation, resulting in haemolytic disease of the newborn.

Figure 3.1 A summary of the development of haemolytic disease of the newborn

If the blood tests show the mother to be Rhesus negative (about 15% of the population have this), she will have several further blood tests to check for the presence of the Rhesus antibodies during her pregnancy.

If necessary, the baby can receive a blood transfusion once it is born, or even whilst still in the uterus. Alternatively, immediately after giving birth to her first Rhesus-positive baby, the Rhesus-positive mother can be injected with a substance which will destroy any foetal blood cells in her circulation before they can trigger the immune response.

Syphilis

Although **syphilis** is now a rare condition, it has such harmful effects on the foetus (see page 36) that a blood test is done to test for its presence. If the result is positive and treatment is given before 20 weeks, the foetus will suffer no ill effects.

Rubella

To check whether a pregnant woman has had **rubella**, or been immunised against it, her blood will be tested for antibodies to the virus.

Haemoglobin estimation

An estimation will be made of the density of red blood cells in the blood. This is

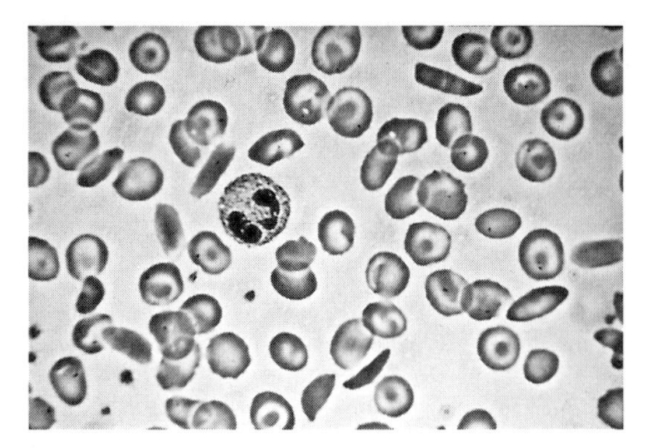

Figure 3.2 Photomicrograph of blood showing sickle cells

expressed either in grammes or as a percentage (14.7 g is equivalent to 100%). The normal haemoglobin level of a pregnant woman (11–13 g) is lower than that of a non-pregnant woman. Haemoglobin tests are made at intervals throughout the pregnancy.

Unusual forms of haemoglobin may also need to be tested for. For example, people of African origin may have an inherited condition known as **sickle cell trait**. This can be detected by checking for the presence of the characteristic 'sickle shaped' red blood cells (Figure 3.2). **Thalassaemia**, another inherited blood disease, may be checked for in women of Mediterranean, Asian or African origin.

Alphafetoprotein (AFP) and human chorionic gonadatrophin (hCG)

At about 15 to 16 weeks into pregnancy, women in the UK are offered a blood test to determine whether or not there is an increased risk of having a baby with **Down's syndrome** or **open neural tube defect** (see the 'Folic acid' section on page 33 in Chapter 2 above). The test measures the amount of two substances in the blood: **alphafetoprotein (AFP)**, a protein produced by the foetal liver, and **human chorionic gonadatrophin (hCG)**, a hormone.

In pregnancies with Down's syndrome, the AFP level tends to be lower than average and the hCG level tends to be higher than average. These measurements are used together with the woman's age to calculate the risk of her baby having Down's syndrome. If this indicates a significant risk (greater than 1 in 250), the result is called 'screen-positive' and she will be offered amniocentesis (see below).

A raised AFP level indicates an increased risk of the baby having an open neural tube defect. If this is found to be the case (i.e. screen-positive), a detailed ultrasound will be done (see below).

Amniocentesis

If blood tests indicate that a woman has an increased risk of having a baby with Down's syndrome, she will be offered **amniocentesis**. An ultrasound scan is used to check the position of the baby in the uterus. A fine needle is then inserted through the abdominal wall and into the uterus to take a sample of amniotic fluid (20 cm^3). This sample contains cells shed by the baby, cells which are then grown. The chromosomes are then examined under a microscope. There will normally be 22 matching pairs plus the two sex chromosomes, giving a total of 46 chromosomes, but a Down's-syndrome baby will have a total of 47 chromosomes. Amniocentesis can also detect some other problems, and will show whether the baby is male or female.

Amniocentesis is generally carried out in the 16th–18th week of pregnancy and takes 3–4 weeks to give a result. Amniocentesis carries a risk of causing miscarriage, and it is estimated that about 1 in 100 women who have the test will miscarry as a result.

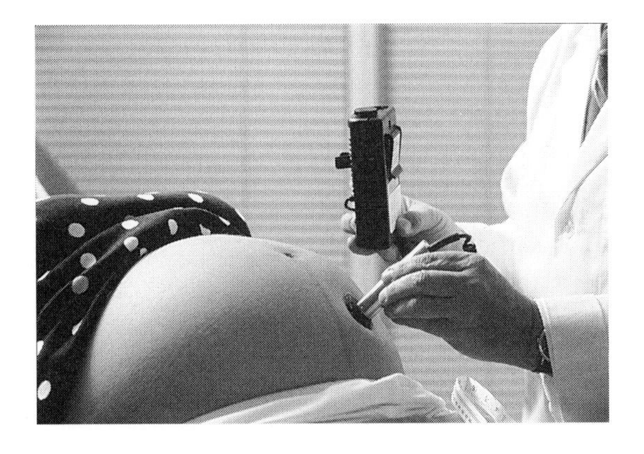

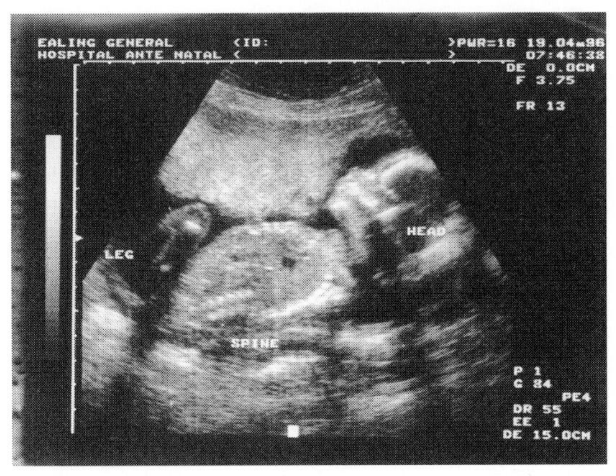

Figure 3.3 (a) The examination of the foetus by ultrasound (b) Ultrasound of foetus

Chorionic villus sampling

This test involves taking a sample of the developing placenta (**chorionic villi**). Using ultrasound to guide it, a fine needle is inserted, either through the vagina or through the wall of the abdomen. The results are usually available after about 2–3 weeks. The advantage of this test over amniocentesis is that results can be obtained much earlier in the pregnancy. However, the main disadvantage is that it carries a significantly higher risk of miscarriage.

Ultrasound

Tissues in the body can be examined by the use of **ultrasound** (high-frequency sound waves). The ultrasound is transmitted into the body, where it is reflected at the boundaries between different types of tissue. The time lapse and intensity loss of the reflected ultrasound (returning signal) allows the nature and position of the tissues to be deduced. The sound waves are generated by a hand-held device which is placed over the area to be scanned (Figure 3.3a). The echo of the returning waves is recorded and analysed by a computer which forms a screen image (Figure 3.3b). Ultrasound scans cause no damage to the tissues, and for this reason are routinely given to pregnant women to monitor foetal development. The scans reveal the size and stage of development and, therefore, the age of the foetus; position of the foetus; multiple births; and any foetal or placental defects. The procedure is also used to guide the needle into the uterus during amniocentesis or chorionic villus sampling (see above).

activity

1 The health checks described above are examples of **screening tests** in which a large number of comparatively healthy people undergo a relatively simple procedure to discover problems. Can you give examples of adult screening procedures? (See Appendix A for example.)

2 Discuss the advantages and the disadvantages to parents of finding out in advance of the birth about any abnormalities their baby has.

HEALTH CHECKS AT BIRTH

As soon as the baby is born, a number of checks will be made on the baby by midwives or doctors. Although these checks are thorough, they may be made so rapidly that the parents are not aware that they are being made. These observations will help the professional to decide if the baby needs additional attention or assistance.

Immediately after delivery, the baby will be given an **APGAR score**. This is based on the baby's heart rate, breathing, muscle tone, colour and reflexes. Table 3.1 shows how these aspects are used to give the baby a score out of 10. This will be repeated at intervals – for example, after 1 minute and after 4 minutes.

The circumference of the head, the length and the weight will usually be measured. The nature of the cry, movement, posture and alertness of the baby will all be observed. To test the **Moro reflex** (see the 'Newborn reflexes' section on page 18 in Chapter 1 above), the baby is pulled up from lying down to an angle

Score	Heart rate	Respiratory effort	Muscle tone	Colour	Reflex
2	Over 100	Strong cry	Good active movement	Body well oxygenated	Irritability (Response to stimulation of foot) Normal cry
1	Below 100	Slow, irregular respirations	Fair, some flexion of limbs	Body oxygenated, hands and feet blue	Moderately depressed grimace
0	No beat obtained	No respirations	Limp	Blue, pale	Absent

Table 3.1 APGAR scoring method
Source: Illingworth (1990)

of 45 degrees, with the examiner's hand behind the head. The hand is suddenly removed, which should elicit the reflex.

All parts of the head and body, including the mouth and eyes, are examined externally for any visible abnormalities.

A **blood sample** will be taken from the baby's foot ('heelprick') in the first few days, which will be used to check for **PKU** (**Guthrie test**) and **hypothyroidism**. Increasingly, this blood sample is also used to carry out a screening test for **cystic fibrosis**.

activity

1 Talk informally to a woman who has a young baby, and ask what tests, if any, she remembers being carried out on the baby within 24 hours of the birth. Was she satisfied with the explanations she was given of these procedures? Would she have liked any further information?
2 If possible, interview a health professional (midwife, GP or paediatrician), and ask both how they go about checking each part of the body, and for specific examples of abnormalities they are checking for.
3 What are the causes, symptoms and treatments of:
   - PKU
   - hypothyroidism?

(See Appendix A for answers.)

Health and developmental checks at 6 or 8 weeks

These checks are carried out by GPs at their surgeries. In some practices, they are done at the same time as the post-natal examination of the mother. Generally, the checks on the baby will only take a few minutes.

- As at birth, measurements will be made of the baby's:
  - weight (with the clothes removed)
  - length
  - head circumference.

  (These data will be plotted on a chart (for example, see Figure 1.6) to check that there are no problems with the baby's growth)
- The doctor carries out the following checks:
  - All parts of the head and body are examined externally for abnormalities.
  - In boys, it is checked that the testes have descended.
  - The abdomen is **palpated** to examine the internal organs.
  - The heart and breathing are listened to.
  - The hips are flexed to check for **congenital dislocation of the hip** (**CDH**).
  - The doctor checks that the results of the blood tests made at birth (for PKU and hypothyroidism) are available.
  - The mother will be asked if she has any worries about the baby's growth, responsiveness, vision and hearing.
  - The doctor will watch to see that the

baby follows the parent's face with its eyes, and will ask if the baby has started smiling.
- The baby's **muscle tone** will be checked by laying the baby on its back and gently pulling it into a sitting position and then lowering it again. It may also be placed on its front to see what ability it has to support its head.

Between this 6- or 8-week examination and the review at 8 months, there are no routine health or developmental checks. However, the doctor will be able to examine the baby when it is seen for immunisation (see page 71 below) or comes to the surgery with minor ailments.

Health and Developmental Checks at 6–9 Months

Every baby will be seen again by the GP when it is between 6 and 9 months old. By this time it will be learning to sit and communicate, and this is the best time for testing hearing by the **distraction method** (see below).

The doctor will make the following **physical** checks:

- The hips will be manipulated to check again for CDH
- The heart will be listened to
- If there is any doubt after the 6/8-week check-up, the descent of the testes will be checked

The following **developmental** checks will also be made:

- The parents are asked:
  - if there are any problems with the baby's growth, health or development
  - if the baby feeds well
  - if the baby recognises familiar people
  - about the baby's **vocalisations**
  - if the baby can roll over from the **prone** position (lying face down).
- The doctor will observe:
  - the baby reaching for a favourite toy, to check its accuracy in reaching and grasping
  - whether the baby has developed a pincer grasp between the thumb and first finger (Figure 1.16), checked by offering a small object such as a currant
  - whether the baby can sit.
- The following measurements will again be made and recorded:
  - length
  - weight
  - head circumference.
- The doctor assesses the baby's hearing in the following ways:
  - The parent is asked if they have any worries about the child's hearing.
  - The parent is asked what evidence they have that the child can hear.
  - Any high-risk factors in the past or family history are considered.
  - A **distraction test** is carried out. The room must be as quiet as possible. Two people are required for this, as well as a carer to hold the baby. The **distractor** sits directly in front of the baby, who is sitting on the carer's lap. He or she moves a toy to attract the baby's attention and then reduces this stimulation by covering or removing the toy. The **tester** makes sounds at approximately 1 metre from the baby, just outside the baby's field of view (Figure 3.4). These sounds must be quiet (less than 40 dB) and at a variety of frequencies

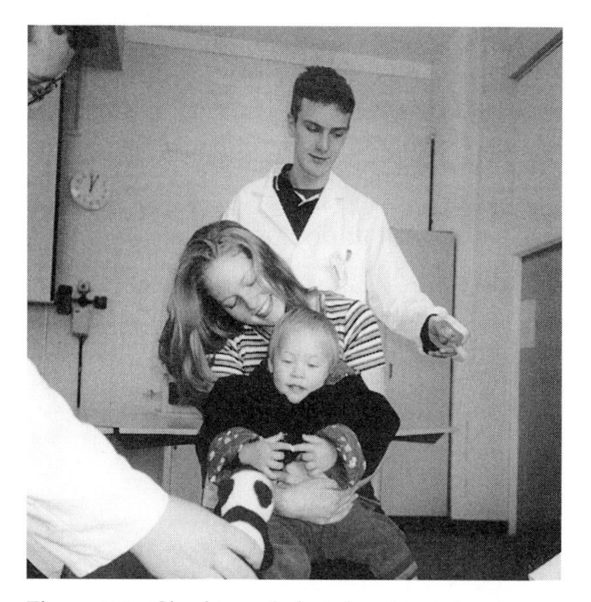

Figure 3.4 Checking a baby's hearing using a distraction test

(i.e. some of high pitch and some of low). They may be vocal, or made with a special rattle or electronic device. To pass, the baby must turn towards both high and low sounds on both sides.

- The doctor checks for any defects in vision by:
  - asking the parent if they have any worries about the child's vision
  - observing the way the child looks around
  - examining the eyes.

activity

1 If possible, observe a baby who is between 6 and 9 months old. What evidence is there that the baby can hear?
2 Look up **glue ear** in the glossary at the end of this book. How can it be treated?
3 Observe a doctor, health visitor or **audiometrician** testing a baby's hearing with the distraction test. Write an account of the process, giving examples of precautions taken and why it may still be unreliable.

HEALTH AND DEVELOPMENTAL CHECKS AT 18–24 MONTHS

- At this age, a physical check is not usually carried out, but the child's height will be measured. Weight will only be measured if there are any concerns
- By 18 months, 97% of children are walking. Any problems in the way the child walks will be checked for
- Parents will be asked if they have any concerns about **language** or **motor development**, vision or hearing. The health professional (doctor or health visitor) will also observe the child to check their use of language and ability to understand instructions
- Because of the high incidence of **iron deficiency** at this age, some doctors offer a screening service to test for anaemia

activity

1 If parents are worried about language development, the child will be referred to a **speech therapist**. Find out how the therapist may test and help the child.
2 At the 18-month check, parents often ask for help with **management issues**. Design a leaflet giving advice on one of the following issues:
   - tantrums
   - sleep disturbances
   - food fads or poor appetite
   - toilet training
   - sibling jealousy

Health and developmental checks at 3 years

By this age, most **physical** problems will already have been identified. However, the doctor still makes the following checks:

- the skin is inspected for unusual marks
- the heart and lungs are listened to
- the descent of the testes is checked
- the spine is checked
- in some districts, routine screening tests of hearing and vision will be made

The child's height will again be measured, but after the age of 2, the standing height rather than the supine (i.e. lying or resting on the back) length will be measured. Standing height is about 0.5 cm less than supine length.

Developmental checks will be made by a combination of direct observation of the child and discussion with parents.

- **Behavioural disorders** and **emotional problems** will be checked for
- The child's **concentration** and **attention** will be considered
- **Language development** will be assessed
- The child's **gross motor skills** (for example, walking) will be assessed

activity

1 Observe a health professional measuring a child. Describe the equipment used and list the precautions taken to ensure the measurements are accurate.
2 If possible, talk to an **orthoptist** and **audiometrician** and find out how the method of carrying out vision and hearing tests varies with a child's age.

Health and developmental checks at school entry

Many health authorities no longer give all children a physical examination at the time they start school. Instead, parents are given questionnaires (Figure 3.5), and children are invited for examination only if the parents have worries or concerns about any aspect of growth or development. The confidential questionnaire is kept as part of the child's school health record.

Other health authorities arrange for every child to be seen in the school by the **school nurse** who may check the following:

- general health and well-being
- vision
- height and weight
- hearing

If this health surveillance is to be carried out, parents are asked to fill in a consent form as well as a questionnaire, and are given the option of being present. If appropriate, the child will also be seen by the **school doctor**.

The health authority is responsible for informing the education authority if the child may have special educational needs, after discussing this first with parents.

Subsequent health and developmental checks

A child will probably have further health and development checks during their first year at junior school (at approximately 8 years old). The school nurse will again ask about general health and well-being, and growth and vision will be checked.

In secondary school, these checks will be repeated, often at about age 11 and 13.

Immunisation

The immune system process

Antibodies are protein molecules produced by white blood cells known as **lymphocytes**. They are produced in response to **antigens** – proteins or carbohydrates that coat foreign material such as bacteria. Antibodies are produced which are each specific to a single antigen. The production of antibodies is not restricted to the blood: they also occur on mucus surfaces – for example, in the respiratory system – and in the alimentary canal.

There are two types of lymphocyte, the **T** and **B cells**, which develop in different ways and have different functions.

- T cells have membranes in which there are receptors for antigens. When one of these cells recognises a complementary antigen, it attaches itself to it and destroys it
- B cells recognise antigens in a similar way to T cells, but respond differently. They are stimulated to produce many **plasma cells**, each of which synthesises and liberates identical antibodies at a rate of nearly 2,000 molecules per second

There are many different ways in which antibodies prevent the replication and harmful effects of **micro-organisms**. These include:

- causing the foreign particles to stick together
- neutralising the **toxins** produced by the **pathogen**
- breaking down foreign material
- stimulating **phagocytosis** (see Figure 3.6)

Richmond Twickenham & Roehampton Healthcare NHS Trust

COMMUNITY HEALTH SERVICES

CONFIDENTIAL HEALTH QUESTIONNAIRE

Please complete this and return it to the school in a sealed envelope, addressed to the School Nurse. The information may be discussed by her with the School Doctor.

CHILD'S NAME .... DATE OF BIRTH ....
OTHER NAMES .... BOY/GIRL
ADDRESS ....

.... POST CODE ....

TEL. No.: (home) .... TEL. No.: (work) ....
FAMILY DOCTOR .... HEALTH VISITOR ....
NAME AND ADDRESS OF CLINIC ATTENDED ....
....
....
SCHOOL..

(1) **MEDICAL HISTORY**

Has your child ever had:–

Whooping Cough Yes/No
Measles Yes/No
Mumps Yes/No
Chicken-pox Yes/No
German Measles (Rubella) Yes/No

(2) Has your child ever had any serious illness? Yes/No
If yes, pleae give details:

(3) Has your child ever attended hospital? Yes/No
If yes, please give details, the age of the child and the name of the hospital:

(4) Did your child have a developmental check between the ages of 3 and 4 years? Yes/No/Don't know

FAMILY HISTORY

Does any member of your family have a disability or suffer from ill health?
e.g. visual or hearing problems, heart disease, diabetes, epilepsy, etc. Yes/No

If so, please give details:

CURRENT MEDICAL INFORMATION

(1) Does your child suffer from:

Bronchitis Yes/No
Asthma Yes/No

Figure 3.5 A sample questionnaire given to parents on child's school entry

	Wheezing cough with colds	Yes/No
	Ear trouble or poor hearing	Yes/No
	Eye trouble (squint, lazy eye, needs glasses)	Yes/No
	Fits, faints or blackouts	Yes/No
	Allergies, e.g. hay-fever	Yes/No
	Skin problems, e.g. eczema	Yes/No
(2)	Does your child receive speech therapy?	Yes/No
	Has he/she ever had speech therapy?	Yes/No
(3)	Does your child take any pills, tablets, drugs, medicines, inhalers, require injections or special health care?	Yes/No
	If so, please give details.	
(4)	Do you have any worries about any of the following?	
	Speech	Yes/No
	Hearing	Yes/No
	Eyesight	Yes/No
	Growth	Yes/No
	Weight	Yes/No
	Eating	Yes/No
	Sleeping	Yes/No
	Behaviour	Yes/No
	Bed Wetting	Yes/No
	Soiling	Yes/No
	Learning	Yes/No
	Clumsiness	Yes/No
(5)	Does your child have any other illness, medical or other problems? Please describe.	

IMMUNISATION

It is very important that these are up-to-date. You can find out which immunisations your child has had or still needs by looking in your child's health book or by checking with the clinic, G.P. or Health Visitor.

Your child should have had:

Three injections (in the first year) against diphtheria, whooping cough, tetanus, usually given at the same time as polio vaccine (drops). Sometimes, for medical reasons, the whooping cough is not given.

One injection against measles (usually between 1 and 2 years of age), or MMR (measles, mumps and Rubella) all in one dose (between 1 and 2 years of age, or when starting school).

A booster against diphtheria, tetanus and polio before starting school at 5 years old.

IMMUNISATION HISTORY

Has your child been immunised against? *Please give dates*

	1st dose	2nd dose	3rd dose
Diphtheria and Tetanus			
Whooping Cough			
Polio (drops)			

Measles, one dose	YES/NO	DATE ....
Measles, Mumps, Rubella (MMR) one dose	YES/NO	DATE ....
Pre-school booster, one dose	YES/NO	DATE ....

For older children:–

Rubella (German Measles)	YES/NO	DATE ....
BCG (against T.B.) sometimes given at birth	YES/NO	DATE ....
Tetanus and Polio booster (15–18)	YES/NO	DATE ....

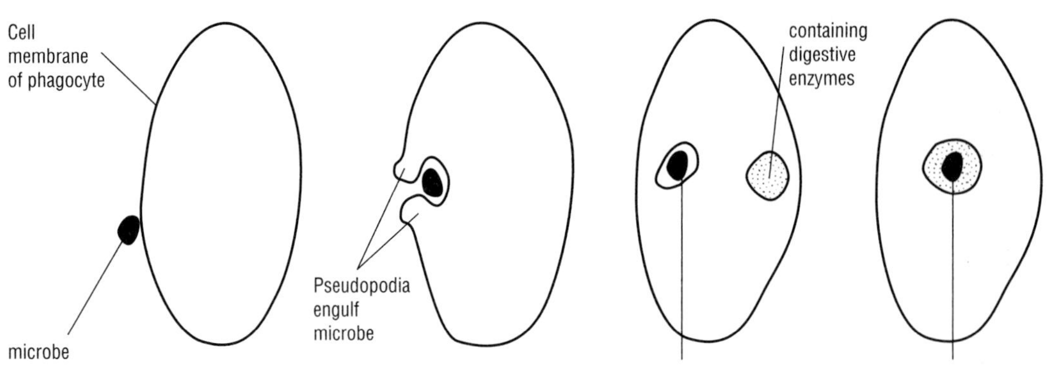

Figure 3.6 The mechanism of phagocytosis

As well as forming antibody-producing plasma cells, the B lymphocytes also produce **memory cells**. These enable an individual who has been exposed to an antigen once to respond more promptly and rigorously in a subsequent encounter (see Figure 3.7). This is called the **secondary response**, and is what gives an individual **immunity** to a disease which they have already encountered.

TYPES OF VACCINE

The immune response can be artificially induced by **vaccination**. When the vaccine is introduced into the bloodstream, the antigens it contains stimulate the production of antibodies without causing the disease itself.

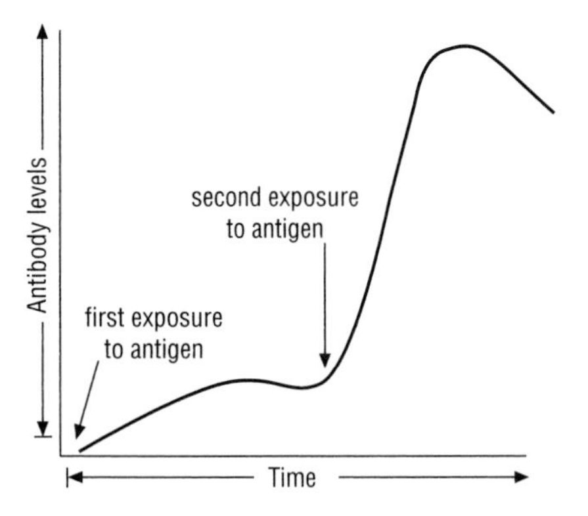

Figure 3.7 The primary and secondary repsonse to an antigen

There are a number of different types of vaccine:

- *Living attenuated micro-organisms.* These are living pathogens which multiply but have been weakened, e.g. by heating or by culturing them outside the human body, so that they are unable to cause the symptoms of the disease. Examples include the vaccines against measles, tuberculosis, poliomyelitis and rubella (German measles)
- *Dead micro-organisms.* Although harmless, these still induce antibody production. Examples include vaccines against typhoid, influenza and whooping cough
- *Toxoids.* In some cases (e.g. diphtheria and tetanus) the toxin alone will cause antibody production. The toxin can be made harmless (e.g. with formaldehyde) and used as a vaccine
- *Extracted antigens.* The antigens can be taken from the pathogens and used as a vaccine. For example, the influenza vaccine can be prepared in this way
- *Artificial antigens.* The genes responsible for antigen production in a pathogen can be transferred to a non-pathogen. This harmless organism can be grown in a **fermenter** where it will produce the antigen which can be harvested and used in a vaccine

All the above methods produce what is known as **active immunity** because they

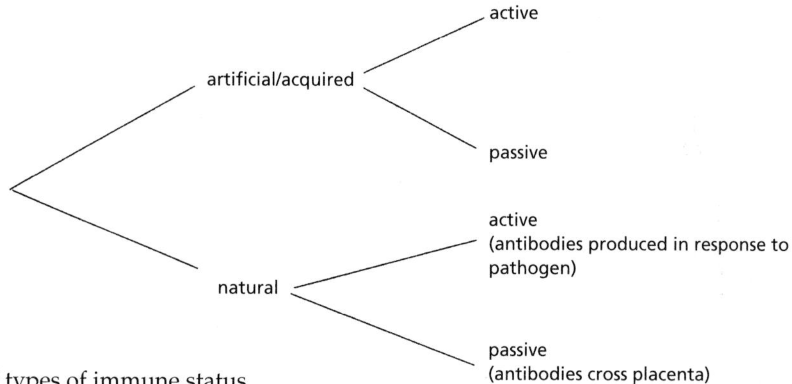

Figure 3.8 A summary of types of immune status

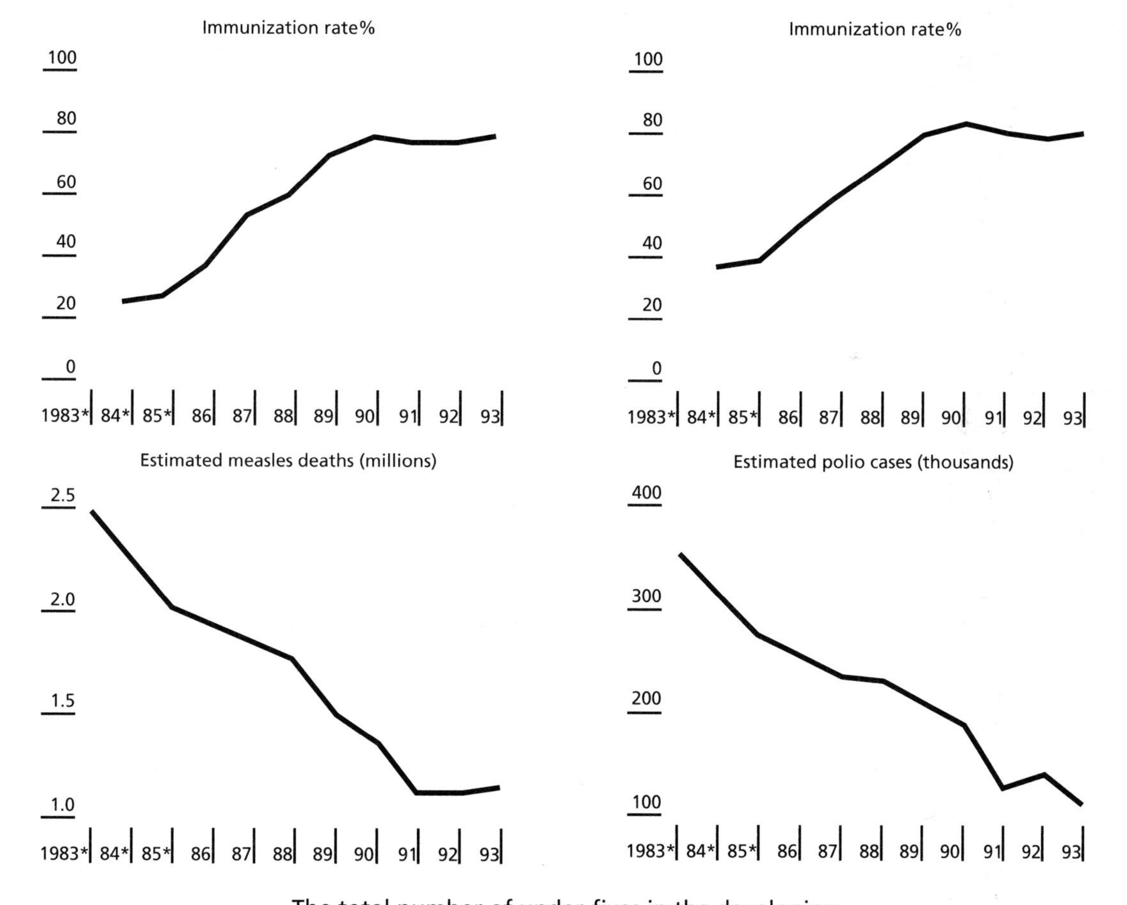

Figure 3.9 Changes in under-five deaths in the developing world (in millions) compared with changes in immunisation (a) measles (b) polio

cause the individual to synthesise their own antibodies. **Passive immunity** involves the acquisition of antibodies. These can be acquired artificially. Antibodies from other mammals, e.g. horses, are injected in the form of a **serum**. For example, tetanus and diphtheria can be prevented in this way.

Immunisation programmes and schedules

The progress made in the control and prevention of infectious diseases has been the result of a number of factors, including improvements in water supply and sanitation, personal hygiene and nutritional status. However, the development of vaccines and immunisation programmes has been the most important factor in the prevention of many infectious diseases. As the immunisation uptake rate has increased, a corresponding fall in the relevant diseases has occurred (see Figure 3.9).

The following account from the NAHAT NHS Handbook 1995/96 describes the most recent developments in immunisation schedules in the UK:

By September 1993, 73 per cent of English districts had reached 95 per cent uptake by the age of two years for polio, diphtheria and tetanus vaccine, 34 per cent for mumps, measles and rubella (MMR) vaccine, and 32 per cent for pertussis vaccine. Increasing numbers of districts are reaching 95 per cent uptake.

In May 1990, the immunisation schedule was changed from one starting at the age of three months and ending between eight and 11 months to an accelerated schedule in which the primary immunisations are given at the ages of two, three and four months.

In October 1992 vaccination against *Haemophilus influenzae* type B (Hib), an important cause of meningitis and other invasive disease in children, was introduced. One year after its introduction, 37 per cent of districts reported 95 per cent uptake at 12 months.

In September 1994, in response to warnings by experts of a possible measles epidemic a campaign to immunise all schoolchildren aged five to 16 was launched at an estimated cost of £20m. Some eight million children were immunised – 94 per cent of schoolchildren in Northern Ireland, 92 per cent in England and 88 per cent in both Scotland and Wales. In March 1995, the Health Secretary said the action had prevented some 50 deaths and about one-third of a million lost working days caring for sick children.

(NAHAT 1996)

– activity –

1 How does rubella harm the developing foetus? (See Appendix A for answer.)

IMMUNISATION SCHEDULE

WHEN DUE	WHICH IMMUNISATIONS	TYPE
AT 2 MONTHS	Hib	ONE INJECTION
	DIPHTHERIA, WHOOPING COUGH, TETANUS – DTP	ONE INJECTION
	POLIO	BY MOUTH
AT 3 MONTHS	Hib	ONE INJECTION
	DIPHTHERIA, WHOOPING COUGH, TETANUS – DTP	ONE INJECTION
	POLIO	BY MOUTH
AT 4 MONTHS	Hib	ONE INJECTION
	DIPTHERIA, WHOOPING COUGH, TETANUS – DTP	ONE INJECTION
	POLIO	BY MOUTH
AT 12-15 MONTHS	MEASLES, MUMPS, RUBELLA – MMR	ONE INJECTION
3-5 YEARS (around school entry)	DIPHTHERIA, TETANUS	BOOSTER INJECTION
	POLIO	BOOSTER BY MOUTH
GIRLS 10-14 YEARS	RUBELLA	ONE INJECTION
GIRLS/BOYS 13 YEARS	TUBERCULOSIS	ONE INJECTION (BCG)
SCHOOL LEAVERS	TETANUS, DIPHTHERIA	ONE INJECTION
15-19 YEAR	POLIO	BOOSTER BY MOUTH

Figure 3.10 Health Education Authority's Immunisation schedule

2 Give an oral, visual or written presentation of an investigation into one named pathogen for which a vaccine is available. Your investigation should include the effect of the pathogen on the body, and the body's response. Investigate the effectiveness of the vaccine through the analysis of statistics, either globally or in one country.

Healthy living practices

There are a number of aspects of the everyday care of children which contribute to their general health and well-being.

SLEEP

Newborn babies spend most of their time asleep (on average, 16½ hours per day during the 1st week). Gradually, the amount of sleep they need decreases. By the end of the 4th week, babies sleep, on average, 15 hours per day, and by the end of 4 months, they sleep less than 14 hours per day. However, children continue to require more sleep than adults.

Sleep is divided into two distinct states:

1 **rapid eye movement** (**REM**), which is termed **active sleep**;
2 **non-rapid eye movement** (**NREM**), which is termed **quiet sleep**.

In REM sleep, the mind is active and processing daytime emotional experiences. In NREM sleep the body rests, and restoration occurs. Babies under 2 or 3 months begin their sleep with active (REM) sleep. As they grow older, the sequence reverses and NREM precedes REM. This is an important developmental change because it shows a shift to the adult pattern.

activity

1 Look at the National Curriculum and note the areas concerned with healthy living practices and the ages at which children will cover these areas.
2 Carry out a survey to find how the numbers of hours of sleep in 24 hours varies with age. Interview parents about the effects of lack of sleep on their children.

Produce a leaflet, aimed at parents, giving advice on strategies to encourage their infants to sleep at night.

NUTRITION

As explained above in the 'Diet' section in Chapter 2, a child's growth and development may be adversely affected by an unbalanced diet. It is therefore important that from an early age children be encouraged to eat a good diet. Not only will this supply the child with the nutrients it needs for healthy growth and development, but there is evidence that individuals who eat well as children, will eat well as adults.

EXERCISE

activity

1 Read the article on p. 79: What evidence is there that children are exercising less? What reasons are given for less exercise being taken? What recommendations would you make to encourage children to take more exercise?
2 Levels of physical activity decline at around 15 years of age, particularly in girls. Carry out a survey to find out why this may be.

PERSONAL HYGIENE

It is important that children be educated from an early age to take care of their skin, hair, nails and teeth.

Skin

General rules for skin hygiene are:

- Wash face and hands in the morning
- Always wash hands after using the toilet and before meals; young children will need supervision. (See information on threadworms in 'Childhood diseases' below)
- After using the toilet, girls should be taught to wipe their bottom from the front to the back to avoid germs from the anus entering the vagina or urethra
- A daily bath is refreshing and enjoyable
- Each child should have their own flannel which must be cleaned regularly
- Skin should always be thoroughly dried,

Heartbeat study proves children are grossly unfit

Scientists have finally proved what parents have long feared: today's children are slackers. They are so inactive that their heart rates are little different awake from when they are asleep.

Using the latest technology to monitor children's heartbeats, university academics discovered that the rate of most pupils barely rose from the time they got up to the time they went to bed. None did the weekly amount of strenuous activity recommended by medical experts to exercise the heart, keep fit and reduce the risk of cardiac disease and obesity in later life.

The findings from the three-year research project – the first to monitor children's heart rates continuously – have alarmed medical experts. They blame the lack of time devoted to sport in the school day, children's reliance on cars for travel, their tendency to spend their spare time watching television or playing videos, and the decline of traditional playground games. In break time at school, the researchers found most pupils simply stood around . . .

The study began in 1993 and tracked 80 boys and girls, aged 9–12, from six primary schools; all wore monitors which used radio waves to transmit a record of cardiac output from electrodes on the chest to a wristwatch-style recorder. They also underwent periodic treadmill tests and checks for cholesterol and haemoglobin. Most children's heartbeat went up by a mere 15 beats a minute, from about 70 in deep sleep to 85 during their normal daily activity. For fitness and to avoid cardiac disease later, the heart rate should go up to about 150 beats a minute for sustained periods of 20 minutes at least three times a week. None achieved such a level.

. . . Calorie intakes for young teenagers had also dropped 50%, from about 3,000 a day in the 1950s to 2,000 a day now, but children were getting fatter. 'There is only reason for it: they are less active,' he said . . .

The main reason for the problem, say doctors and educationists, is the low priority given to school sport, plus the sale of playing fields.

'Although private schools offer more sport than state schools because they have more resources, overall physical activity in children is most strongly related to how physically active the mother is, so we can partly blame the parents.' . . .

Joanne Welsman of Exeter University's child health and fitness research centre, said children generally performed well on treadmill tests because they had not lived long enough for a sedentary lifestyle to affect their in-born fitness. 'It is the implications for their twenties, thirties and forties that we are worried about.'

(The Sunday Times, 17 March 1996)

taking special care with areas such as between the toes and under the armpits

- Observe the skin for any defects such as rashes, dryness or soreness, and act appropriately

Hair

General rules for the care of the hair are:

- Hair should be washed twice a week

- Children with long or curly hair benefit from the use of a conditioner to reduce tangles
- Hair should be rinsed thoroughly in clean water
- It should not be brushed until it is dry, as hair can be damaged if brushed when wet
- Each child should have their own brush and comb
- Afro-Caribbean hair tends to dryness and may need special oils or moisturisers applied. If the hair is braided, it may be washed with the braids intact
- Rastafarian children with hair styled in dreadlocks may not use either combs or shampoo, preferring to brush the dreadlocks gently and secure them with braid
- Devout Sikhs believe that the hair must never be cut or shaved, and young Sikh children usually wear a special head covering
- See information on headlice in the 'Childhood diseases' section on page 90 below

Nails

General rules for nail care are:

- Nails should be scrubbed daily with a soft nail brush. (See information on threadworms in the 'Childhood diseases' section on page 88 below)
- They should be cut regularly, but not too short
- Toe nails should be cut straight across
- Never dig into the sides of nails to remove dirt

Teeth

See 'Gum disease and tooth decay' in the 'Childhood diseases' section on page 88 below.

activity

1 Nutrition:

- Plot a graph to display the data given in Table 3.2. Put 'age' on the x axis. Look back at Figure 1.2. Describe the relationship between the percentage of food intake used for growth, and the rate of growth, at different ages (see Appendix A for answer.)
- Many parents complain that their children will not eat healthy food. If possible, talk to a child who the parents think has an unhealthy diet. Find out what the child eats for a period of at least three days. Do you think their diet is unhealthy? (You

Age	At birth	3 months	1 year	10 years	15 years	Adult
% total intake of food used in growth	40	40	20	10	15	4

Table 3.2 The percentage of food intake used for growth

may want to use a computer programme to help you decide.) What factors influence what the child will and will not eat?

In the light of your findings, write three daily diet sheets which would give the child a healthy diet.

- In developing countries, bottle-fed infants are 25 times more likely to die than infants who have been exclusively breastfed for the first 6 months of life. Why is this, and why do many women in the Third World insist on using a commercial milk formula?
- 200,000 children in the Third World become blind each year because of a lack of vitamin A, and 3.25 million suffer **cretinism** because of a lack of iodine. What foods could be added to a person's diet to prevent these conditions?
- Write guidelines for a carer who is:
  (a) going to bottle-feed a newborn baby
  (b) weaning a baby onto solid foods

2 Personal hygiene:

- If possible, observe a baby being bathed. Write a list of instructions on how to do this, aimed at a new parent.
- Design a poster aimed at encouraging a child to take care of either their skin, hair, teeth or nails.
- What is **cradle cap**, and how should it be treated?

Accident prevention

Facts:

- Accidents are the most common cause of death in children between the ages of 1 and 14
- Accidents account for half of all deaths in children of this age
- Three children in the UK are killed in accidents every day
- 10,000 children are permanently disabled each year
- Each year 1 in 4 children attend accident and emergency departments

In the long-term strategy set out in *Health of the Nation* (1992), the government declared its objective to reduce the death rate from accidents among children aged under 15 by at least 33% of the 1990 rate by 2005 (from 6.6 per 100,000 population to 4.4 per 100,000) (Figure 3.11).

Carers of children can reduce the risk of an accident by the following means:

- *Be a good role model.* For example, don't run across busy roads. Instead, find a safe place and wait until it is safe to cross.

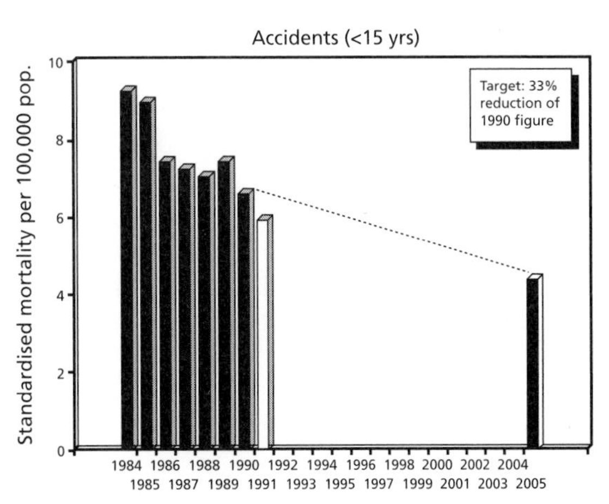

Figure 3.11 Target for the reduction of deaths from accidents in children aged under 15

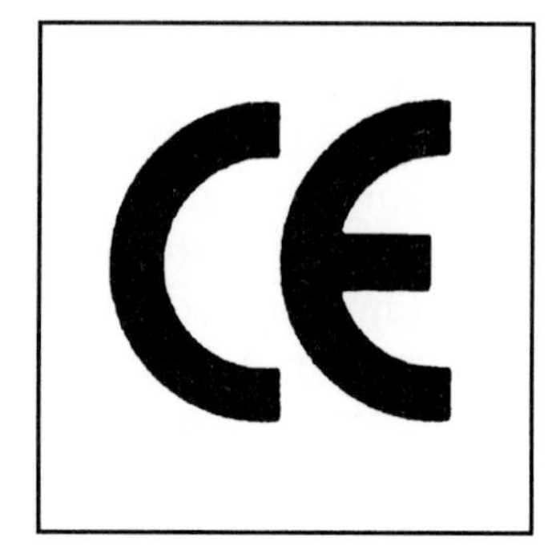

Figure 3.12 Safety symbols

- *Teach children about safety.* Even very young children can be made aware of dangers in their environment.
- *Never leave children alone in the house.* Children under 7 should never be left alone, even if apparently safely asleep.
- *Anticipate danger.* For example, children often injure themselves with objects their parents thought they could not reach.
- *Check for the appropriate safety symbol when buying goods.* Figure 3.12 shows the symbols to look for.
- *Make the child's environment as safe as possible.* The recommendations below aim to make the child safe in the home, garden and street.

SAFETY IN THE HOME

Choking and suffocation is the largest cause of accidental death in babies under 1 year, and older children playing or eating on their own are also at risk.

- Do not use a pillow for babies under 1 year old
- Baby nests should only be used for carrying a baby, not for leaving a sleeping baby unattended
- Do use a firm mattress which meets British Standard No. 1877
- Don't leave a baby alone with a propped-up bottle
- Check for hanging cords, for example of a window blind
- Keep all plastic bags away from babies, and teach older children never to put plastic bags on their heads
- Dummies must have holes in the flange to meet safety standards in case they are

drawn into the back of the throat. It is dangerous to have them on long ribbons in case they twist around the neck. For the same reason, care should be taken with coats with strings around the hood or collar

Children are at risk from **burns and fire**. These risks can be minimised if you take the following precautions:

- Fit smoke alarms upstairs and downstairs
- Keep a fire extinguisher in your kitchen
- Don't leave burning cigarettes in ashtrays
- Never smoke in bed
- Teach children the dangers of fire, and talk to them about what to do if a house fire breaks out
- Keep matches away from children
- By law, children's nightwear must satisfy the flammability performance requirements specified in British Standard No. 5722
- By law, upholstered articles (e.g. armchairs and sofas) must have fire-resistant filling material; most cover fabrics must have passed a match-resistance test; and the combination of the cover fabric and filling material must have passed a cigarette-resistance test
- Guard open fires with a spark guard
- Keep heaters away from furniture
- At night, switch off all but essential electrical appliances (unless they are designed to be left on overnight)
- Keep children away from hot cookers, and turn saucepan handles inward
- Make sure children cannot reach, or climb up to, water heaters or central heating boilers
- Keep kettles and hot drinks out of reach of children
- Don't use tablecloths that children can pull down on top of themselves
- Don't leave a hot iron unattended
- Test bath water before putting a child in. Always run the cold water in before the hot water

From time to time, all children will *fall*, but precautions should be taken to minimise this, and to ensure that the falls are not serious.

- Babies should never be left unattended, even for a moment, on a raised surface (e.g. a bed). Lay them on the floor instead.
- Stairgates should be used at the top and bottom of stairs. When old enough, the child should be taught to come downstairs backwards on all fours.
- Childproof window safety catches should be fitted, and where necessary, vertical bars.
- A harness should be used in high chairs, push chairs and supermarket trolleys.

Accidents with **poisons** are most likely to happen between the ages of 1 and 3 years old. To avoid this:

- keep all medicines in a locked cupboard
- use childproof containers
- don't store dangerous chemicals, such as bleach, under the sink. Keep them in a higher, locked cupboard
- don't transfer dangerous chemicals into other containers, such as lemonade bottles

Each year, over 7,000 children are treated in hospital for **cuts** caused by glass.

- Use special safety glass in doors
- Use plastic cups and bottles
- Keep all knives, razors and scissors safely away from children

Babies and young children can **drown** in only a few inches of water, so they should never be left unsupervised in the bath, or even with a bucket containing a few centimetres of water.

Electric sockets should be covered or fitted with dummy plugs to prevent children from poking objects into them and receiving **electric shocks**.

SAFETY IN THE GARDEN

Young children should not be left to play unsupervised in the garden, and every effort should be made to make it as safe as possible. The following recommendations are taken from a leaflet produced by The Consumer Safety Unit, Department of Trade and Industry, in association with the Consumers Association and the Royal Society for the Prevention of Accidents:

- Keep chemicals, like weedkillers, insecticides, wood preservatives and fertilisers out of sight and reach of children, preferably under lock and key, and always in their original containers.
- Garden ponds, paddling and swimming pools are dangerous places for children who make a bee-line for water. Most at risk are the under-fives. Ideally, garden ponds should be filled in and made into sandpits until the child is older. Paddling pools should be emptied immediately after use. Swimming pools should be securely fenced off or covered with a child-proof fixed cover. Although learning to swim is important, it is not a safeguard against drowning. Most important of all is adult vigilance, at all times, when children are near water.
- Children's play equipment must always be firmly fixed and checked for wear and tear. Keep swings well away from any glass, trees and bushes. If there is any risk of falling, bark chippings form a safer alternative surface for play areas – avoid hard surfaces such as gravel or paving.
- Children cannot resist putting things in their mouths. So be particularly wary about plants, berries and fungi that you suspect might be poisonous or a choking hazard. Before buying new plants check whether they are poisonous or liable to cause allergies.
- A broken fence or an open gate is an invitation to an inquisitive child who may not realise the dangers from traffic outside. Check fences and gates regularly ensuring that any damage is repaired and gates are kept shut.

And two additional points:

- Make sure young children are secure in the garden and cannot, for example, wander out onto a road
- Keep children away from bonfires and barbecues

ROAD SAFETY

Children must be educated to walk or cycle safely on roads, and precautions must be taken to allow them to travel safely in cars.

Children as pedestrians or cyclists

- Children should wear light clothes and/or luminous bands when out at dusk, or walking on country roads without pavements
- The **Green Cross Code** is a very good method of teaching road safety:

1 Find a safe place to cross, then stop. Safe places include Zebra and Pelican crossings, or where there is a lollipop person or traffic island. Never cross between parked cars.
2 Stand on the pavement, near the kerb.
3 Look all round for traffic, and then listen.
4 If traffic is coming, let is pass. Look all around again.
5 When there is no traffic near, walk straight across the road. Never run.
6 Keep looking and listening for traffic while you cross.

Children as passengers in cars

- Babies not yet sitting are best transported in a rear-facing restraint which doubles as a baby seat at home. These must not be used in the front passenger seat if the car is fitted with an air bag
- Once the baby can sit up, a child safety seat with the BSI Kite mark should be used in the back of the car until the child is 4
- When the child is too large for this seat, either a child harness or a special adjustable adult seat belt may be used, with a rigid booster cushion

activity

1 Check your home for any of the above hazards. How safe an environment would it be for a toddler?
2 What advice would you give to children about what to do if a house fire were to break out? How would you give this advice to children without frightening them?
3 Go to a shop, or look at a catalogue selling baby equipment. What safety equipment is on the market? How much would it cost to make your home safe for a child?
4 Every local authority employs a **Road Safety Officer**. Find out about the role played by this person in your area in educating children in road safety. Find out, also, about programmes run by the Royal Society for the Prevention of Accidents with the same aims.
5 A first-aid box should be kept in the home and in the car. Write a list of the essential contents of these.

Environmental health

In the sections on factors affecting growth and development in Chapter 2, and the 'Childhood diseases' section on pages 88–95 below, there is a description of some of the detrimental effects of air, water and noise pollution on children's health. Because of the harm caused, it is essential that every effort be made to limit these factors.

In April 1996, the new **Environment Agency (EA)** was launched by the government to take over the duties of the National Rivers Authority (NRA), Her Majesty's Inspectorate of Pollution (HMIP) and waste-disposal authorities. The EA is directed by eight Regional Environmental Pollution Advisory Committees (REPAC).

CONTROL OF WATER POLLUTION

The Environmental Protection Act 1990 is the legislation which allows the control of water pollution from major industrial sources. In addition, there is the Water Resources Act 1991 which is a very important anti-pollution law. There are various regulations linked to this Act which relate to specific water-pollution problems. One example is a regulation which allows areas to be designated as **nitrate-sensitive**, and the entry of nitrates into the water in these areas can then be controlled by law. Industrialists, farmers and others who cause pollution are given advice and warnings by water inspectors. If they do not respond, a prosecution will result.

In order to prevent water having any adverse effects on health, it is necessary to ensure that there is:

- a source of clean water for domestic purposes
- an effective sewage-disposal system

activity

1 Arrange a visit to a local water-treatment works. Write a report on your visit. In the report, include a flow diagram of the processes involved in the treatment of water in your area.

2 Plan a visit to your local sewage-treatment works. Which type of process is employed here, biological filter or activated sludge? Write a report on your visit. Especially note any precautions that are taken to test the quality of the effluent before it is released into the river. Does this sewage works deal with any trade or industrial waste?

CONTROL OF AIR POLLUTION

The Environmental Protection Act 1990 and the Clean Air Act 1993 are the most important laws on the control of air pollution. European law has also had a major impact on the recent control of pollution.

The Environmental Protection Act 1990 attempts to control air pollution caused by industrial processes. There is a list of noxious and offensive gases in the legislation that are specified as pollutants. These include over 3,000 industrial processes and about 2,000 major plants. Inspectors must be satisfied that an industrial process is operating using the best practicable means both for preventing the escape of noxious or offensive gases and for rendering gases harmless whenever possible. In practice, the inspectors check that approved anti-pollution equipment is installed and working effectively. There are minimum heights for industrial chimneys, and concentration levels for gases that are emitted are also specified. Unfortunately, although tall chimneys stop noxious gases from causing air pollution locally, they encourage the transport of sulphur dioxide and other pollutants over long distances, causing regional hazes and acid rain.

The local authority, i.e. the district or borough council, is responsible for local air-pollution control, and it operates through special provisions made in the Environmental Protection Act 1990 and the Clean Air Act 1993. Much of the latter act is concerned with the prevention of pollution by smoke.

There are also regulations about the sulphur and lead content of fuel used in motor vehicles, and about the sulphur content of oil fuel used in engines and furnaces. The burning of fuels in vehicles produces about 40% of the total oxides of nitrogen released into the air, as well as other air pollutants.

- Lean-burn engines have been designed which can cut down levels of nitrogen oxides in car exhausts by 75% at a cost of only about £60 for each car
- Catalytic converters can be fitted to cars. Since lead interferes with the conversion process, cars with converters have to run on lead-free petrol. These converters cost over £500 per car, and usually have to be replaced after the car has travelled 50,000 miles

activity

1 Find examples of schemes in the UK and abroad which encourage people to use their cars less. How successful are these schemes?
2 What pressure groups are concerned with the reduction of air and water pollution? What do they do to attempt to achieve this?
3 What steps can an individual take to limit air and water pollution?

CONTROL OF NOISE POLLUTION

Many noise problems, particularly those involving neighbours, can be solved by talking them through. However, if informal solutions do not work, then the law can help. The Environment Protection Act 1990 in England and Wales and the Control of Pollution Act 1974 in Scotland empower local authorities to deal with noise from **fixed premises** if they consider that the noise amounts to a 'statutory nuisance'. This is defined as a 'noise emitted from premises so as to be prejudicial to health or a nuisance'. Proceedings may be taken against noise from factories, shops, pubs, dwellings and stationary vehicles.

The Noise and Statutory Nuisance Act 1993 makes noise in the *street* a statutory nuisance. Traffic noise is excluded from this (see below), but it does include noise from car repairs and car radios and alarms. It restricts the use of loudspeakers in the streets.

To complain about noise, the following steps can be taken:

1 Complain to the **local authority** by contacting the Environmental Health Department. They must investigate

your complaint. If they agree that the noise is a nuisance, they will contact the offender, informally at first, but with an **abatement order** if necessary. If the offender fails to respond, they can take proceedings in the **magistrates' court** (the **sheriff court** in Scotland) or seek an injunction in the **High Court**.

2 An occupier of premises affected by noise can complain directly to the magistrates' court.
3 **Civil action** can be taken, but it is expensive, and legal advice should be taken.

One of the most widespread sources of noise nuisance, and the most difficult to control, is **road traffic**. Surveys show that 23% of the population are bothered by noise from this source. The Motor Vehicles (Construction and Use) Regulation 1986 limits the noise made by motor vehicles:

- They must be fitted with an efficient exhaust silencer
- The engine must not be run unnecessarily when stationary
- Horns may not be sounded in a restricted road between 11.30 pm and 7.00 am, and not by a stationary vehicle unless there is a danger to another moving vehicle
- Private vehicles must not be fitted with a gong, bell, siren or two-tone horn

Complaints about a noisy vehicle should be made to the police, and suggestions about traffic control should be made to your local traffic authority.

1 What steps can be taken to soundproof a home or school from external noise?
2 What could you do to make sure that noise from your home does not irritate neighbours?
3 What could you do about the following sources of noise?
   - general neighbourhood noise (e.g. barking dogs, noisy parties, alarms)
   - construction noise
   - noise at work
   - aircraft noise
   - noise from road traffic

Childhood diseases

Many of the so-called 'childhood diseases' can actually occur at any stage in a person's life, although they are more common in the early years. They are generally caused by one of a variety of **pathogens** (disease-causing organisms). Some of the most common examples are described below:

DISEASES CAUSED BY BACTERIA

Gum disease (or gingivitis) and tooth decay (or caries)

These are examples of conditions caused by **bacteria**. A child with **gingivitis** will have swollen, tender gums which bleed easily. Bacteria in **plaque** attached to the surfaces and neck of the teeth break down sugar in the food and form acid. This acid damages both the gums and the enamel of the teeth.

To a great extent, both of these conditions are preventable.

- Children should be given food containing added sugar (e.g. sweets) *with* meals and not *between* them
- Regular dental check-ups are needed, even for the first set of teeth. (Decay in a baby tooth can affect the permanent tooth lying underneath)
- As soon as a baby's first tooth appears, regular brushing should commence
- An adequate amount of **fluoride** is needed in the diet. If there is insufficient fluoride in the drinking water, fluoride drops should be given, but care should be taken not to exceed the recommended dose as this causes discoloration of the teeth

Whooping cough (pertussis)

This is a highly infectious bacterial disease, spread by exhaled droplets (for example, talking, coughing and sneezing). It is most common in pre-school children, and most serious in babies of under 6 months old. The **incubation period** (the time taken between picking up the pathogen and showing the symptoms) is 8 to 14 days. The child is infectious from a week before the onset of symptoms until 3 weeks after the cough starts.

The disease starts with a cold, and then the child begins to cough. Gradually, this cough becomes worse, and comes in spasms lasting half a minute or more. Breathing in after a cough produces the characteristic 'whoop', although this is not always present, particularly in young children. The child may vomit and have nose bleeds and may suffer from weight loss and convulsions. The cough may last for many months. It may lead to complications such as **pneumonia** and lung or ear infections. Even when the child starts to recover, they frequently suffer relapses.

Diseases caused by viruses

German measles (rubella)

This disease is most common in children between 4 and 12 years old. The incubation period is 14 to 21 days. The child is infectious from a week before the symptoms appear until about 5 days after the symptoms appear.

The symptoms include headache, sore throat and slight fever, followed by swelling and soreness of the neck and the appearance of a rash of minute pink spots, spreading from the face and neck to the rest of the body. In young children, the symptoms may be so mild that the disease is not diagnosed. Infection in early pregnancy can harm the development of the foetus (see the 'Diseases' section in Chapter 2, page 36 above).

Measles

Measles is a viral infection which is spread through droplets. From just before feeling ill until 4 days after the rash appears, the person will be highly infectious. The incubation period is 8 to 14 days. Early symptoms are like those of a cold often accompanied by a high temperature, conjunctivitis, dislike of light, a dry cough and perhaps small white spots on the inside of the mouth. On the third to fifth day, a blotchy, slightly elevated rash appears which lasts for 3–5 days. When the **rash** appears, the temperature usually rises sharply; the child stops eating and has a stomach ache; the **lymph glands** in the neck are swollen; and there may be **diarrhoea** and vomiting.

Mild or severe complications are common and include pneumonia, ear infections or even **encephalitis**. For this reason, it is important that all children be vaccinated against the disease (see pages 71–76).

Mumps

Mumps is a viral infection most common between the ages of 5 and 15. It is spread through exhaled droplets. The sufferer is infectious for a week before and a week after the symptoms first develop. The incubation period is 14 to 21 days.

The first symptoms are a fever, headache and loss of appetite, and sometimes vomiting. A day or two later, the most characteristic symptom of swelling of the **salivary glands** below and in front of the ear and under the chin develops. The mouth feels dry and hurts when eating or talking, and foods that stimulate the production of saliva cause pain in the swollen salivary glands. These swellings last for about a week. Complications are rare, but include meningitis and encephalitis. Now that most children in the UK are vaccinated (see above) against mumps, the numbers of cases has fallen dramatically.

Chickenpox

This viral infection is spread by direct contact (touch) or droplets. It is highly infectious, particularly before the rash appears, and remains infectious until all the spots have formed scabs. The incubation period is between 13 and 17 days. The first symptoms are probably a headache and fever. The rash is made up of red spots which turn into itchy blisters. The spots come out in crops, mainly on the trunk, but frequently on the limbs, face, scalp and even in the mouth. These dry to form scabs which can last for a few weeks. If they are scratched or get infected, they will leave a scar.

Common cold

The average child, between 4 months and 2 years, has about six or seven colds a year. These are caused by a virus spread in exhaled droplets. We are all familiar with the symptoms of the common cold, but in young children these may also include sickness or diarrhoea caused by the swallowing of nasal discharge.

Illnesses due to other parasites

Parasites live and feed on another living organism, called the **host**. As well as bacteria and viruses, these include protozoa (single-celled organisms), fungi, worms (**flat worms** and **round worms**) and **arthropods**. Although these parasites are not strictly childhood illnesses, they can contribute to secondary symptoms of ill health.

Threadworms (or pinworms)

These are the most common bowel parasite in children in the UK, and are described in the article on p. 91.

Headlice (nits)

Headlice are tiny insects about the size of a pin head. They can only live in hair, and so cannot be caught from cushions, hats or combs. To check for headlice:

- check pillows and collars for little black specks. These are the droppings and shed skins of lice.

Some tips to keep out those unwelcome creepy-crawlies

by Jean Waterworth, health visitor

Of all the creepy-crawlies that from time to time take up residence in or on us – and there are quite a few – worms seem to cause the most distress.

Head lice, for example, have almost achieved social respectability (not many young children escape them altogether) whereas threadworms are still a taboo subject, despite the fact they are surprisingly common, specially in children.

Threadworms look, as their name implies, just like thin white cotton threads and can sometimes be seen in the bowel motion.

The worms live in the lower part of the bowel and emerge at night to lay eggs on the skin around the anus (back passage). This causes irritation so the child scratches himself and contaminates his fingernails with the eggs.

If he subsequently puts his fingers in his mouth he will be re-infested; likewise if he touches food, whoever eats it will become infected.

The eggs then pass through to the bowel, and the whole process starts all over again.

The good news is that although threadworms are a nuisance they aren't harmful. They seldom have any effect other than keeping children awake with itching or possibly making them wet the bed.

Doctors will prescribe a medicine to get rid of the worms and will probably advise the whole family to be treated – adults as well as children.

This is important as symptomless infection is common and if one member of the family is left untreated he could re-infect the rest.

Other measures should include making sure everyone uses their own flannel and towel, changing the child's pyjamas or nightie and sheets as often as possible and vacuuming the carpet frequently.

To prevent threadworms keep your children's fingernails short and clean and teach them to wash their hands after using the toilet and before eating.

If your family is affected take comfort form the fact that so are plenty of others – it's just that nobody talks about it.

And a final tip – if you floss your teeth, don't throw your used bits of floss down the toilet, it might cause unnecessary panic!

(Okehampton Times, 3 February 1994)

- comb the hair over a sheet of paper with a detection comb (obtain from a pharmacist). This will dislodge the lice.
- look behind the ears and the nape of the neck at the hair close to the scalp for **nits**. These are the tiny cream-coloured egg cases stuck to the hair shafts.

It is important that these checks be made as the itching only begins about 2–3 months after infection and stops after a while as the scalp becomes insensitive. Children are particularly susceptible to catching headlice because of the amount of close head-to-head contact at school.

But it is important that adults too regularly check their hair for the presence of lice.

- *To treat the infection:* use a lotion or shampoo which contains an **insecticide** (seek advice from your local pharmacist, health visitor or school nurse on the type you should use, and treat the whole family at the same time)
- *To prevent infection:* comb the hair regularly, at least twice a day and always at bedtime. This will kill any lice

(a)

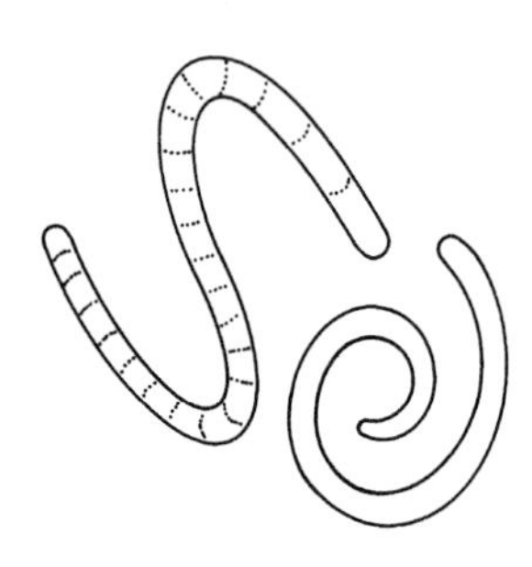
(b)

Figure 3.13 (a) Headlouse (b) Threadworms

It is important to let children know that if they have headlice this does *not* mean they are dirty. Remember:

- headlice love clean hair
- having headlice is like other infections such as a cold, in that you catch it from someone else

Environmental illnesses/disease

Environmental illnesses may be caused by air or water pollution. Asthma and lead poisoning are examples of two environmental illnesses which affect children in particular.

Asthma

In recent years, there has been an increase in the number of children suffering from **asthma**. This has been blamed on an increase in air pollution (see the 'Air pollution' section in Chapter 2 on page 57 above).

A report sponsored by the National Asthma Campaign (NAC) revealed a link between high ozone levels and increased hospital admissions for respiratory diseases over the four-year period up to 1996.

As the following article written by a health visitor explains, air pollution is not, however, the only factor that triggers the condition.

Lead poisoning

Lead is the most serious heavy-metal pollutant in the atmosphere. The lead in car exhaust fumes accounts for about 80%, with the remainder coming from industrial processes. Children are particularly susceptible to lead poisoning due to several factors such as their small ratio of volume to body surface area, their higher metabolic rate and oxygen consumption, and their different body composition. Even very low levels of lead in the blood

Why you should always choose a teddy bear with big ears . . .

by Jean Waterworth, health visitor

For reasons no-one quite understands asthma – especially among children – appears to be on the increase.

Asthma is basically a condition which affects the airways of the lungs.

These airways have a tendency to narrow and become inflamed, allowing less room for air to get through.

This in turn causes difficulty in breathing and sometimes wheezing, chest tightness or coughing.

It can start at any age, and, it seems, be grown out of at almost any age. It does often run in families.

Attacks can be triggered by many different things ranging from stress, excitement, exercise, infections, cold air, smoky atmospheres, pollen, fur, feathers and probably above all, house dust mites (tiny bugs that breed in dust).

If your child has been newly diagnosed as asthmatic there are many things you can do to help: being calm and reassuring, encouraging swimming (which helps breath control), buying mattress covers, washable hypo-allergenic duvets and pillows, damp dusting, hoovering regularly (when he or she isn't around) and so on.

Alerting the school is a good idea, and if you smoke, now is the time to give up!

It can be a dilemma though for parents knowing just how far to adapt their lifestyle . . .

But perhaps compromises can be reached – such as making rules about pets not going upstairs, and not having too many ornaments or fluffy toys in the bedroom . . .

. . . [the average teddy bear harbours two to six hundred thousand dust mites]

Perhaps letting the child have only one fluffy toy at a time in bed is sensible – along with a regular teddy wash. The bigger the ears, the better for hanging up to dry!

Many practices now have Asthma Clinics run either by a GP or a Practice Nurse.

The beauty of these clinics is that the patient can be seen by someone with a particular interest in asthma and be given more time than in surgery.

This is necessary because it is important that the patient really understands when and how to use the drugs prescribed.

With modern medicines, used properly, asthma should not restrict one's lifestyle in any way.

Asthma is unfortunately complicated by the fact that it doesn't always present itself as the classic wheezing breathlessness.

Sometimes the first clue is a persistent, dry, irritating cough especially at night.

If that sounds familiar, it would be sensible to consult your doctor.

Of course your child might simply have a dry irritating cough – but best to get it checked out.

Stop press: another way of killing teddy's house-dust mites, if he is getting too old or fragile to withstand frequent washing, is to pop him in the freezer overnight!

(Okehampton Times, 10 November 1994)

adversely affect cognitive development and behaviour, with potentially long-term effects; and higher levels result in damage to the kidneys, liver and reproductive system. Growth is impaired and blood synthesis is interfered with.

Lead level in children 'nearing danger point'

Thousands of Bradford schoolchildren have dangerously high levels of lead in their blood, according to a report commissioned by the area health authority, details of which have been passed to *The Observer*.

More than a hundred youngsters are suffering from lead poisoning, with nearly 10 per cent of the primary-school population considered 'at risk'.

There is considerable evidence that lead can damage the brains of young children and lead to intellectual retardation. In another study, Dr Neil Ward of Surrey University last week claimed to have established a link between high levels of lead in children and poor reading.

In September, school inspectors will monitor the reading ability of young children following a leaked report earlier this month from nine education authorities which showed a dramatic decline in standards . . .

The Bradford study shows children from poor families to be at greatest risk. Richard Stainton, a senior official of the National Union of Teachers, said yesterday the survey illustrated the link between the environment, poverty and educational performance . . .

Lead poisoning is widespread in Victorian, industrial cities because of old housing stock with lead plumbing often decorated with lead paint. Dr Ward's findings, however, are based on research with children in non-industrial Berkshire. He sampled hair and saliva taken from 31 primary-school pupils from a new housing development built without lead pipes, next to a dual carriageway.

'About half the group had a high level of lead and low reading ability,' said Dr Ward, 'The children with the highest lead content had the lowest reading ability.' . . .

(The Observer, 1992)

activity

1 For each of the diseases listed above (pp. 88–94), explain how you would care for a child so as to help alleviate the symptoms.

2 Make a table which gives the following information for each of the diseases, described above (pp. 88–90), which are caused by either a bacterium or a virus:

- the type of pathogen involved
- the way in which it is spread
- the incubation period
- the time the child is most infectious
- symptoms
- treatment
- prevention

3 Read the article by the health visitor on threadworms on page 91 above and then complete the following tasks:

- What are the symptoms in a child who has threadworms?
- Sketch a flow diagram to show how infection and reinfection occur
- Design a poster or leaflet which includes information on how to prevent threadworms
- Threadworms can cause **enterobiasis**. Find out what the symptoms of this disease are

4 Read the article by the health visitor on asthma on page 93 above and then answer the following questions:

- What factors may trigger an asthma attack?
- How can attacks be prevented?
- Find out what medicines may be given to help asthma sufferers

activity

Produce a record of an investigation of the key stages of physical development and the factors affecting them. This record should include:

- a description of each stage of physical development and all the factors affecting them from pre-conception until birth (using annotated diagrams).
  (This description could be in the form of a leaflet or poster aimed at prospective parents)
- a description of the norm for all categories of physical development, from birth to 7 years
- an explanation of factors which affect the physical development of children (include social and economic factors)
- an explanation of the importance of screening, monitoring and assessment procedures, from conception to 7 years
- a description of the symptoms, and possible complications, of four childhood diseases
- a description of how good child health can be promoted and maintained

The last five descriptions and explanations above could be presented in the form of leaflets or posters aimed at new parents.)

- an explanation, with examples, of physical development in middle childhood leading to puberty and adolescence, noting the gender differences.
  This explanation could be presented in the form of a leaflet aimed at an 11-year-old child)
- a description of the ageing process in adulthood.
  (This description could be presented as a poster)

References and resources

Baum, D. and Graham-Jones, S. (eds) (1989) *Child Health. The Complete Guide*, London: Viking Penguin.

Blackburn, C. (1991) *Poverty and Health: Working with Families*, Oxford: Oxford University Press.

Bourne, G. (1984) *Pregnancy*, London: Pan.

Bremner, J. G. (1994) *Infancy*, Oxford: Blackwell.

Bromwich, P. (1989) *BMA Family Doctor Guides: Menopause*, publ. by Equation, Wellingborough, Northamptonshire NN8 2RQ, in association with the British Medical Association (BMA).

Carter, M. (1992) *Genetics and Evolution*, London: Hodder & Stoughton.

Cole, M. and Cole, S. R. (1993) *The Development of Children*, 2nd edn, New York: Scientific American Books.

Grant, P. (1995) *The State of the World's Children, 1995*, Oxford: Oxford University Press, for UNICEF.

Green, N. P. O., Stout, G. W., Taylor, D. J. and (ed.) Soper, R. (1990) *Biological Science*, Cambridge: Cambridge University Press.

Gregory, J. (1995) *Applications of Genetics. Cambridge Modular Sciences*, Cambridge: Press Syndicate of the University of Cambridge.

Hall, D., Hill, P. and Elliman, D. (1994) *The Child Surveillance Hand Book*, 2nd edn, Oxford: Radcliffe Medical Press.

Illingworth R. S. (1987) *The Development of the Infant and the Young Child, Normal and Abnormal*, Edinburgh: Churchill Livingstone.

—— (1990) *Basic Developmental Screening 0–4 Years*, Oxford: Blackwell Scientific Publications.

Karmiloff-Smith, A. (1994) *Baby It's You*, London: Ebury Press, Random House UK Ltd, for Channel 4.

Manginello, F. P. and DiGeronimo, T. F. (1991) *Your Premature Baby*, New York: John Wiley & Sons, Inc.

Moore, K. L. (1988) *Essentials of Human Embryology*, Toronto and Philadelphia: B.C. Decker Inc.

NAHAT (1996) *NAHAT (National Association of Health Authorities and Trusts) NHS Handbook 1995/6*, 10th edn, Tunbridge Wells: JMH Publishing.

Overmeir, J. B. and Seligman, M. E. P. (1967) 'Effects of inescapable shock upon subsequent escape and avoidance learning, *Journal of Comparative and Physiological Psychology* 63: 23–33.

Oxford Reference Dictionary of Nursing (1990), Oxford: Oxford University Press.

Simpkins, J. and Williams, J. I. (1993) *Advanced Human Biology*, London: Collins Educational.

Stanway, P. and Ting, R. (1989) *The Mothercare Guide to Child Health*, New York: Prentice Hall Press.

Thomson, H. and Manuel, J. (1996) *Further Studies in Health*, London: Hodder & Stoughton.

Timberlake, L. and Thomas, L. (1990) *When the bough breaks . . .*, London: Earthscan Publications Ltd.

Tizard, B. and Hodges, J. (1978) 'The effect of early institutional rearing on the development of eight year old children', *Journal of Child Psychology and Psychiatry* 16: 61–73.

Tortora, G. J. and Anagnostakos, N. P. (1987) *Principles of Anatomy and Physiology*, New York: Harper and Row.

United Nations Environment Programme (UNEP) (1990) *Environmental Data Report. 1989–90*, Oxford: Blackwell.

Werner, E. and Smith, R. S. (1982) *Vulnerable but Invincible: a Longitudinal Study of Resilient Children and Youth*, New York: McGraw-Hill.

Useful addresses

Asthma Helpline
0345 01 02 03 (local rates)

The International Autistic Research Organisation
49 Orchard Avenue
Shirley
Croydon CR0 7NE
Tel.: 0181 777 0095
Fax.: 0181 776 2362

National Asthma Campaign
Providence House
Providence Place
London N1 0NT
Tel.: 0171 226 2260

The National Society for Clean Air and Environmental Protection (NSCA)
136, North Street
Brighton BN1 1RG
Tel.: 01273 326313

NHS Health Information Service
Freephone 0800 66 55 44
(Members of the public and health professionals can use this national service which is open from at least 10.00 am to 5.00 pm Monday to Friday, and calls are routed through to the correct area so that relevant local information can be given.)

The Noise Abatement Society
PO Box 518
Eynsford
Dartford
Kent DA4 0LL
Tel.: 01695 725121

The Wellcome Centre for Medical Science
183, Euston Road
London NW1 2BE
Tel.: 0171 611 8722
Fax.: 0171 611 8726
(This has an excellent information service, open to members of the public from Monday to Friday: 9.45–5.00 pm (except public holidays). Enquiries can be answered over the phone. There is a reference library; video viewing facilities; information on 250 different UK research charities; and health-related database resources).

PART

II

COGNITIVE AND LANGUAGE DEVELOPMENT

CHAPTER 4

Cognitive Development *from* Birth *to* Adulthood

Empiricism: Early theorists, such as the philosopher John Locke, believed that the newborn child was like a 'tabula rasa', or a blank slate, upon which experiences were imprinted. William James asserted that sensory inputs to the infant are 'one blooming buzzing confusion' and that it is only later, through experience, that the child manages to discriminate and make sense of them.

Nativism: A contrasting view was proposed by Descartes and Kant, philosophers writing in the 17th and 18th centuries, who believed that infants have an innate capacity to perceive space and would actively attempt to create order and organisation in their perceptual world.

Cognitive development has been studied by many psychologists:

Classical conditioning (Pavlov) allows infants to form expectations about the connections between events in their environment. **Operant conditioning** (Skinner) allows new behaviours to emerge as a result of the positive or negative events they produce.

Social Learning Theory (Bandura) allows learning to occur through imitation and modelling, without the need for direct reinforcement.

Constructivism (Piaget) assumes that the child is an active agent in her own development, adapting to the environment by changing her basic *schema*.

Social constructivism (Vygotsky) also assumes that the child is an active constructor of knowledge and understanding, but stresses the importance of *social inter-*

action. Bruner also embraces social constructivism but recognises a greater role for *adults* in the cognitive development of children.

Concept formation is an important aspect of cognitive development; the early years curriculum emphasises *active learning*, which involves concrete real-life experiences. Such experiences and situations encourage the formation of concepts. Other related aspects of cognitive development are memory, concentration, imagination, creativity, problem solving and self-expression.

Adolescents think in different ways from younger children: their thinking is more abstract and metaphysical. In adulthood and old age, most skills are developed further as part of *crystallised intelligence*, but certain abilities, such as short-term memory and the memory for names usually deteriorate.

Intelligence may be defined as the ability to solve problems or as cognitive functioning in a wide variety of behaviours. Intelligence tests (IQ tests) compare a child's performance to that of others of the same age; they do not provide an accurate picture of the many different facets of intellectual functioning.

Play is central to a child's learning. The *process* is always more important than the *product*. Piaget defined three stages of play; this is known as the social constructivist view on play and includes sensorimotor play, symbolic play and games with rules.

What is cognitive development?

Cognitive – or **intellectual** – **development** refers to the development of the parts of the brain concerned with perceiving, reasoning, acquiring knowledge and understanding. Physical and cognitive development take place side by side; from the moment of birth, a child is absorbing knowledge about the environment through the senses of sight, sound, touch, smell and taste. Cognitive and **language development** are essential components of the **learning process** and go along together. Progress in one area affects progress in the other.

During childhood, the brain grows rapidly. Every brain cell – or **neuron** – that the person will ever use throughout life is present at birth; the baby's experiences of the world are vital to the restructuring of the brain, which forms increasingly specialised pathways to control different behaviours. By the age of 1 year, the baby's brain will have reached three-quarters of its adult size, and up until middle childhood, the two **hemispheres** of the brain become more interconnected and specialised. (See Figures 4.1 and 4.2.)

Theories of human development often focus on the central issues of **nature** and **nurture**.

The nature–nurture debate

The **nature–nurture** debate is about the relative importance of inherited and envi-

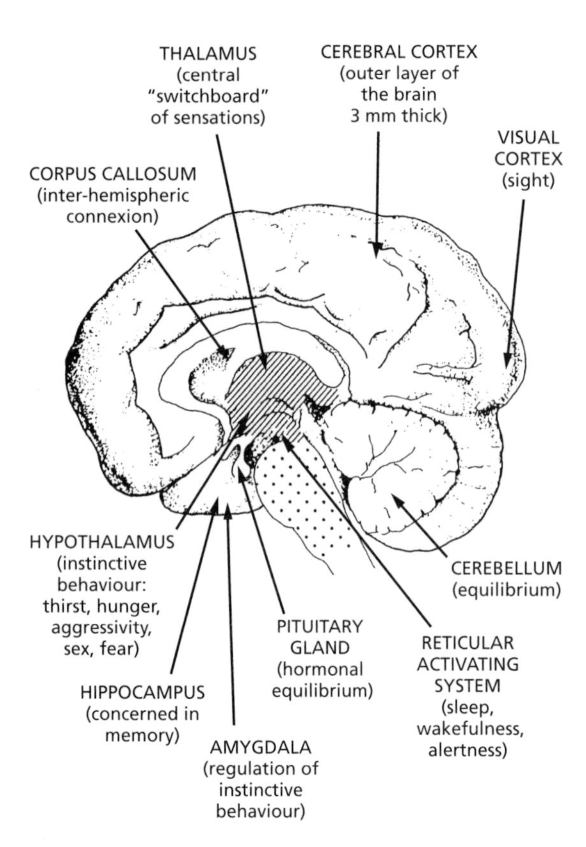

Figure 4.1 Side-view of the human brain: right hemisphere (inside)

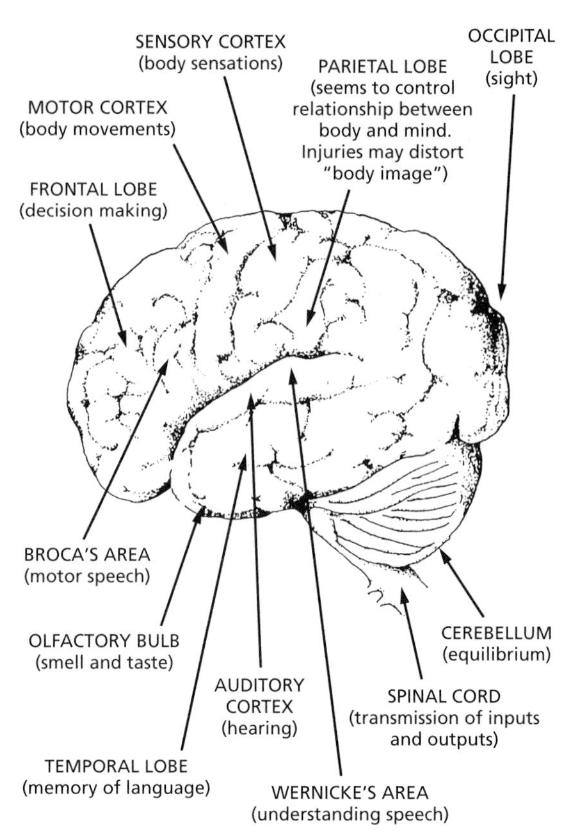

Figure 4.2 Side-view of the human brain: right hemisphere (outside)

ronmental influences on human characteristics. **Developmental psychologists** are divided into two broad camps:

1 *empiricists* – who stress the role of learning and environmental influence on human characteristics;
2 *nativists* – who stress genetic (hereditary) influences.

Theories of cognitive development

The systematic scientific study of child development began in the twentieth century, and may be explored through the work of six leading theorists:

1 Ivan Pavlov – classical conditioning
2 B. F. Skinner – behaviourism and operant conditioning
3 Albert Bandura – social learning theory
4 Jean Piaget – constructivism
5 Lev Vygotsky – social constructivism
6 Jerome Bruner – social constructivism.

Ivan Pavlov (1849–1936)

Ivan Pavlov was a Russian physiologist who discovered a type of **associative learning** called **classical conditioning**. Most of his experiments were carried out on dogs, but the underlying principles may also be applied to human learning. Pavlov harnessed a dog to an apparatus which, by means of a tube inserted in the animal's cheek, measured the amount of salivation elicited during the experiment.

Salivation is a normal **reflex** response to food in the mouth. Pavlov found that a hungry untrained dog does not salivate when a bell is sounded; but if food was offered after sounding a bell, eventually the dog would **associate** the bell with the food and would salivate merely at the sound of the bell. (See Figure 4.3.) Pavlov paired a **conditioned stimulus (CS)** – a bell – with an **unconditioned stimulus (UCS)** – food in the mouth. The bell is called a conditioned stimulus because the behaviour it elicits is 'conditional' on the way it has been paired with the unconditioned stimulus. Food in the mouth is called an unconditioned stimulus because it 'unconditionally' causes salivation. Salivation is called an **unconditioned response**, because it is 'unconditionally' elicited by food in the mouth. When the unconditioned response (salivation in response to food in the mouth) occurs in

Figure 4.3 Pavlov's dog

response to the conditioned stimulus (the bell), it is called a **conditioned response (CR)** because it depends upon the pairing of the CS (the bell) and the UCS (the food). The key sign that learning has taken place is that the CS elicits the CR before the onset of the UCS.

Example: a recent study by Lewis Lipsitt (1990) used classical conditioning techniques to show that newborn infants will form a conditioned response to a disagreeable stimulus. Lipsitt paired a tone (CS) with a puff of air to the eyes (UCS). Infants under one month old learnt to shut their eyes (UCS) when the tone sounded 1.5 seconds before the puff of air. The shutting of their eyes became a conditioned response, as it was not conditional on the puff of air to the eyes. (See Figure 4.4.)

B. F. Skinner (1904–90)

Burrhus Frederic Skinner was a behavioural psychologist whose work was concerned with the way in which the external environment controls individual behaviour. He started his experiments on **operant** (or **instrumental**) **conditioning** using rats, but argued that similar systems of using **reinforcers** or rewards could be used in the education of young children. Operant conditioning refers to behaviour which operates on the environment in order to produce an outcome. Skinner invented an apparatus known as the 'Skinner box' – see Figure 4.5. A rat was placed in this box, which was empty apart from a lever and a food tray. After the rat depressed the lever, a pellet of food was automatically released into the food tray. Skinner's learning theory relies on the **law of reinforcement** which states: 'actions which are immediately followed by rewards (reinforcement) are repeated and learned whereas actions or behaviour which are not followed by reinforcement are dropped'. The rat in

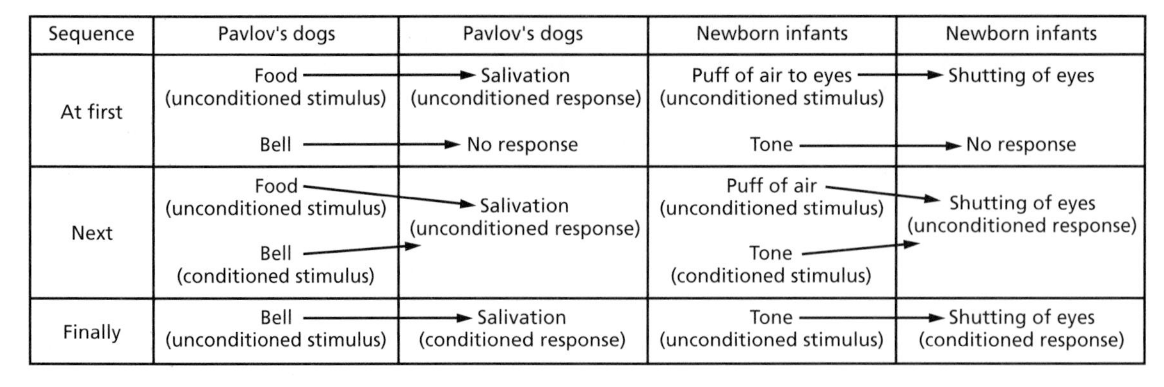

Sequence	Pavlov's dogs	Pavlov's dogs	Newborn infants	Newborn infants
At first	Food → (unconditioned stimulus) Bell →	Salivation (unconditioned response) No response	Puff of air to eyes → (unconditioned stimulus) Tone →	Shutting of eyes No response
Next	Food → (unconditioned stimulus) Bell → (conditioned stimulus)	Salivation (unconditioned response)	Puff of air → (unconditioned stimulus) Tone → (conditioned stimulus)	Shutting of eyes (unconditioned response)
Finally	Bell → (unconditioned stimulus)	Salivation (conditioned response)	Tone → (unconditioned stimulus)	Shutting of eyes (conditioned response)

Figure 4.4 A summary of classical conditioning

Skinner's box learnt that food was provided whenever it depressed the lever. Skinner used the term **reinforcer** to apply to anything which would make the animal repeat the response. Reinforcers may be tangible rewards, such as toys, sweets or money, or intangible rewards, such as praise or affection.

Example: a child may receive a sweet after behaving in a desirable way, perhaps by tidying their toys away. The child's behaviour is thus **shaped** by learning that certain actions result in a reward.

In his animal experiments, Skinner also used **negative reinforcements**. The rat may have its behaviour reinforced when we stop something which the rat does not like. Skinner applied an electric shock to the rat which could only be avoided by the rat jumping into a shuttle box – a **learned response**. Such a reinforcement is not the same as punishment as the intention is different: in punishment, the intention is to stop a behaviour from occurring rather than to make it more likely to happen. **Behaviour therapy** often uses operant-conditioning methods in order to treat individuals with mental illness or behaviour disorders. Another use in education is **programmed learning**, which allows students of mixed ability to progress at their own pace by moving from simple responses to complex problem-solving activities.

Example: an **open learning workshop** allows students to work through a sequence of exercises on the computer. The rewards or reinforcers enable steady progress through a structured sequence of programs, usually using words of praise and encouragement.

Figure 4.5 A Skinner box experiment with a collared dove

For Skinner, cognitive development consists of a history of reinforcements that shape behaviour in particular ways. Lack of reinforcement leads to a behaviour decreasing in frequency and being eliminated.

ALBERT BANDURA

Bandura is a social psychologist who took the work of the behaviourists and applied it to human development. Whereas Skinner and the early behaviourists concentrated on observable stimuli and responses, Bandura emphasised the role of **observation** and **modelling** in the learning process. Bandura and his colleagues conducted various experiments to support his **social cognitive theory**, also called **observational learning**.

Bandura argues that learning may occur merely as a result of watching someone else perform some action, and that direct reinforcement is not always necessary for such learning to take place.

Examples: children learn ways of hitting from watching violent scenes on television. Children learn physical skills such as swimming or bike-riding partly from observing these skills being demonstrated by others.

Bandura also found that children are more likely to imitate the behaviour of, or use as role models:

- those people who are warm and loving towards them
- those who are competent or powerful
- those who are seen as receiving rewards for their behaviour
- those who are most similar to themselves, e.g. the same gender

From as early as one hour old, a baby will imitate an adult's gestures. If the baby is held in front of her mother and the mother pulls her tongue in and out, the baby will almost always respond by moving her own tongue in and out (see Figure 4.6a). Experiments have proved that *movement* is essential for imitation to take place; a static tongue already protruded will not evoke imitation in the neonate.

The social component of Bandura's learning theory is found in his concept of **intrinsic reinforcements** or **intrinsic rewards**. These reinforcements are internal to the individual and may be expressed as pride, satisfaction or the simple enjoyment which follows achievement.

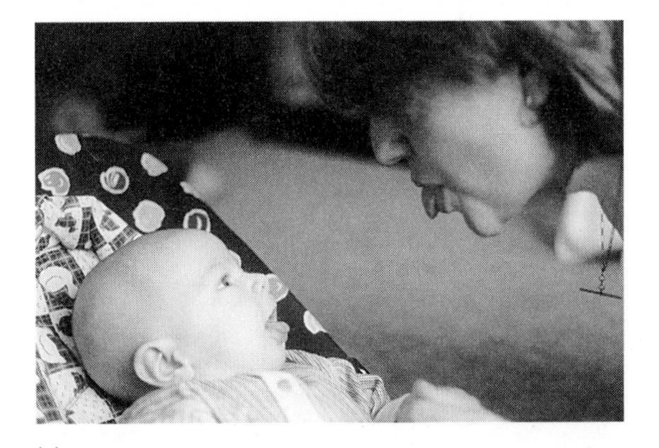

(a)

(b)

Figure 4.6 Imitating behaviour (a) Ben pulls his tongue out in response to his mother (b) He tries to copy the expression on his father's face

Example: a child who has learnt how to write his name or to tie his shoe laces will feel satisfaction or pride.

Bandura also argued that the inner mental processes, previously ignored by strict behaviourists, are central to the development of learning. Learning from a model is not merely a matter of imitation but also involves the setting of goals, the prediction of outcomes and the evaluation of individual performance. Social cognitive theory recognises that it is people's ideas about the stimulus, not the stimulus itself, that controls behaviour.

CASE STUDY

A LEARNING SITUATION

One day, Alex and his mother were playing in the living room, with the TV on in the background. Alex was not paying much attention to the TV: he was more interested in playing a sort of wrestling match with his mother. At age 4 years, he had not acquired much appreciation for the plot of the space adventure film that was on TV. However, when a noisy commercial for a new chocolate bar called 'Boomer' interrupted the film, Alex stopped playing with his mother and began to watch the TV with rapt attention. In the commercial, a boy a little older than himself ran into a shop, bought a 'Boomer' bar, walked briskly outside and then peeled back the sweet wrapper and took a bite. The boy was immediately surrounded by attractive friends who smiled and laughed and invited the boy to come and play with them. Alex seemed visibly impressed.

activity

1 What factors in the commercial might have caught Alex's attention?
2 Identify the probable conditioned stimulus (CS), the unconditioned stimulus (UCS) and the conditioned response (CR) and unconditioned response (UCR) involved in the commercial (see the section on classical conditioning on page 100 above).
3 From an observational-learning (Bandura) viewpoint, identify the factors in the commercial that might cause Alex to want to imitate the boy and buy a 'Boomer'.

(Answers in Appendix A.)

JEAN PIAGET (1896–1980)

Jean Piaget was originally a biologist who became interested in the intellectual development of children whilst studying clinical psychology and working with Alfred Binet in Paris. Binet was involved in the standardisation of intelligence test procedures, and Piaget became interested in the variety of responses children gave to the standard test questions. In particular, he was intrigued by the nature of children's thinking which was demonstrated when they gave a number of similar *wrong* answers. Why did children make such similar mistakes?

Piaget saw the child as an active participant in the development of knowledge, **constructing** his own understanding and **adapting** to the world around him in increasingly efficient ways. In Piaget's view, babies are born with the ability to adapt to and learn from the environment; their innate mental processes are basic patterns of actions – Piaget called them **schemas**. The reflexes of a newborn baby (see Chapter 1, page 18) are primitive schemas which provide frameworks for action and are later transformed into new schemas through the process of **adaptation**.

The process of adaptation

Piaget maintained that the method of developing schemas involves the following processes:

- *assimilation:* during assimilation, the child takes in new information and tries to make it conform to what is already known from previous experiences.

  Example: sucking is a primitive schema, present as a reflex in the newborn baby; when lightly touched on the cheek by a nipple, the baby will turn and start sucking on the nipple. Later, the baby may find their thumb or finger touching their cheek – because it feels not unlike the nipple, the child will start sucking on it. (The schema itself changes little but now includes the possibility of a new object.)
- *accommodation:* accommodation is the adjustment which takes place in one's understanding of something following new experiences; the schema adapts itself, or **accommodates**, to the new situation.

  Example: when babies encounter another object, e.g. a blanket, they may try to suck it. However, as the blanket is very unlike the nipple or thumb, it is not assimilated into the sucking schema. Babies then make some **accommodation**: they will modify the existing sucking schema to take account of the new experience, perhaps by choosing one corner of the blanket or by only sucking the smooth satin binding.
- *equilibration:* this third part of the adaptation process involves a periodic restructuring of schemas into new structures. Children are motivated to develop schemas by the process of equilibration since it restores equilibrium – or balance – and so reduces tension.

  Example: a child has a pet dog called Max. At first, they may think that all dogs are called Max – or even all cats. However, they gradually learn that dogs are similar to but also different from cats. They also learn that other people's dogs have different names, and that although dogs and cats are different, they are both animals. Their concept of dogs and animals continues to develop through this process of assimilation → disequilibrium → accommodation → equilibrium

Piaget's stages of cognitive development

Piaget believed that there are four major developmental stages between birth and adulthood, corresponding to infancy, early childhood, middle childhood and adolescence. (See Tables 4.1 and 4.2.) This theory was based on many years of testing and observing children's behaviour and recording their responses in problem-solving situations. Piaget maintained that the young baby's mind works very differently from an adult's, and that the child's thinking passes through a sequence of consecutive changes on the path to adulthood. All cognitive development proceeds as a result of a child performing **opera-**

Age	Stage	Description
Birth–18 months (approx.)	Sensorimotor	Infants are developing their first **schema**; coordinating their sensory perceptions and simple motor behaviours; they are totally **egocentric**. See Table 4.2 for substages.
2–7 years (approx.)	Pre-operational	Young children are developing a range of schemas; they can represent reality to themselves through the use of symbols, including mental images, words and gestures. They begin to classify objects into groups, tend to overgeneralise and often fail to distinguish their point of view from those of others. They are still egocentric.
7–11 years (approx.)	Concrete operational	Children can now **decentre** and reason logically. They are able to do such things as addition and subtraction providing the problem is related to experience. Such operations are considered concrete because they are carried out in the presence of the objects and events being thought about. Children are less egocentric now, but cannot yet deal with abstract concepts and ideas.
12 years onwards	Formal operational	Children are now able to reason logically and to deal with abstract concepts. They can think about and imagine things that have not happened yet or that have never been seen. They can now think in a rational, scientific way and can approach problems in a systematic and thought-out manner.

Table 4.1 Piaget's stages of cognitive development

tions on their environment. An operation may be mental or physical; it is anything the child does which has an effect on their environment.

Object permanence

Piaget believed that there are a series of steps involved in the child's emerging understanding of **object permanence**. Object permanence is the recognition that an object continues to exist even when it is temporarily out of sight. The first sign that the baby is developing object permanence comes at about 2 months of age. If you show a toy to a child of this age and then put a screen in front of the toy, the child shows a surprised reaction, as if they knew that something should still be there. However, babies of this age show no signs of searching for a dropped toy or one that may have disappeared beneath a blanket.

Substage 1 Birth–6 weeks	**Reflex schemas exercised** The reflexes present at birth provide the initial connection between infants and their environments. Involuntary rooting, sucking, grasping and looking all produce stimulation in addition to responses to stimuli. *Example:* when infants suck, they experience tactile pressure on the roof of the mouth; this stimulates further sucking, which produces more tactile pressure, and so on.
Substage 2 6 weeks–4 months	**Primary circular reactions** This is the repetition of actions which are pleasurable in themselves. Existing reflexes are extended in time or are applied to new objects. Such actions are termed primary because they are centred on the baby's own body; they are termed circular because they lead only back to themselves. *Example:* infants may suck between feeds, or may suck their thumbs. They may also wave their hands about and kick their feet, purely for the pleasure experienced through such actions.
Substage 3 4–8 months	**Secondary circular reactions** Infants begin to realise that objects are more than extensions of their own actions; their focus is on objects external to themselves. Infants will repeat actions that produce interesting changes in the environment. *Example:* when babies make a noise and their mother responds, they will repeat that noise. Similarly, a baby may enjoy shaking a rattle or bell.
Substage 4 8–12 months	**Coordination of secondary circular reactions** Infants combine actions to achieve a desired effect; such coordinated effort is seen as the earliest form of true problem-solving. Infants now understand that objects have an existence independent of themselves. *Example:* infants will knock a pillow away in order to reach for a desired toy.
Substage 5 12–18 months	**Tertiary circular reactions** Infants begin to 'experiment'; they try out new ways of playing with or manipulating objects in order to see what the consequences will be. Improved motor skills also aid wider exploration of the child's environment. *Example:* Piaget's son, Laurent, aged 10 months, is lying in his cot: 'He grasps in succession a celluloid swan, a box etc., stretches out his arm and lets them fall . . . Sometimes he stretches out his arm vertically, sometimes he holds it obliquely, in front of or behind his eyes, etc. When the object falls in a new position (e.g. on his pillow), he lets it fall two or three times more on the same place, as though to study the spatial relations; then he modifies the situation.'
Substage 6 18–24 months	**Beginnings of symbolic representation** Infants use images, perhaps words or actions, to stand for objects. They indicate that they can carry out actions mentally and think about objects that are not present. This substage is really the beginning of the next major stage: pre-operational thought. *Example:* the child will search for a hidden object, certain that it exists somewhere (object permanence).

Table 4.2 Substages of sensorimotor development (Piaget)

activity

Ask a willing parent of a baby aged between 6 and 12 months of age if you can try the object-permanence activity with the baby:

1 Ask the parents for one of the baby's favourite playthings. Place the baby in a sitting position or on their stomach in such a way that they can reach for the toy easily.
2 While the baby is watching, place the toy in full view and within easy reach. Note if the baby reaches for the object.
3 Again, in full view of the baby, cover part of the toy with a cloth so that only part of it is visible. Note if the baby reaches for the toy.
4 If the baby reaches for the toy, cover it completely with the cloth. Note if the baby continues to reach for it.
5 While the child is still interested in the toy, and again in full view of the child, cover the whole toy with the cloth once more. Note if the baby tries to pull the cloth away or to search for the toy in some way.

Research shows that Step 3 – i.e. continuing to reach for the partly covered toy – is typically experienced at about 6 months, Step 4 at about 7 months and Step 5 at about 8 months. Write up the results of your activity and compare with others.

The pre-operational stage: 2–7 years

Piaget described the radical change that takes place in children's thinking at around the age of 2 years in terms of the child's ability to use **symbols**, but he tended to focus on what the child still *cannot* do rather than on what the child *can* do. Characteristics of the pre-operational stage of cognitive development are:

Egocentrism

Egocentrism is the inability of the child to **centre** on more than one aspect of a situation at a time. Children in the pre-operational stage look at things entirely from their own perspective. This should not be construed as selfishness or arrogance; the child assumes that everyone sees the world in the same way.

Example: the 'three mountains' task. A model of three mountains with different

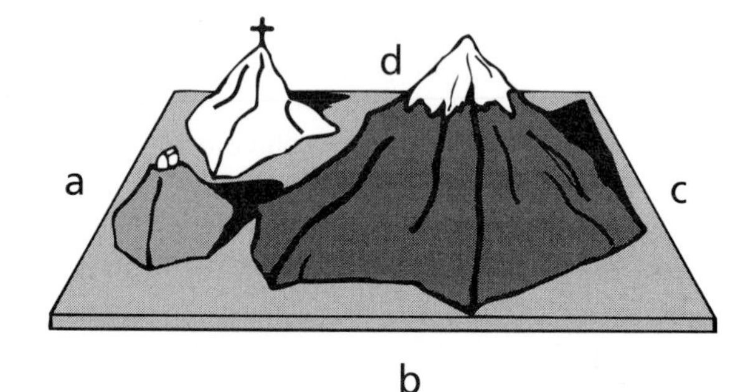

Figure 4.7 The three mountains task

features was placed in front of the child. The child was asked to describe the model from her point of view, saying which mountain was closest and which furthest away etc. A small doll was then placed at position C (see Figure 4.7), with a different perspective from that of the child. The child was then asked to describe the scene from the point of view of the doll. Piaget and Inhelder (1956) concluded from the results of this task that children at this stage were unable to **decentre**, i.e. the child described the view entirely from her own perspective.

The 'hiding from policemen' experiment

This task was devised by Martin Hughes to present children with a task that was more meaningful in everyday terms than the Piaget 'three mountains' experiment. Children aged between $3\frac{1}{2}$ and 5 years of age were tested individually using an apparatus consisting of two walls which intersected to form a cross. In the first instance, the child was asked to judge whether a 'policeman' doll could see a 'boy' doll from various positions; then the child was asked to 'hide the doll so that the policeman can't see him', with the policeman at a given fixed position. In the second instance, another policeman was introduced (see Figure 4.8), and the child was asked to hide the doll from *both* policemen. This required the child to consider and coordinate two points of view. Look at Figure 4.8 and decide where the child should be placed (in this instance, the only effective hiding place is at C). This task was repeated three times so that each time a different section was left as the only hiding place. The results were dramatic: 90% of the responses given by the children were correct.

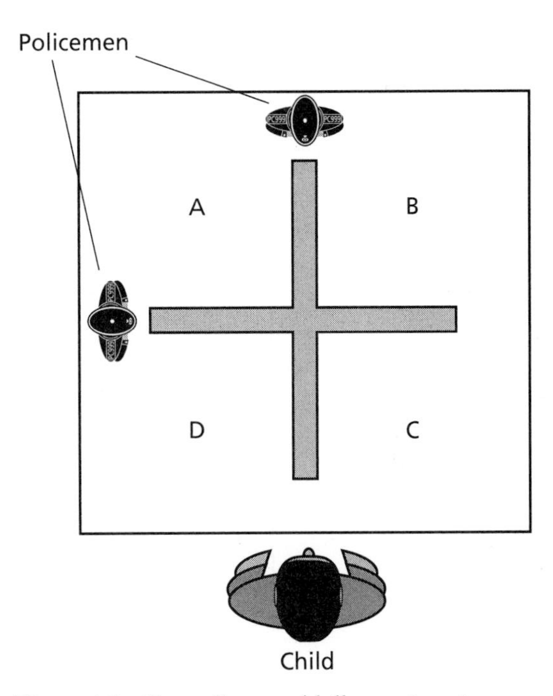

Figure 4.8 The policemen/doll experiment

Conservation
This is the idea that objects remain the same in fundamental ways, such as in mass or number, even when there are external changes in shape or arrangement. Children at this pre-operational stage are likely to be misled by the visual appearance of the object and say that the amount or mass has changed. (See Figure 4.9.)

Example: two identical glasses contain equal amounts of water. The water from one of these glasses is poured into another, differently-shaped glass (tall and thin, or short and squat), and the child is asked if there is still the same amount to drink in each glass containing water. A child under 5 years old will rarely **conserve**, i.e. such a child will assume the amount of liquid to have been altered.

CONSERVATION SKILL	BASIC PRINCIPLE	TEST FOR CONSERVATION SKILLS	
		Step 1	Step 2
Number	The number of units in a collection remains unchanged even though they are arranged in space.	Two rows of buttons arranged in one-to-one correspondence	One of the rows elongated or contracted
Substance	The amount of a malleable, plastic-like material remains unchanged regardless of the shape it assumes.	Modelling clay in two balls of the same size	One of the balls rolled into a long, narrow shape
Length	The length of a line or object from one end to the other end remains unchanged regardless of how it is rearranged in space or changed in shape.	Strips of cloth placed in a straight line	Strips of cloth placed in altered shapes
Area	The total amount of surface covered by a set of plane figures remains unchanged regardless of the position of the figures.	Square units arranged in a rectangle	Square units rearranged
Weight	The heaviness of an object remains unchanged regardless of the shape it assumes.	Units placed on top of each other	Units placed side by side
Volume	The space occupied by an object remains unchanged regardless of a change in its shape.	Displacement of water by object placed vertically in the water	Displacement of water by object placed horizontally in the water

Figure 4.9 Conservation experiments

Figure 4.10 A possible reason for wrong answers to conservation tasks

Class inclusion

This is the relationship between classes of objects such that a subordinate class is included in the larger class, as apples are part of the larger class 'fruit'. Children at the pre-operational stage confuse classes (e.g. a set of animals or a set of flowers) with subclasses (e.g. dogs or roses).

Example: a child may know that several different words may be used to label their dog – terrier, dog, puppy, animal, and the dog's name. Although the child may use all these names, they do not yet grasp the concept of **class inclusion**: that all individual dogs like their terrier are included in the category of dog, and that all dogs are included in the larger category of animal. Experiments in conservation:

– activity –

1 Conservation of mass:

- Take two balls of play dough or plasticine which the child agrees are the same
- Take one of the balls and, in front of the child, roll it out into a cylinder – or sausage – shape
- Ask the child if the two pieces of dough are the same amount

2 Conservation of number:

- Make two rows of buttons which the child agrees have the same number
- Spread one row out to make a longer row, and ask the child which row contains more buttons

Piaget states that children under 7 years old will say that the cylinder shape of dough is bigger and that the longer row of buttons contains more buttons.

See Table 4.3 for a summary of cognitive development at this stage.

The concrete operational stage of cognitive development: 7–12 years

As **concept formation** develops, children begin to think about objects in a new way. In middle childhood, their thinking becomes more 'mobile', and they become capable of mental operations, internalised actions that fit into a logical system. Piaget thought the most critical of these concrete operations was **reversibility**: the understanding that both physical actions and mental operations can be reversed.

Example: the ball of play dough can be made into a cylinder shape and then reformed back into a ball shape.

Another feature of this stage of development is that children can take into account several features of an object at the same time, when they are **classifying** and **seriating**. This means that they no longer **centrate**, i.e. they are able to concentrate on more than one thing at a time.

According to Piaget, children begin to master the principle of conservation at

Centration	**Piaget's work** Children at this stage usually focus on one aspect of a situation. This means that they ignore all others. A major demonstration of this is **egocentrism**. Children tend to assume that objects have consciousness (**animism**). *Example:* they may be cross with – and kick – a chair that they have bumped into. Children fail to consider both the height and width of containers in order to compare their volumes. (See the conservation section on page 110.) Children cannot **reverse** their thought processes. If a boy says he has a sister and is then asked if his sister also has a brother, he is likely to reply that his sister does not have a brother: he has difficulty reversing his own role. Similar difficulties arise in early mathematics – e.g. 3 + 4 is seen as different from 4 + 3. Children confuse classes with subclasses (see the **class inclusion** section on page 110.) **Criticisms of Piaget's work** Researchers have found that even very young children can **decentre** and see things from somebody else's point of view, including babies (see the policeman/doll experiment on page 109). When children are in a situation which makes what Margaret Donaldson (1978) calls 'human sense' they *can* **conserve** and understand **reversibility**. Children find formal test situations rather difficult. This is because it is very hard for a young child to understand what is actually being asked of them (see Figure 4.11).
Confusion of appearance with reality	Children may believe that a straight stick partially submerged in water actually does become bent. Children behave as if a witch's mask actually changes the identity of the person wearing it. Children lack the ability to question the reality of figures such as Father Christmas or the Tooth Fairy (e.g. 'How could Father Christmas deliver toys to everyone at night?')
Moral realism	Children at this stage of cognitive development are characterised by illogical thinking. They base what is right or wrong on what happens. Morality is seen as something imposed from the outside – it does not take **intentions** or **motives** into account. *Example:* a child helping to wash up breaks a cup. A child takes a valuable cup from the cupboard, having been told not to, but does not break the cup. A child at this stage will believe that the child who broke the cup was the naughtier of the two children.

Table 4.3 A summary of the pre-operational stage of cognitive development

about the age of 8 when they recognise that it is *logically necessary* for the amount of liquid, mass, number etc. to remain the same despite the change in appearance. They now understand certain logical relationships through the following related mental operations:

- *identity:* the child recognises that a change limited to outward appearance does not change the amounts involved. The child might explain: 'the balls of dough were equal to start with and nothing was added or taken away, so they are the same.'
- *compensation:* the child understands that changes in one aspect of a problem are mentally compared with and compensated for by changes in another. The child might explain: 'The cylinder-shaped ball of dough is longer, but it's thinner, so it's the same.'

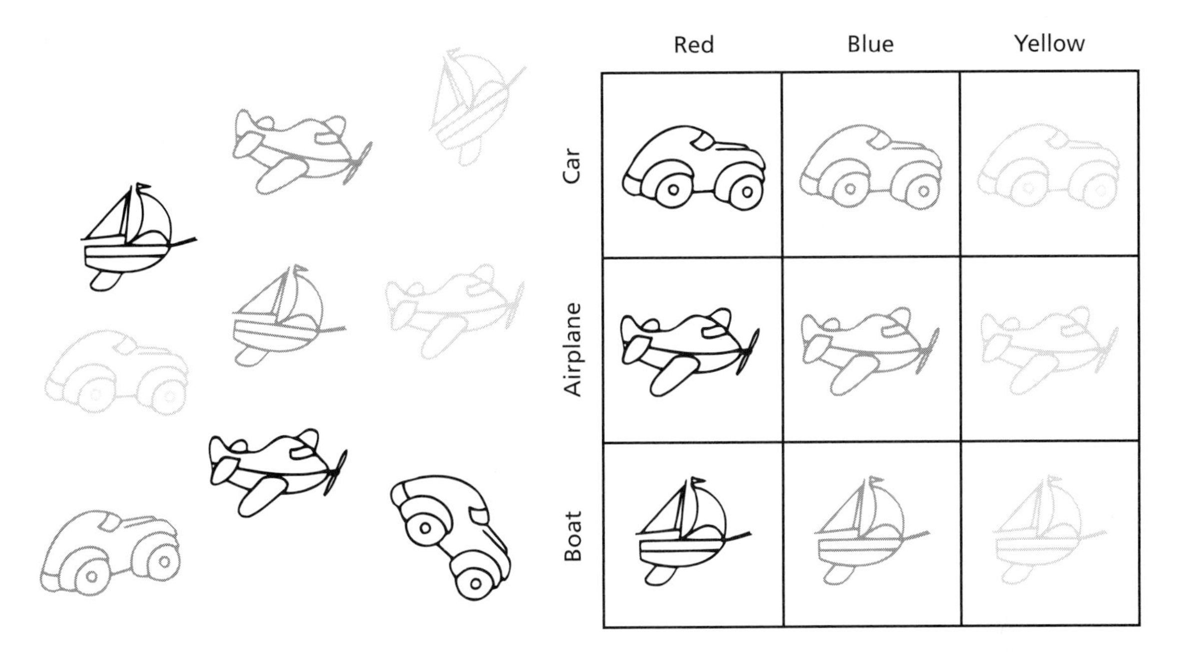

Figure 4.11 Logical classification

- *reversibility:* the child realises that one operation will reverse the effects of another. The child might explain: 'If I changed the cylinder shape back into a ball, it would be the same.'
- *classification:* the child can now grasp relationships between objects and is able to separate a collection of objects according to multiple criteria. For example, the child might have a stamp collection which is organised first by country, then by picture identification (e.g. animals, birds or flowers) and then perhaps by size or shape. (See Figure 4.11.) **Class inclusion** is now fully understood.
- *inductive logic:* the child can now go from their own experience to a general principle. The child might reason: 'I have added another animal to this set of animals and counted it. This set now has one more, so adding always makes it more.'

See Table 4.4 for a summary of cognitive development at this stage.

The formal operational stage (from 12 years onwards)

Piaget believed that there is a fairly rapid eruption of development over a period of years, starting at about the age of 12 and nearing completion at about 15 years of age. The major elements of this new level of abstract thinking are:

- the understanding of **abstract concepts**, such as democracy, peace or justice
- the use of **deductive logic**; the testing of hypotheses to solve problems
- the use of **combinational logic** to solve complex problems, e.g. algebraic formulas
- the ability to separate the **real** from the **possible**, rather than relying on concrete situations

Decentration	Children no longer concentrate on just one thing at a time, but are able to take into account several features of an object or an event at the same time; they are now able to classify and seriate more competently.
Conservation	Children understand that certain properties of an object will remain the same even when other, superficial ones are changed. They know, for example, that when a tall, thin glass is emptied into a short, fat glass, the amount of liquid remains the same (conservation of liquid). The same is true for conservation of mass, number, volume etc.
Identity	Children understand that if nothing has been added or taken away, the amount must remain the same.
Compensation	Children can mentally compare changes in two aspects of a problem and see how one aspect compensates for the other.
Reversibility	Children realise that certain operations can reverse or negate the effects of others.
Inductive logic	Children apply their own experience to a general principle. In primary-school science, children make systematic observations and then try to reason why things happened in a particular way.
Egocentrism declining	Children can now see things from somebody else's point of view; they can think about how others perceive them (social perspective taking), and can also understand that a person can feel one way and act in another way.
Changes in social interaction	Children understand about rules and begin to play rule-based games. They make moral judgements of 'good' and 'bad' behaviour (autonomous moral reasoning), and believe that the punishment must fit the crime.

Table 4.4 A summary of the concrete operational stage of cognitive development

Piaget recognised that the adolescent is highly impressed with the power of thought and naively underestimates the practical problems involved in achieving an ideal future. Although egocentrism continues to decline, it often persists until the individual enters the job market.

Some adults never reach the formal operational stage of development and manage to lead a fulfilled adult life without ever using formal thinking.

Lev Vygotsky (1896–1934)

Vygotsky was born in Russia in the same year as Piaget. His study of psychology and cognitive development was greatly influenced by the rise of Marxism in 1920s Russia. Whereas Piaget was an only child and apparently solitary by nature, Vygotsky was one of eight children growing up in a culture that valued the importance of the social group. After an initial training in law, Vygotsky worked at the

Combinational logic	At this stage, adolescents are able to consider both a situation and all its possible alternatives. *Examples:* (a) planning a trip to the seaside by car, adolescents can mentally review all the possible routes by systematically assessing which is the shortest or fastest route. Or, in a more abstract sense: (b) when asked what the Prime Minister could have done in a certain situation, a teenager will come up with a variety of alternatives, some real and some impractical.
Separating the real from the possible	At this stage, adolescents can reason about hypothetical problems; they can think about possibilities as well as actualities. *Example:* if asked the question: 'If all Martians have green faces and this creature has a green face, is it a Martian?', the adolescent can reach a logical conclusion, whereas a 7 year old is likely to say 'I don't know' or 'Things don't have green faces.'
Hypothetical-deductive reasoning	This is the ability to form hypotheses and to use scientific (or deductive) logic, often called the scientific method. *Example:* the pendulum problem: an adolescent observes an object hanging from a string and attempts to discover what determines how fast the object swings. She is shown how to vary the length of the string, the height from which the pendulum is released, the force of the push on the pendulum and the weight of the object. One or several of these variables could control the speed of the swing. In order to solve this problem, she will systematically test predictions from each hypothesis. She will employ hypothetical-deductive reasoning. (A child at the concrete-operational stage will approach the problem in a haphazard fashion, by experimenting with all the variables in an inconsistent manner.)
Using abstractions	Adolescents have the ability to accept propositions that are contrary to reality and to separate themselves from the world. They are able to use abstract rules to solve a whole class of problems, and can deal with material that is not observable. The adolescent is concerned with the world of ideas, and will debate with friends such issues as human rights, the morality of wars and political problems. *Example:* an adolescent understands higher-level concepts such as liberty and democracy as well as the abstract meaning of proverbs. Whereas the child at the concrete operational stage may interpret the proverb 'A stitch in time saves nine' as meaning only that if a shirt is falling apart at the seams, one stitch now will prevent the need for many stitches later on, the adolescent can *abstract* from the proverb and conclude that if you do a small amount of work ahead of time, you reduce the number of problems you may encounter later on.

Table 4.5 A summary of the formal operational stage of cognitive development

Moscow Institute of Psychology. He certainly read Piaget's work, but developed his theory of child development independently.

Like Piaget, Vygotsky saw the child as an **active constructor** of knowledge and understanding. The main features of Vygotsky's theory are:

- *the zone of proximal development (ZPD):* each child has a zone of proximal development ('proximal' meaning 'next') which is achievable only with the help and encouragement from another person or persons; this could be guidance from an adult or collaboration with more competent peers. Vygotsky stresses the importance of someone who knows more than the child being able to help the child to learn something that the child would find too difficult to do alone. This 'expert intervention' can only enable learning if it is far enough ahead of the child's present level to be a challenge, but not so far ahead that it is beyond comprehension.
- that *concepts, language and memory* are mental functions which come from the **culture** and begin with the interaction between the child and another person.
- *the importance of social interaction:* the process of development involves **internalising** social interactions. What starts as a social function becomes internalised so that it then occurs *within* the child.
- *reconstruction:* children experience the same situations over and over again as they grow, but each time they can deal with them at a higher level and reconstruct them.
- *the importance of play:* children benefit from play as it allows them to do things beyond what they can do in 'real' life – such as pretend to drive a car. Play is another way through which children reach their zone of proximal development.
- *the cultural context:* social relationships and the cultural context are at the heart of a child's learning.

activity

Encouraging cognitive development:

1 Plan an activity for children in an education setting which will encourage the development of cognitive skills. Use a structured approach:

   – *aim:* what particular skill or skills you are hoping to promote;
   – *rationale:* the reason for your choice of skill area for the particular child or children targeted;
   – *plan:* include a timed plan, resources needed (people, space, equipment and materials, and details of the activity);
   – *activity:* implement the activity with the child or children;
   – *evaluation:* describe how the activity went; did you have to modify your plan? Did you meet your aim? (What were the learning outcomes for the children?) If you were to do the activity again with different children, would you alter anything? What did you personally learn from the activity? etc.;
   – *health and safety:* outline the measures taken to ensure health, hygiene and safety during the activity;
   – *equal opportunities:* explain the relevance of **equality of opportunity** in terms of gender, race, disability etc.

Always discuss the proposed activity with your placement supervisor and gain written permission.

2 Match the following statements in column 2 to the correct name or title in column 1:

Column 1	Column 2
A class inclusion	1 everything that exists has consciousness
B zone of proximal development	2 unable to take another's perspective
C egocentrism	3 first found in concrete operational stage
D schema	4 theory associated with Albert Bandura
E animism	5 involves reinforcers and rewards
F equilibration	6 Pavlov's theory – stimulus/response
G deductive logic	7 feature of Vygotsky's theory of cognition
H social learning theory	8 maintaining balance between assimilation and accommodation
I classical conditioning	9 action, strategy or skill
J operant conditioning	10 reasoning from the general to the particular (formal operational stage)

(Answers in Appendix A.)

Jerome Bruner (1915–)

Jerome Bruner is a psychologist who believes that adults can be a great help to children in their thinking. Bruner's theory of infant skill development has the following features:

- *enactive thinking:* children need to move about and to have real, first-hand, direct experiences; this helps their ideas and thought processes to develop.
- *iconic thinking:* children need to be reminded of their prior experiences; books and interest tables with objects displayed on them are useful aids to this recall of prior experience.
- *symbolic thinking:* 'codes' are important; languages, music, mathematics, drawing, painting, dance and play are all useful codes which Bruner calls **symbolic thinking**.
- *scaffolding:* adults can help develop children's thinking by being like a piece of scaffolding on a building. At first, the building has a great deal of scaffolding (i.e. adult support of the child's learning), but gradually, as the children extend their competence and control of the situation, the scaffolding is progressively removed until it is no longer needed.

Bruner claimed that 'any subject can be taught in some intellectually honest form to any child at any stage of development' (Bruner 1963). Developing Vygotsky's concept of the zone of proximal development (ZPD), Bruner and his colleagues investigated the role of scaffolding in learning. They concluded that scaffolding has particular aspects:

- *recruitment:* the tutor's first task is to engage the interest of the child and to encourage them to tackle the requirements of the task.

- *reduction of degrees of freedom:* the tutor has to simplify the task by reducing the number of acts required to reach a solution. The child needs to be able to see whether they have achieved a fit with the task requirements or not.
- *direction maintenance:* the tutor needs to maintain the child's motivation. At first, the child will be looking to the tutor for encouragement; eventually, problem-solving should become interesting in its own right.
- *marking critical features:* a tutor highlights features of the task that are relevant; this provides information about any inconsistencies between what the child has constructed and what they would perceive as a correct construction.
- *demonstration:* modelling solutions to the task involves completion of a task or explanation of a solution already partly constructed by the child. The aim is that the child will imitate this back in an improved form.

Parents routinely act as tutors in the manner outlined above through the rituals and games which are a part of normal adult–child interactions.

Examples: when a child is trying to describe a new experience, the adult(tutor) may guide them in the choice of appropriate words and images.

Figure 4.12 Mathew concentrates on the story, as his father engages his attention

During a book-reading session with the child, the 'tutor' or parent will demonstrate the process by (a) engaging the child's attention, e.g. by saying 'Look'; (b) simplifying the task by focusing on one question, e.g. 'What's that?'; (c) maintaining motivation by encouraging any responses; (d) giving information about objects in the book, e.g. 'It's an X'; (e) giving appropriate feedback, e.g. 'That's right, it's an X', and encouraging repetition on the part of the child.

activity

Scaffolding an activity:
Choose an activity which is appropriate to the age group you are working with, and plan how the activity could be scaffolded to assist learning. Examples could include: a story session with 'props' for a group of nursery-school children; a session which explains the concept of time for a child or an adult with learning difficulties.

The scaffolding process often comes naturally to parents and those working in care and education settings, but it is useful to examine the underlying process and to evaluate its effectiveness.

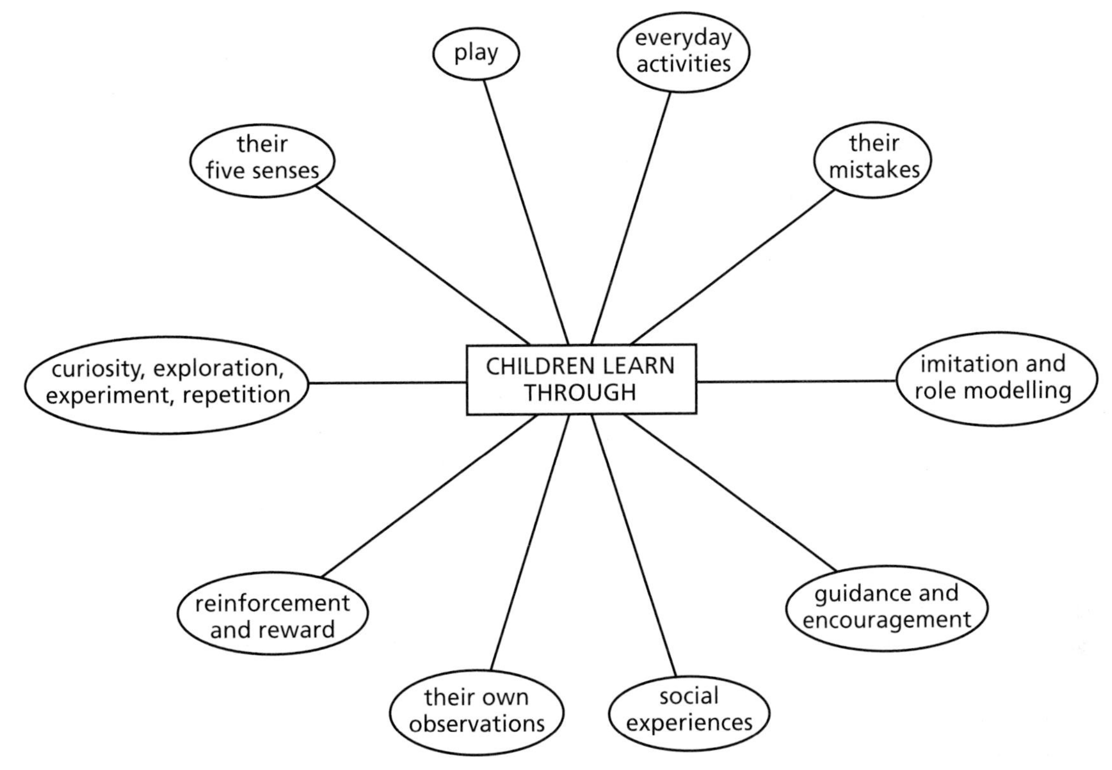

Figure 4.13 A summary of how children learn

From sensation to perception

Sensation is the process by which we receive information through the senses: sight, hearing, taste, smell, touch and **proprioception** – the sense which tells the infant the location of the mobile parts of their body (e.g. their legs) in relation to the rest of them.

Perception is making sense of what we see, hear, touch, smell and taste. Our perception is affected by previous experience and knowledge and by our emotional state at the time. There are, therefore, wide variations in the way individuals perceive the same object, situation or experience.

Until fairly recently, the generally accepted view of infant perception was summed up in the quote: 'The baby, assailed by eyes, ears, nose, skin and entrails at once, feels it all one great blooming buzzing confusion' (William James, writing in 1890). This is the **empiricist** view of perception, which argues: that infants have very little perceptual ability; that only the simplest form of perception (e.g. distinguishing a figure from its background) is innate; and that all the rest of our perceptual abilities are learnt or are determined by our environment. The **nativist** view of perception argues that, under normal circumstances, perceptual processes develop in an orderly manner controlled by the genetic blueprint.

The infant's perception at birth differs from adult perception because the perceptual system is immature and needs time to develop. Research into infant perception depended on the use of appropriate methodologies, and these were not developed until the 1960s and 1970s. Newborn infants are not easy subjects for psychologists to study because:

- they spend much of their time asleep; and even when awake, they are likely to be involved in feeding
- they cannot communicate verbally
- they are only **alert** (and therefore receptive to experimental study) for short periods of time, on average for less than 10 minutes at a time

STUDIES IN INFANT PERCEPTION

The ability to discriminate and make sense of what is experienced by the senses develops as the nervous system matures. The development which takes place in the **cerebral cortex** (see again Figure 4.1) enables the infant to store information and to retrieve what is needed to respond to different situations. **Cognition** or 'knowing' refers to what results when our brain does more than register something (an object or a situation) in the world and construct a perception of it. Cognition is the relating of this perception to other previous perceptions.

Three important research techniques are:

- *spontaneous visual preference*
- *habituation*
- *operant conditioning*.

The **spontaneous visual preference** technique was introduced by Robert Fantz in 1961. Where two stimuli were presented at a time, the observer recorded the 'visual preference' for one stimulus over the other. In Fantz's experiment, babies were placed on their backs in a specially designed 'looking chamber' and shown various forms. An observer looked down through the top of the chamber and

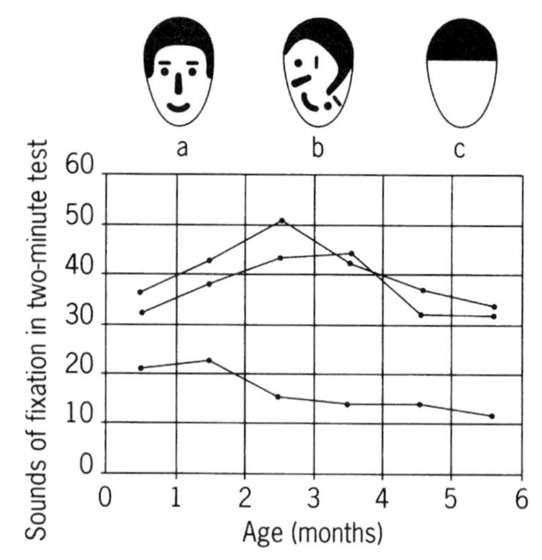

Figure 4.14 Visual preference of infants for (a) a schematic face, (b) a scrambled schematic face, and (c) a non-facelike figure

recorded how long the infants looked at each form. Fantz found that infants showed a preference for looking at **patterned** figures, such as faces and concentric circles, rather than for plain ones. In later studies, Fantz presented a schematic face and a form in which facial elements (i.e. nose, mouth and eyes) had been scrambled. He found that infants could apparently distinguish the two forms and that they showed a preference for the schematic face. (See Figure 4.14.)

Example: babies will actually search out and stare at human faces during their first two months of life; as babies focus on objects at 8 to 10 inches away (see Chapter 1, page 19), they are perfectly placed to focus on a parent's face when cradled in their arms.

Habituation techniques rely on response patterns. The infant is repeatedly presented with sight or sound until they show loss of interest by stopping looking or no longer turning towards a sound. Then some aspect of the stimulus is changed: the frequency of the tone or the arrangement of objects in a visual display. If the infant's interest is renewed, we may conclude that the infant could sense the change. Habituation means that we *adapt* to what is familiar and *attend* to what is new. Pavlov discovered this phenomenon in 1927 and called the first response to a novel stimulus an **orienting reflex**, in which the animal turns towards and attends to the stimulus. The decline of attention as the stimulus is repeatedly presented is what is called habituation.

Example: an everyday example of habituation is the fact that we do not notice a clock ticking or a fan whirring in the background. The habituation technique has been used to test a wide variety of abilities in infant development: learning, memory, perceptual discrimination and categorisation.

Operant conditioning

A recent study by Walton, Bower and Bower used a method called 'operant conditioning of high-amplitude sucking'. Newborn infants were placed in front of a TV screen and then shown two photograph-like images. One image was of their own mother's face; the other image was of a complete stranger, but one whose image was matched to the mother's for hair colour and style, eye colour and complexion. Every time the infant sucked fairly hard on a pressure-sensing dummy, an image appeared on the screen. Which image appeared – the mother's of the stranger's – depended on how fast the infant sucked. In this way, the infant controlled not only the presentation of the stimulus, but also which stimulus they saw. A control was applied to the experiment: for some infants, sucking fast produced their mother's face; while for others, this produced the stranger's face. The researchers found that newborn infants produced significantly more sucking responses in order to see an image of their mothers' faces as opposed to an image of strangers' faces, using a preferential operant sucking procedure.

Sensory deprivation

A congenitally blind baby (i.e. a baby who is *born* blind) will develop a more sophisticated sense of touch than a sighted baby, although both kinds of baby start life with the same touch potential. As the sense of touch develops, so the area of the brain normally assigned to touch increases in size for the blind baby, while the area of the brain normally assigned to sight decreases. The ability to use sound information in this particular way decreases with age. A study by Gregory in 1963 concerned a 54-year-old man who had been blind from birth and received his sight back after an operation. It was found that if he had had previous experience of handling objects, then he was able to 'see' them much better than objects that he had not previously touched.

Similarly, in a congenitally deaf baby, the part of the brain which normally receives auditory stimuli is taken over by the visual input from sign language.

The 'visual cliff'

Small children often fall down stairs, and it was thought that the reason for this was that they could not perceive depth. E. J. Gibson and R. D. Walk devised an experiment to examine depth perception in infants. They constructed an apparatus known as the 'visual cliff'. This consists of a central board laid across a sheet of plate glass which is supported about a metre above the floor (see Figure 4.15). On one side of the board, immediately under the glass surface, was stuck some black-and-white checked material; on the other side, the black-and-white checked material is at floor level, i.e. about one metre below the board. The effect was therefore of a visual deep drop or 'cliff'. Gibson and Walk tested 36 infants aged between 6 and 14 months. Each baby was placed on the central board, and the mother called to the baby from the 'deep' side and the 'shallow' side successively. The babies were extremely reluctant to venture onto the deep side – in fact, only 3 out of 27 did so – but they were all quite willing to crawl on the 'shallow' side. Gibson and Walk concluded that infants can discriminate depth as soon as they can crawl. The reason for infants falling down stairs is not therefore an inability to perceive depth, but is likely to be that they have limited control over their movements.

Cross-modal perception

Cross-modal perception is the ability to connect information across two senses or **sensory modalities**. We do not perceive the world through one sensory pathway (or modality); we integrate information from different senses.

Example: matching the shape of the mouth with the sound being spoken (sight and sound); or, having seen an object previously, being able to pick it out by touch in the dark (sight and touch).

Piaget believed that cross-modal perception was simply not possible until late in the baby's first year, after gaining experience of the way different objects looked, sounded and felt. Empirical studies show that cross-modal transfer is possible as early as 1 month and becomes common by 6 months.

Cross-cultural studies

Cross-cultural studies show the effects of different life experiences on certain aspects of perception. Segal, Campbell and Herskovitz (1963) found that members of African tribes living in jungle conditions were much less susceptible to the Müller–Lyer Illusion (see Figure 4.16). Although the two horizontal lines in this Illusion are the same length, most of us would say that the line at the bottom looks

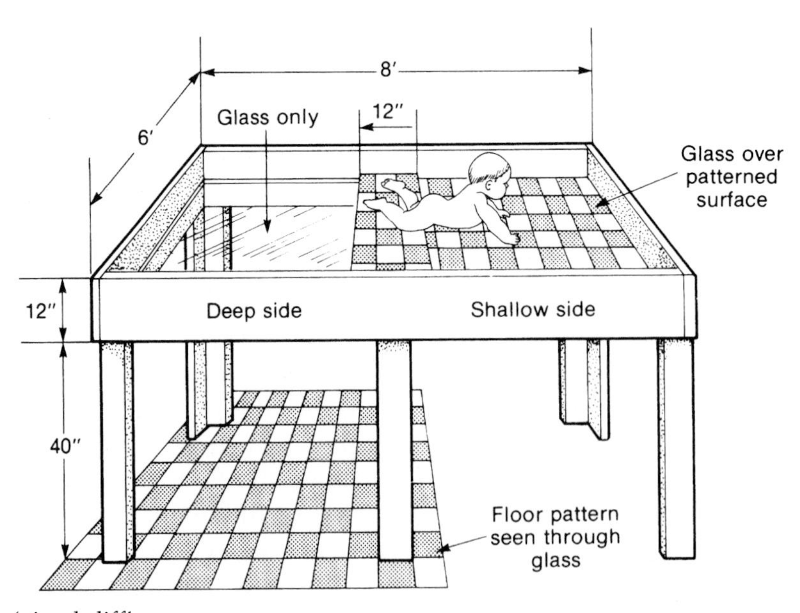

Figure 4.15 The 'visual cliff'

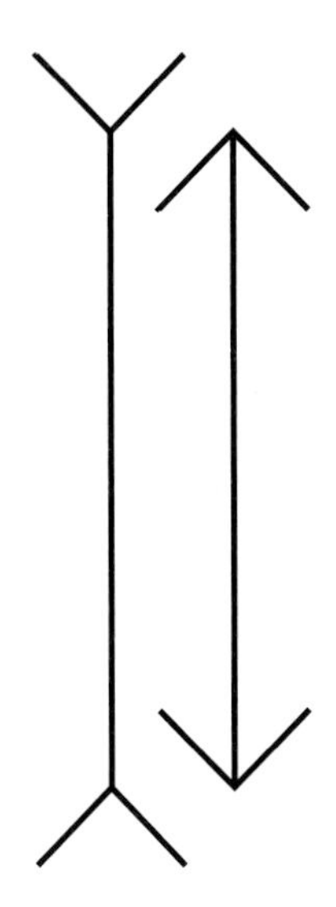

Figure 4.16 Muller-Lyer illusion

longer. The African tribesmen, however, tended to say that they were of equal length. The probable reason for this cultural difference is the extent to which people are accustomed to interpreting two-dimensional drawings and pictures – a skill we take for granted in the world of photographic images.

– activity –

Design and make a game or toy which will encourage a child's sensory development. Think about the stage of development the child has reached, and plan to make a toy that will promote the development of one or more of that child's senses. Examples: sound lotto, 'feely' bag, matching smells, odd one out, or a mobile for a very young baby. Points to consider are:

- safety
- hygiene
- suitability for purpose

Try to describe the way in which the senses may be developed by using your game or toy, and if possible, write a detailed observation of the child playing with it.

Interrelated components of cognitive development

The interrelated components or parts of cognitive development are:

- *concentration:* the ability to give undivided attention to a task. This involves an intense mental application, whether it be a playful activity or a demanding problem-solving activity.
- *attention and attention span:* **attention** involves being aware, thinking, being observant, concentrating on the task in hand; **attention span** refers to the length of time for which an individual is able to give attention to a task or to the activity of listening.

  Example: the average attention span for a 3-year-old child is 5–10 minutes; for a 5 year old, 15–20 minutes; and for an adult, 20–30 minutes.
- *memory:* the ability of the brain to store and recall past thoughts, sensations and knowledge. It is the sum of everything retained in the mind. Without **memory**, learning would be impossible. The two types of memory are:

  1. *short-term memory:* the retention of specific details for a period of time – e.g. detailed knowledge of specific information for an exam.
  2. *long-term memory:* the continual retention of known details – e.g. your name and address, the fact that snow is cold, your childhood experiences.

- *sensory perception:* the process of obtaining information about the world through our senses. Our perception is our interpretation of objects, people and events using this information form our senses together with our learned knowledge and expectations.
- *readiness* as a biological condition linked to prior learning. This is the view that each stage of development, learning and understanding is dependent upon the previous stage, e.g. sitting and standing precedes walking; an understanding of 'full' and 'empty' is reached before the conservation of capacity.
- *imagination:* the ability to produce mental images of something that is not visible and has not been experienced. It involves creativity, ingenuity, insight, originality and resourcefulness.
- *creativity:* **creativity** is closely linked to imagination. It is often characterised by originality of thought, and is a productive, inventive and original talent.
- *self-expression:* this is being able, in whatever context, to communicate what you feel and think. It does not have to be oral communication: it could be in any form, e.g. mime, dance, art, drama, music etc.
- *problem-solving:* the ability to come up with a strategy for sorting out, clarifying or resolving any puzzle, difficulty, complication or question.
- *divergent thought:* the ability to think up a number of different ways of dealing with a problem or situation. Some feel it to be a vital component of creativity. However, it is not always helpful – in a multiple-choice exam paper, for example, the single correct solution demands **convergent** thinking instead.

Concept formation

The formation of **concepts** is a major task for the development of thought. A concept may be defined as:

- an idea – formed in the mind
- a 'big' idea made up of many small ideas and given a name, e.g.: an attribute – colour, shape, size; a type of object – fruit or ball; or an abstract notion – good and evil, truth and falsehood
- an individual idea. Although many people's concepts are very similar, no two people have exactly the same concepts
- an idea which develops over time, as experience, language and thinking come together. Some concepts develop before others – e.g. the concepts of shape and colour precede the concepts of size and shape
- a product of **categorisation**, which is the process by which entities are grouped together because they are similar to each other in certain respects

The formation of concepts is often called **conceptualisation**. Piaget's theory of conceptualisation describes two significant processes: assimilation and accommodation (see page 105 above).

THEORIES OF CONCEPT FORMATION

The classical theory

The classical theory of concept formation can be traced back to the writings of Aristotle in ancient Greece. It states that all the examples of some concept share a number of common properties or features. When a list of common features is drawn up, a concept is further defined as possessing both *necessary* and *sufficient* features.

Example: a concept of a square may be described thus: (1) it is a closed figure; (2) it has four sides; (3) it has sides which are equal in length; (4) it has four equal angles. The classical view of a concept specifies the properties or features that every member of the concept must have.

A concept of a cat is not so easily described: (1) it is a four-legged animal; (2) it is covered with fur; (3) it has claws on each paw; (4) it has whiskers; (5) it has a long tail etc. The classical concept view receives a challenge, however, when we consider a Manx cat, which does not have a tail. The Manx cat is obviously perceived as a cat, but does not fit all the features described as normally belonging to a cat.

The family resemblance theory

In this theory, put forward by the linguistic philosopher Wittgenstein, the list of features which make up the concept in the classical view lose their *necessary* and *sufficient* aspects. Instead, these features are related in a **probabilistic** way; in other words, these features are highly **correlated**, i.e. they exist in a mutual, reciprocal relationship.

Example: a famous example from Wittgenstein's own writing discusses the concept of **games**. We are all able to use the term 'game' in a wide variety of contexts. It is part of our vocabulary, but covers a huge variety of games: card games, team games, ball games, computer games, games played by one person, competitive games etc. It would be impossible to draw up a list of features, as in the classical view, to cover all the common features of games. However, the term **family resemblances** may be used to describe the indefinite pattern of relationships (or correlations) between individual instances. Although the presence of a tail is **highly correlated** with the presence of fur and claws in the concept of cat, it is not a *necessary* feature, and so we may still recognise a Manx cat as fitting in with our previous concept of cat.

The prototype theory

Eleanor Rosch and Carolyn Mervis sustained the view put forward by Wittgenstein but further developed it with the idea that humans represent concepts as idealised versions – or **prototypes** – and then use these to evaluate real-world instances. Rosch gave research participants a series of statements which described items as belonging to a given concept ('a peach is a fruit', 'a cable car is a vehicle', etc.). The participants had to say, as quickly as possible, whether the statement was true or false. Rosch found that people took longer to judge items which were very different from the prototype than they did to judge ones that were similar.

Example: it took longer for the participants to give the answer to 'a cable car is a vehicle' than it did to give the answer to 'a truck is a vehicle'.

The prototype theory recognises that all prototypes are *individually* constructed, and that one person's prototype, therefore, may not be exactly like another's. However, these prototypes are similar enough for us to share meanings and to be able to argue about specific instances.

The connectionist model theory

Vygotsky and Piaget both believed that children pass through stages in conceptual development, and that their concepts are fundamentally different from those of adults. The **connectionist model** approach to concept formation argues the *opposite* case, i.e. that children have the same conceptual system as adults but differ in their ability to *use* this system. This difference in ability is explained by the fact that children are in the process of acquiring information and experience. Connectionist models store information as a pattern of neurons, which are part of a complex network in the human brain.

Example: a computer model was given a series of inputs, none of which was in the prototype form. The model was then tested to see its reaction to various new examples, and it was found that the model responded most accurately to a prototypical example even though it had not been presented with one in the training phase. In other words, the connection was made without any prior experience being necessary for the establishment of a link.

DEVELOPING CONCEPTS

Everyday concrete (i.e. not abstract) concepts such as chairs, dogs or apples are understood by very young children through the adult's use of labelling items. The categorisation of such concepts in the larger sets of 'furniture', 'animals' or 'food' will not occur until the child is around 6 years of age.

There are many ways in which children can be helped to develop concepts:

Colour

Young babies are attracted to bright colours. Adults should provide an environment and toys which use bright primary colours. Matching games can be introduced (see the Activity on page 128 below). It is important to name the object as well as the colour when playing 'colour' games with young children – e.g. 'Find me a red pencil' rather than 'Is this red?' – otherwise they may believe that a red pencil is a 'red'.

Number

Learning to count involves not just simply reciting the names of numbers but also knowing that two always means two no matter what is being counted – two buttons, two cats, two feet etc. Rhymes such as 'Five currant buns in a baker's shop' and 'One, two, buckle my shoe' help to introduce the child to repeating a sequence of numbers. Counting accurately involves knowing that each object counted must be matched to a single number; this is called **one-to-one correspondence**. At first, a child will need plenty of experience in handling and counting objects and in grouping and sorting numbers of things. The conservation of number gradually develops around the age of 5 or 6, and the idea of 'more than' and 'less than' can be introduced.

Margaret Donaldson and James McGarrigle used toy cars and garages. They arranged the cars on two shelves, one directly above the other. On one shelf there were five cars, on the other four. These were placed in one-to-one correspondence, starting from the left, so that in one row an extra car always projected to the right.

Children of nursery-school age were asked which shelf held more cars; in one instance, with the garages present as shown in Figure 4.17, and in another instance, with the garages absent. Without

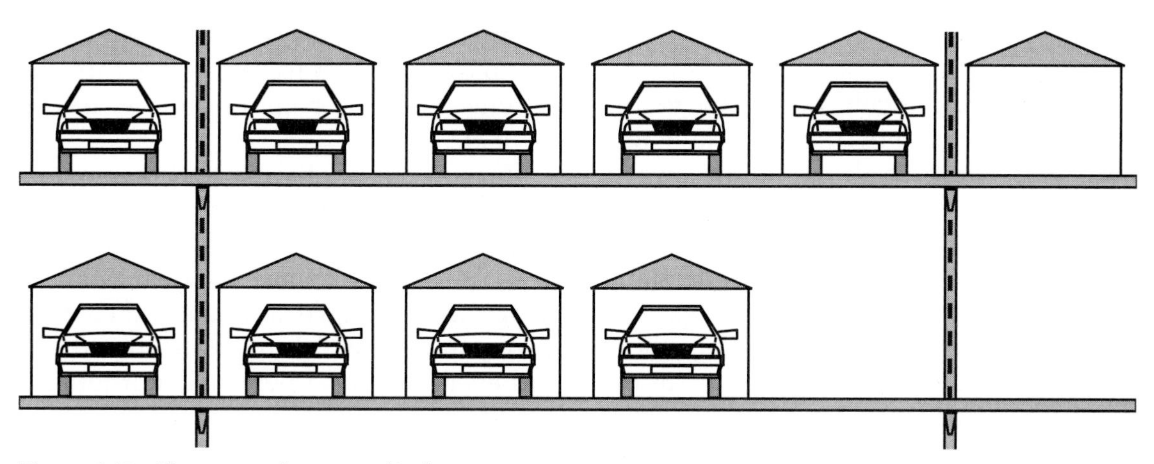

Figure 4.17 The cars and garages display

the garages, all the children gave the correct response, which seems to show that they know the meaning of 'more'. However, when the garages were present as shown, about one-third of the children stated that the shelf holding only four cars had more than the shelf with five! Donaldson concludes that the interpretation of the term 'more' is affected by the way in which the situation is understood as a whole. When the garages are present, the children tend to read the situation in terms of the full set of cars which would be appropriate to the garages, so that the row of five cars in the six garages is seen as lacking a car. The children were attending to the 'fullness' of the garages rather than to the number of cars.

Shape

From birth, babies are interested in shapes and patterns, and they appear to respond more to the shape of the human face than to any other shape. Adults can help children to develop their visual discrimination by providing names for shapes, by letting them handle solid shapes and by encouraging drawing and writing about shapes. A 4-year-old child will be able to draw a circle and a square but not yet a triangle. Once at school, children will be given opportunities to make patterns and to sort into sets both two-dimensional and three-dimensional shapes. They will learn to draw a triangle and a diamond shape, and the idea of **tessellation** is introduced. The increasing ability to discriminate and remember shapes helps in the acquisition of reading and writing skills.

Weight, size and spatial relationships

These concepts are difficult to understand as they involve **relativity** – e.g. in the concept of weight: 'heavier than' and 'lighter than'. Children can experience weight, size and space in their everyday play: when they first go on a see-saw with a heavier person at the other end; when they have to hold on tightly to a balloon as it is light enough to blow away; when they use climbing frames or crawl in and out of boxes etc. Stories such as 'Goldilocks and the Three Bears' and 'Three Billy Goats Gruff' provide ideal opportunities to compare the relative size of things.

Time

Time is a very difficult concept for young children. There are two specific skills that need to be developed: one is the awareness of the passing of time, and the other is the ability to tell the time by looking at a clock. Young children do not understand that each moment is joined to the next and that they live in the present but have both a past and a future. A basic routine for the day with regular mealtimes and bedtimes will help children to develop a concept of time and to grasp the idea of a sequence of events. Adults can also help by familiarising children with terms such as month, year, later, before and after.

Abstract concepts

An **aesthetic awareness** of form and beauty first shows itself when a child refers to a 'pretty flower' or dances with enjoyment to a piece of music. Adults can help to develop a love of form and beauty by offering experiences which help children to express their feelings – e.g. through activities such as painting, music, movement etc.

The concept of **sharing and ownership** may not be grasped until about the age of 3 years. Very young children are only able to see the world from their own point of view. Games of give and take and cooperative games in which roles are shared out and everyone has a personal contribution need to be encouraged.

Other concepts such as peace and justice do not develop until early adolescence or even adulthood.

Metacognition and metamemory

Metacognition is a loosely used term describing an individual's knowledge of their own thinking processes. It means that you know both what you know and

activity

A colour game:
Rationale for the activity: to help the child (or children) to remember a colour while they are engaged in looking for a similar object elsewhere (this is called **mapping**).

Plan and implement the following activity with a child (or a group of children) aged between 3 and 5 years:

1 Assemble the necessary equipment:
   - a box of coloured crayons
   - pieces of string
   - different-coloured objects (avoid patterns/keep to single-colour objects)
2 Set out the crayons in a line, and lay out the objects so that each is next to the crayon of the matching colour.
3 Ask the child to use the pieces of string to link each object to its colour.
4 When the child has matched the colours, rearrange the objects and ask the child to join them up again, even though the strings will cross over each other.

Write an **observation** of the activity and then **evaluate** the cognitive development that may have taken place.

how you manage to remember and learn.

Metamemory is a subcategory of metacognition, and it describes knowledge about your own memory processes.

Examples: if you are faced with an important exam, you will be able to explain what study methods you could use and which tasks will be the most difficult – and why. If you are given a list of things to remember and are then asked later to explain the processes you had undergone in trying to remember, you will be able to describe those processes. You may even have considered various different strategies before selecting the most effective one.

Cognitive changes from adolescence to later life

The thinking of adolescents often exhibits five characteristics not usually seen in the thinking of younger children. These were proposed by Daniel Keating in 1980:

1. *thinking about possibilities:* adolescents are likely to think about alternative possibilities that are not directly observable; younger children, on the other hand, rely heavily on their **senses** to apply reasoning.
2. *thinking ahead:* adolescence is a time when young people start to plan ahead, often in a systematic way. Younger children may look forward to a holiday, for example, but are unlikely to focus on the preparation required.
3. *thinking through hypotheses:* adolescents are more likely than young children to engage in thinking that requires them to make and test hypotheses and to think about situations that are contrary to fact.
4. *thinking about thought:* otherwise called **metacognition** (see page 128 above), this thinking about one's own thought processes becomes increasingly complex. Adolescents also acquire the ability to engage in **second-order thinking**; i.e. they can develop rules about rules, holding two different two rule systems in mind as they think them over. At the same time, they are able to think more systematically about other people's points of view.
5. *thinking beyond conventional limits:* issues which have preoccupied human beings for centuries – such as morality, religion and politics – are thought about by adolescents as they become aware of the disparities between the ideals of their community and the reality of the individual behaviour observed.

Piaget described this as the formal operational stage of cognitive development (see page 115 above). The core of Piaget's evidence relating to this stage comes from observations of adolescents working on scientific experimental problems. In some societies, virtually no adults can solve these tasks, and critics of Piaget's stage theory see this as a weakness; some theorists prefer to emphasise the importance of language and/or the cultural context in the development of cognition in adolescence.

How well are cognitive abilities maintained in old age?

The ability to perform certain intellectual tasks seems to decline during adulthood, whereas the ability to perform other tasks seems to remain the same or even to improve. There are changes in **memory**, but only in certain aspects. Long-established skills, such as money management, playing a musical instrument or gardening, remain unaffected in old age, whereas the memory for names and everyday actions may be affected. Sometimes, the ability to distinguish between an imagined event and one that really happened is impaired:

Example: some elderly people may believe that they have turned the gas off, when in reality they have only *thought* about turning it off.

The ability to recall information from the distant past improves slightly into middle age, and by the age of 60 shows only a slight decline.

John Horn and Gary Donaldson (1980) see these changes as a reflection of two fundamentally different kinds of intelligence:

1 *crystallized intelligence:* intelligence that is built up over a lifetime on the basis of experience. Abilities that **improve** over the course of adulthood make use of this kind of intelligence. **Crystallized intelligence** consists of culturally organised, accumulated experience which continues to increase until the biological foundations that support all behaviour have markedly deteriorated;
2 *fluid intelligence:* intelligence that requires the manipulation of new information to solve a problem. Abilities that begin to **decline** during adulthood make use of this kind of intelligence. **Fluid intelligence** is largely an inherited biological predisposition that parallels other biological capacities in its growth and decline.

Intelligence

Intelligence is often defined as the ability to solve problems. It is, however, best regarded as a descriptive term which refers to a number of different abilities which result in behaviour which is appropriate to the environment.

D. O. Hebb, in 1949, argued that much of the difficulty about the relative importance of nature and nurture to intelligence

activity

Cognitive changes – adulthood to old age:

1 In groups, discuss the strategies which could be used to help elderly people to remember important actions and events.
2 Find out about the range of magazines specifically targeting elderly people. Obtain copies of some of these magazines and analyse their content in terms of their appeal to their audience:
   - the overall impression of the magazine: is it upbeat, informative, serious, etc.?
   - the types of images used: are all the models conventionally attractive? Is there a mix of ethnic groups represented? Are the genders equally represented?
   - What sort of advertisements predominate?
   - If possible, show the magazines to someone over 65 years old and ask for their opinions.

arose from confusing three separate types of intelligence. These he describes as follows:

1 *Intelligence A:* this is genetically inherited intelligence (part of our **genotype**), and it may be termed **potential intelligence**. Whatever happens to the individual child after conception can either help or hinder this potential to be realised, but it cannot *alter* the potential itself;
2 *Intelligence B:* this describes the part of intelligence that *does* develop and is a result of the interaction of an individual's genetic make-up with the effects of their environment;
3 *Intelligence C:* **Intelligence C** was proposed by Philip Vernon, a British psychologist, and refers to an unknown amount of Intelligence B which can be measured by **intelligence tests**.

THREE THEORIES OF THE NATURE OF INTELLIGENCE

1 *The psychometric (or 'power') theory.* This theory, which went unchallenged until the middle of the twentieth century, asserts that intelligence, or intellectual power, is defined by how well or how quickly a child can perform cognitive tasks. These tasks are problem-solving and the analysis of complex situations. The idea that children are labelled and even ranked according to this aspect of intellectual power led directly to the development of intelligence tests.
2 *The cognitive developmental (or 'structure') theory.* This theory was developed by Piaget and his followers, and focuses on the development of **cognitive structures** rather than on intellectual power. It recognises that intelligence is 'plastic': it can stretch, grow and increase. Children can increase their intelligence:
   - by mixing with adults and other children who help them to develop their intelligence
   - if they experience a stimulating environment which promotes thinking and the development of concepts

   In this view, it is the *patterns* of development which are common to all children that are important, rather than the individual differences.
3 *The information processing theory.* This theory stresses the importance of the underlying **processes** or strategies that make up all cognitive activity. It offers an integration of the two preceding theories by examining the basic elements involved in memory and in the processing of information. On the computer analogy, information enters the system (the brain) and is held very briefly in the sensory store. Information that is **attended to** passes next to the short-term memory for temporary storage or operations. Information that is examined and interpreted is then transferred to the long-term memory for permanent storage. The deficiencies in cognitive ability noted by Piaget in the pre-operational stage are merely a reflection of **immature** processing and memory skills. The ability to process information increases both with age and with greater input from a stimulating environment.

MULTIPLE INTELLIGENCES

Howard Gardner proposed a theory of **multiple intelligences**, each of which follows a separate developmental path. Each type of intelligence has its own 'peak' time: e.g. musical intelligence often appears at an early age; logical mathematical intelligence appears in late adolescence; and the kind of spatial intelligence relied upon by artists may not reach its peak until much later. (See Tables 4.6/7.) Gardner believed that these types of intelligence are partly genetic but also open to cultural influences; they can also be promoted through education. Intelligence tests can therefore only measure a small part of an individual's intelligence.

Normative measurement

Normative measurement is concerned with **milestones** in a child's development. These show what *most* children can do at a particular stage (see page 16 in Chapter 1). Mary Sheridan wrote a 'paediatric tool' – *Children's Developmental Progress From Birth to Five Years* – which aimed to familiarise all professionals working with children with the accepted milestones (or **stepping stones**) of development. She was particularly concerned that children with physical, mental, emotional or social disabilities were identified and fully assessed as early as possible so that appropriate help could be given to promote development.

The **value** of some means of normative measurement lies in:

- an early identification of children who may be experiencing difficulties
- a comparison of a child's progress over a period of time
- anticipating and responding appropriately to certain types of age-related behaviour, e.g. temper tantrums
- providing reassurance that the child is developing normally
- guiding the adult in providing for the child's developmental needs

The **limitations** of normative measurement are:

Type of intelligence	Features
Linguistic	Special sensitivity to language, which allows one to choose exactly the right word or turn of phrase and to grasp new meanings easily
Musical	Sensitivity to pitch and tone, which allows one to detect and produce musical structure
Logical-mathematical	Ability to engage in abstract reasoning and to manipulate symbols
Spatial	Ability to perceive relations among objects, to transform mentally what one sees, and to recreate visual images from memory
Bodily-kinaesthetic	Ability to represent ideas in movement, characteristic of great dancers and mimes
Personal	Ability to gain access to one's own feelings and to understand the motivations of others
Social	Ability to understand the motives, feelings and behaviours of other people

Table 4.6 Gardner's ideas of multiple intelligences

- It may result in the child being labelled as 'below average' or as 'very bright', and expectations may then be lowered or raised inappropriately
- It may cause unnecessary anxiety when a child does not achieve milestones which are considered average for their age
- The child's performance may be affected by a number of factors, e.g. tiredness, anxiety, illness

Tests of normative measurement should ideally be supported by other means of assessment; **observations** are a very useful tool in the assessment of development.

Intelligence tests

The first **intelligence test** was designed by Alfred Binet in Paris as a practical method of identifying children who had learning difficulties in some particular skills such as arithmetic or language. The Binet tests were never intended to be used as a general test for all children; nor were they designed to assess general intelligence. Binet devised a simple formula to give each child a score – or **intelligence quotient** (**IQ**): the score, or IQ, is obtained by multiplying the child's mental age by 100 and dividing by their chronological age.

Examples: a child aged 10 years with a mental age of 10 scores 100 (average intelligence); a child aged 8 years with a mental age of 10 scores 125 (above-average intelligence); and a child aged 10 years with a mental age of 8 scores 80 (below-average intelligence).

The value of intelligence testing is:

- It helps to assess a child's intellectual ability and to compare it with classroom performance. (For example, an exceptionally gifted child may not be achieving their potential)
- It may help to identify a child who has a specific learning disability (e.g. dyslexia)

It may be used with other assessments in order to plan a programme of remedial help for any child who is falling behind their peers in class.

The limitations of intelligence testing are:

- it can lead to the labelling of a child as 'average', 'dull' or 'bright'
- It may lower or raise expectations of a child inappropriately
- It can only assess the child's performance on a particular day
- It does not measure common sense and the ability to function in the real world
- It may only serve to show that a child is good (or, not good) at *school-type* learning

Optimal times

Although it is useful to consider the development of children as an ordered sequence of stages, recent research shows that it is never too late for a child to catch up on missed learning. Children should not be pushed into achieving milestones such as becoming potty trained or learning to read and write: there are optimal – or best – periods which are individual to each child. These are the most sensitive periods in which learning can take place most easily. If a child is, for any reason, held back from development during these optimal times, they will have more difficulty in achieving those skills later on. What helps one child does not necessarily help another. Different children need different sorts of help in learning. A thorough knowledge of all aspects of child development can help parents and caregivers to recognise these optimal times and to provide both a stimulating environment and the tools for learning.

The role of play in cognitive development

Play is central to a child's learning. It helps children to use what they know and to understand things about the world and the people they meet. From a very early age, children learn best by doing, seeing and touching, and they perceive very little difference between work and play. Play is open-ended: even when there is a goal in sight, such as building a tower of blocks, the **process** is more important than the product.

THE SOCIAL CONSTRUCTIVIST VIEW ON PLAY

Piaget and Vygotsky emphasised the child as an active learner. Children use objects, props, other people – children and adults – and a variety of different concepts for their play.

Piaget defined three stages of play:

1 *sensorimotor play (from birth to 18 months):* the child explores and manipulates objects using all the sensorimotor schemas at their command. They 'mouth' objects, shake them, bang them, or move them along the floor. They build up an idea of what objects do, by the process of assimilation. Once a skill is mastered, it is repeated at every opportunity. Piaget called this **mastery play** or **practice play**.
2 *symbolic play (from 18 months to about 5 years):* in symbolic – or make-believe – play, the child makes something stand for something else. A child who can already drink from a cup may use the cup to give a doll or teddy a drink. Later on, the child will use objects to stand for something altogether different; e.g. a broom becomes a horse, or a cardboard box becomes a car. Symbolic play repeats and organises images and symbols (schemas) that the child already has by assimilation. Any emotional experiences can be consolidated and 'acted out' in symbolic play. Reality is not important as the child is still **egocentric**.
3 *games with rules (from 5–12 years onwards):* the child is able to play more cooperatively and take part in games with rules. Children can make and use these rules in their own invented games, such as elaborate games of hide

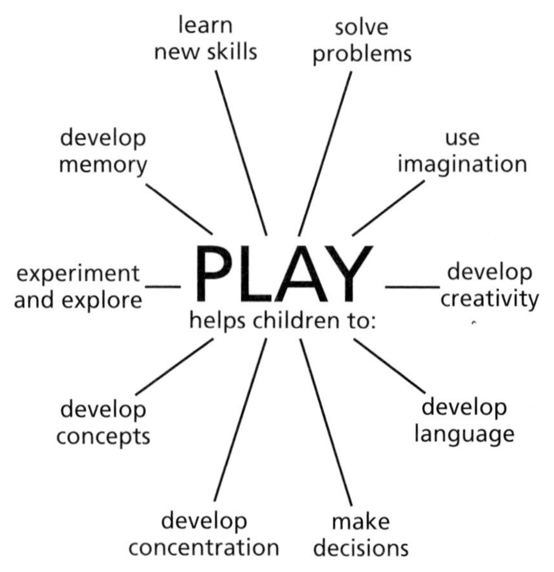

Figure 4.18 The role of play in cognitive development

and seek. When the child is at the concrete operational stage, they **decentre** and realise that other children have feelings and appreciate sharing toys etc. The child will become more altruistic: instead of personal enjoyment overriding everything else, they will recognise that to succeed in a football team, they must cooperate – as a team member – by passing the ball. At the formal operational stage, children cease to play quite so much – except for games with rules. These include computer games and board games.

Piaget's theory about play has been criticised because he suggests that children play at whatever activity they have just learned and that during the play reality will be distorted to suit the child's needs. Furthermore, the social and environmental aspects of play have been largely ignored in his theory. For example, Piaget says little about the amount of distortion that occurs in play, and whether this can be modified by interaction with adults.

Vygotsky believed that children (and parents) do not appear to play in order to promote cognitive or social development, but do so for pleasure and enjoyment. He warns against the over-intellectualising of children's play.

D. W. Winnicott, writing in 1964, emphasised the importance of play for the emotional and social development of the child, but stated that all developmental stages in a child's play are related to the child's capacity to learn. He introduced the concept of the development of **potential space** between the mother and the infant. The idea of the **transitional object** is central to this concept. A transitional object may be a cuddly toy, a blanket or a piece of rag to which the baby becomes especially attached. It symbolises the union of the baby and mother at the time they are becoming sepa

Figure 4.19 Make-believe play: getting ready to go shopping

rate in the baby's mind, and has been described as the 'first *not-me* possession'. The child's passage through this transitional stage of development is fundamental to the future development of symbolic thinking.

Reasons why play may not develop

Play can be described as the child's work, as it involves the highest levels of learning. Not all children play, however, and there are many reasons why play may not develop:

- chronic illness or disability
- emotional upset or trauma
- physical or sexual abuse
- intellectual neglect: a lack of stimulation – e.g. the sad instances of children in Romanian orphanages being confined to a cot all day

activity

Playing with dough:
Find a recipe for play dough and obtain the ingredients (flour, salt and colouring, and water). If possible, arrange to make and use the dough in a session at a nursery school or playgroup.

Draw up a **plan** for the activity to include:

- the **rationale** – or reason – for the activity
- a description of the **preparation**, including materials used
- a **timed plan** of the activity and how many children you intend to involve

Take the necessary ingredients into the nursery and prepare the play area appropriately. **Implement** the plan with the children, and include:

- a description of the making of the dough, i.e. how did the children manage the measuring of the flour, salt and water? What language was used? Did the children enjoy the dough-making?
- a description of the playing with the dough, e.g. did you use rolling pins, cutters or other tools? How did the children enjoy the experience? What language was used?
- a record of any deviation from your original plan, with reasons
- an evaluation of the activity: what were the benefits for the children? What learning took place? How could the experience for the children have been improved? What changes would you make if doing the same activity again?

- intellectual abuse – the child who is under pressure to achieve in advance of optimal times of development may suffer 'burn-out' as young as 8 or 9 years old, and can be put off school
- communication difficulties
- Attention Deficit Disorder (ADD) and Attention Deficit Hyperactivity Disorder (ADHD)

Factors influencing cognitive and language development

The interplay of various factors will influence the way in which an individual child develops intellectually. These have been summarised in Figure 4.20. Each of these factors may prevent or delay a child developing cognitively or linguistically (the latter will be the focus of the next chapter). One factor may affect another; for example, physical factors such as a hearing deficit may affect a child socially and emotionally and lead to lack of confidence and motivation. If a child lacks stimulation in their environment – in any area of development – they will miss out on important early learning activities which help in the development of concepts.

Conditions such as Down's syndrome are usually, but not always, associated with learning difficulties. Language and comprehension may be very slow to develop, and children will need lots of encouragement to communicate; some children will require help with **signing**. Deafness has serious effects on both language and cognitive development, even when the condition is temporary, as in 'glue ear'. Many of the reasons why children may not play (outlined above) apply equally to the cognitive development of children.

Genetic
- sensory impairment
- Down's syndrome

Environmental
- effects of poverty
- lack of stimulation
- poor provision for play

Social
- poor role models
- limited social opportunities
- lack of a stable relationship with adults

Physical
- temporary or permanent hearing loss
- effects of poor nutrition
- lack of opportunity for physical activity
- effects of physical disability or chronic illness
- lack of sleep

Emotional
- lack of self–esteem and confidence
- effects of trama/event such as bereavement, abuse, new baby, etc.

Cultural
- different cultural expectations and experience

Figure 4.20 Factors influencing cognitive and language development

CASE STUDY

LAURA, AGED 4 YEARS

Laura is an only child who has **cerebral palsy** (**CP**). She is able to walk slowly with the aid of special leg splints, but has difficulty controlling her arm movements. Chewing and swallowing present a challenge at mealtimes. Laura also has trouble making herself understood when speaking, as the muscles which control speech are affected. Laura is a cheerful, inquisitive child who likes to play with others in the home corner at the day nursery she attends. She is receiving therapy using the Bobath technique.

activity

1. How might Laura's learning and comprehension be affected? List the areas which may present problems now and in the future.
2. List the ways in which you could help to promote Laura's cognitive and language development.
3. Find out about the therapies available for children with cerebral palsy – in particular, conductive education and the Bobath technique.

Name	**Pavlov**	**Skinner**	**Bandura**
Theory	Classical conditioning	Operant conditioning	Social cognitive theory
Main ideas	An example of associative learning: a response becomes connected to a stimulus where previously no such association existed	An example of associative learning or instrumental conditioning: an individual's behaviour operates on the environment so as to produce an outcome	Often called observational learning. The majority of our behaviours are learned through observation; there is no need for reward or conditioning

Name	**Piaget**	**Bruner**	**Vygotsky**
Theory	Constructivism	Social constructivism	Social constructivism
Main ideas	Often called the cognitive-developmental theory: the child is a constructivist, an active explorer oriented towards interacting with and understanding the environment	Children learn through doing, imaging things that they have done and through using symbolic codes (e.g.talking, writing or drawing). Adult scan help by making learning more manageable	The zone of proximal development means that the child can do with help now what the child will be able to do independently later in life. Play is very important for children under 7

Table 4.7 A summary of theories of cognitive development

CHAPTER 5

Language Development *from* Birth *to* Adulthood

Language is the basis of all social communication. Children develop at different rates, but the *sequence* of development is the same.

Language has four components: (1) Listening and understanding – receptive speech; (2) talking, – expressive speech; (3) reading; and (4) writing. All language involves the use of symbols, that is, making one thing stand for another. Language does not have to be oral, i.e. spoken; it also includes sign language, drawing and painting etc.

There are four main theories about how language is acquired: (1) Imitation theory; (2) nativist theory; (3) interactionist theory; and (4) input theory. Kuczaj proposes a combined view which makes a distinction between input and intake; in this view, it is the child's *use* of the input – from adults and others – that is crucial to developing language.

Literacy is the ability to read and write. Writing involves putting language into a code, and reading is decoding what has been written down. Reading skills are more easily learnt if they are taught within a context that makes 'human sense' to the child.

Both participation in human activity and exposure to language as part of that activity are needed for development of the full range of language abilities. Studies of children who have suffered extreme forms of deprivation show a similar sequence of language development to children reared normally, once they have been placed in a nurturing environment.

Language development

Language sets human beings apart from the rest of the animal world. The ability to learn language appears to be uniquely human, despite numerous attempts to teach it to other species. Language is the basis of all social communication. It allows the transmission of a culture from one generation to another, and it provides tools for thought. All children develop at slightly different rates, but the *sequence* of development is the same in all children.

Natural language has the following features:

- *it is symbolic:* all languages are made up of **symbols**. Symbols are a way of making one thing stand for another; for example, a drawing of father or the word 'Daddy'. Daddy does not have to be there: these symbols, the drawing or the word, will stand for him when he is not there.

- *it is arbitrary:* there is no necessary connection between the symbol (whether word or gesture) and the object or idea to which it refers. The word 'Daddy' *looks* nothing like a man, and different languages say 'Daddy' in different ways.
  In French it is 'Papa', and in Japanese it is 'Chichi'.
- *it is systematic:* the symbols must be used **systematically**. For example, in the sentence 'Peter hugged Sarah', we know that it was Sarah who was hugged and that it was Peter who did the hugging. If we reverse the order of the sentence, to read 'Sarah hugged Peter', the words are exactly the same but the meaning of the sentence has changed. Each of the 5,000 living human languages is governed by a different set of rules. Speakers of a language know these rules, even though they may not be able to state what they are.
- *it is creative:* when we use language, we are not merely repeating sentences that we have previously heard. Rather, we are constantly speaking and understanding sentences that we have heard before.

The development of language is closely allied to children's **intellectual and conceptual development**. It is an important milestone for the developing child as it enables higher levels of communication and a channel for expressing emotion and interacting with others.

There are four main ways in which language is used:

1 *listening and understanding* – receptive speech
2 *talking* – expressive speech
3 *reading*
4 *writing*.

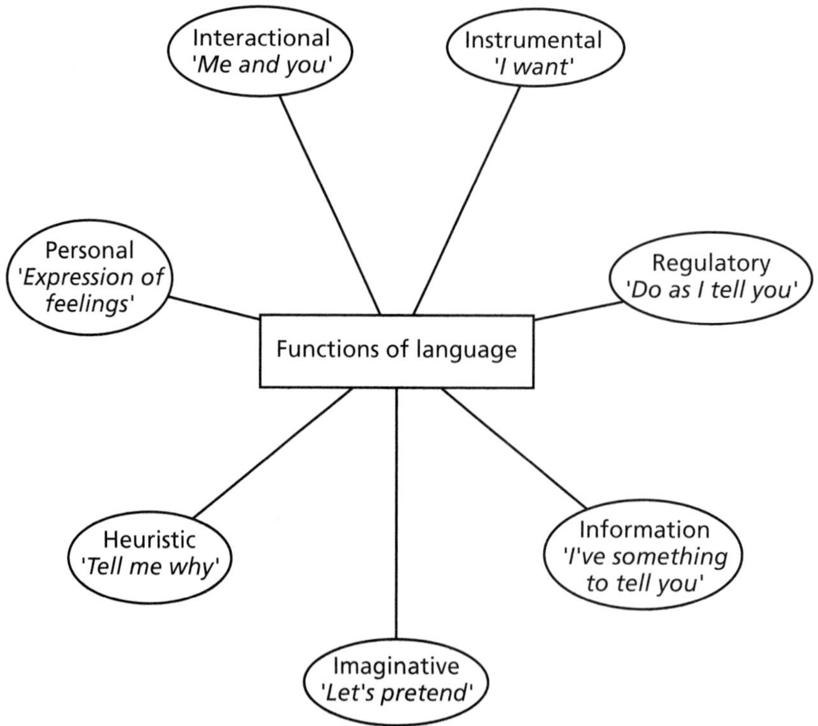

Figure 5.1 The functions of language

Phonemes and morphemes

The smallest individual sounds which go to make up any language are called **phonemes**, and the system by which sounds are combined to make words is called **phonology**. English uses 45 phonemes, although the human vocal apparatus is capable of generating many more.

Example: the 'keh' sound at the beginning of 'cat' is a phoneme in spoken English. By changing only one phoneme in many English words, it is possible to change their meaning; e.g. 'cat' can be changed to 'rat' by substituting 'reh' for 'keh'.

Morphemes are the smallest units of sound which have meaning. Phonemes are put together to form morphemes. A morpheme may be a whole word or only part of one.

Example: 'unhappiness' consists of three morphemes: 'un - happi - ness'. Each morpheme has a meaning in isolation: 'un' carries a negative meaning; 'happi' plainly has a meaning, and 'ness' expresses a state or quality.

Words and sentences

Morphemes are put together to form **words**. With words come meanings, or what linguists call **semantics**. In order to convey precise meaning to a listener when putting words into sentences, we must follow a set of grammatical rules. This set of rules is called **syntax**.

Language and grammar

Every language has its own kind of **grammar**. Grammar involves the rules that make the language work; it does not prescribe *how* a language should be spoken. Typically, grammar will include:

- **nouns**, which might involve either a *subject* – 'the *girl* ran to the door' – or an *object* – 'the girl ran to the *door*'
- **pronouns**, used in place of a noun – such as '*she* liked *it*'
- **adjectives**, used to describe nouns – 'She was *happy* to be playing with her *two* friends'
- **verbs**, which are action words – 'I am *going* home'
- **prepositions**, used to mark a relation between nouns, or pronouns and other words – 'he looked *under* the bed'
- **conjunctions**, used to join words and phrases – 'He likes music *and* dancing'
- **adverbs**, used to describe verbs – 'The child *quickly* walks away'
- **interjections**, or words of exclamation – '*Gosh!* I almost fell over'
- **apostrophes**, or marks which indicate possession – 'the *boy's* teddy' (the teddy that belongs to the boy)

Theories of language acquisition

There are four main theories about how language is acquired:

1. imitation
2. nativist
3. interactionist
4. input.

1 Imitation theory

For a long time, it was thought that language was acquired or 'picked up' by a simple process of imitation and reinforcement. This learning theory is particularly associated with Skinner, and has the following features:

- Adults – especially parents – react to random babbling sounds made by infants. They conclude that the child is asking for something, e.g. 'bi-bi' or 'bis-bis' = biscuit. They respond by providing the biscuit or whatever they think is requested and giving the correct name for it. As the child is eating the biscuit, she repeats the sound 'bi-bi', and the association between the sound and the child's experience of eating the biscuit is reinforced by the adult saying 'Yes, that's right, you've got a biscuit'.
- Children may also acquire language through imitating and echoing sounds made by adults in particular situations; e.g. the adult says 'Tom's gone to school', and the child echoes 'school' or 'kool'. A child has learnt that, by saying 'I want ... (my teddy, a biscuit, Mummy)', they will get what they want, will learn to preface all requests with the word 'I want' by a process of **reward** and **reinforcement**
- Sounds and words that are not part of the language that the child will eventually speak are not reinforced and are therefore extinguished (this is called **operant conditioning** – see page 101 above)

Criticisms of imitation theory

This theory of imitation does not explain the rules of grammar which are applied in children's speech. For example, children often make simple errors when using plurals which they cannot have heard adults use: 'boaties', 'shoppies' and 'mouses' for boats, shops and mice. Similarly, when a child says 'taked' or 'digged', she is actually demonstrating an understanding of the rule of making regular past tenses (i.e. by adding the regular suffix '-ed').

The theory that language is acquired through imitation and **reinforcement** is not supported by research into the habits of parents when communicating with small children. Parents rarely correct their children's grammar; and when they do so, studies by Katherine Nelson (1988) show that these children have smaller vocabularies than those children whose parents corrected less. The idea that parents 'shape' their children's learning in this way is therefore flawed.

2 Nativist theory

This theory was proposed by Noam Chomsky, an American psycho-linguist writing in the 1960s. Chomsky argued that much of a child's speech was composed of original constructions and could not, therefore, have been copied from an adult. Children must be born with an **innate** capacity for language development, and the sequence of development of language may be expressed as follows:

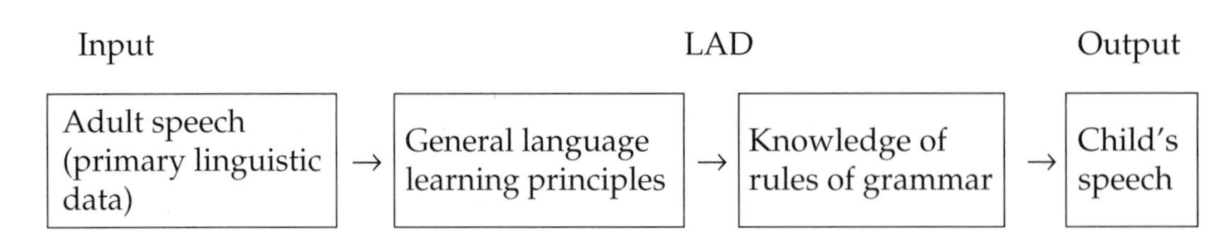

Figure 5.2 The Nativist Theory of Language Acquisition

The main features of the **nativist** (or **innateness**) **theory** are:

- Human beings are born with a biological (innate) capacity for language; it is part of their genetic inheritance. Chomsky termed this the **Language Acquisition Device** (**LAD**). The LAD is programmed to recognise the universal rules that underlie the particular language that a child hears. Using the machine analogy, the LAD may be described as computer hardware
- All children possess innate mental structures which allow them to recognise and to use the complex grammatical rules of a language
- All languages share universal key rules – nouns and verbs and ways of posing questions, issuing commands and expressing negatives
- Children could not possibly learn all they know through imitation, as many behaviourists argue
- Experience cannot modify the way the LAD works as that is innate – i.e. something we are born with
- The **critical period hypothesis** – the nativist view describes an apparent critical period for language acquisition; if the left cerebral hemisphere (which is responsible for the specialisation of language functions) is damaged, the extent of potential recovery from damage is determined by age and is at its highest prior to puberty

Chomsky proposed that language development should be described as 'language growth' because the 'language organ' simply grows like any other organ. He later abandoned the term LAD, but the importance of innate mental structures in cognitive development remains the core of nativist theory.

Criticisms of nativist theory

If all children are born with an innate capacity for language, it does not account for the years taken to develop language skills. It also does not explain the mistakes made by children and the use of **over- and underextension** (see page 147 below for overextensions). And it also fails to explain the wide variation in language ability between individual children. Furthermore, an adult is able to learn a second language to proficiency, which means that the critical period hypothesis is also called into question.

3 Interactionist theory

This theory argues that language acquisition must be viewed within the context of a child's cognitive development. **Piaget** associated language acquisition with the emergence of **representational thought**, which he saw manifested in a variety of ways, including in the search for hidden objects and pretend play. The main features of interactionist theory are:

- Children's language development is closely linked to their cognitive achievements; and skills learnt provide essential resources for language acquisition
- Children do not use hypothetical statements until they have formed **concepts**, rather than having simply acquired grammar
- The cultural view of language acquisition (offered by Bruner and others) emphasises that the social environment is organised to incorporate the child as a member of an already-existing language-using group. Bruner uses the term **format** to refer to a socially patterned activity in which adult and child do things to each other and with each

other; an example of a format is the game of 'peek-a-boo'

Piaget saw language as depending entirely on thought, simply mirroring what was in the child's mind. Bruner saw language as a tool which amplifies and enhances thought. Vygotsky also offered an interactionist explanation of language acquisition: he saw language, on the one hand, primarily as a **social** skill, i.e. one concerned with social interaction, and thought, on the other hand, as the child's individual way of making sense of the world.

Criticisms of interactionist theory

Piaget's approach to the development of language fails to explain the ability of very young children to use and understand complex grammatical structures. Language would not develop ahead of the child's fundamental thought processes. For example, before the child can use expressions of comparison – e.g. 'This cake is bigger than that' – they need first to have developed the conceptual ability to make relative judgements of size. There is currently more acceptance of the interactionist view proposed by Bruner and Vygotsky, which stresses the importance of social interaction in language development.

4 Input theory

This theory (also referred to as **connectionist theory**) stresses the importance of the language used by adults – particularly mothers. In the 1970s, this language was called **motherese**, but is usually now called by the less sexist term **Baby Talk Register** (**BTR**). Many adults talk differently to young children from the way they speak to adults. Baby Talk Register has the following features:

- It is spoken in a higher-pitched voice
- Sentences are shorter, and key words are emphasised
- Speech is slower, and the sentences use simple grammar
- It is highly repetitive: the same sentences, or variations of the same sentences, may be used over and over again, e.g. 'Where is the teddy? Can you see the teddy? There is the teddy!' The adult often repeats the child's sentences, sometimes correcting the grammar in the repetition. A child using **telegraphic speech**, e.g. 'Daddy car', may obtain the response 'Yes, Daddy has gone to work in his car'
- The vocabulary is limited to words that the child will understand, and tends to refer to concrete objects that are immediately present
- Diminutive or reduplicative words are common, e.g. 'doggie' or 'choo-choo'. English makes particular use of a 'y/ie' ending, and similar forms are found in other languages, e.g. the Japanese '-ko'
- There is a high frequency of question forms, and many sentences end on a higher intonation, e.g. 'Yes?' and 'All right?'

Although BTR, or something resembling BTR, exists in most cultures and contexts, it is not found in every society. Research has shown that even newborn infants can discriminate between Baby Talk Register and adult-directed speech, and that they *prefer* to listen to BTR. This may be due to the lilting, musical quality of the speech patterns. The input theory relies on the fact that children who hear a lot of language develop vocabulary more rapidly in the early years than do those who are talked to less.

Criticisms of the input theory

Research into the language development of children from other cultures has shown that in cultures where the parents do not speak in BTR, the children still manage to learn the language. Although the amount of input from adults in terms of modification of speech (as in BTR) and greater involvement in story-telling and symbolic play does affect the rate at which language is learned, it does not appear to be *necessary* for language learning.

A COMBINED PERSPECTIVE

Each of the four theories outlined above has some insight to offer on the acquisition of language, but a more useful perspective is provided by Stan Kuczaj. He makes the distinction between **input** and **intake**. Although adult input is important to some extent, it is the child's **use** of the input which is crucial. Kuczaj in fact argues that language development is affected by three things in all:

1. *innate organising predispositions:* this is the basic brain structure which forms the basis for neural connections. Very young infants are 'pre-programmed' to pay attention to the beginning and ending of strings of sounds, and especially to stressed sounds;
2. *input:* the set of language experiences actually encountered by the child. Many of the studies on the use of BTR concentrate on the *frequency* of use of BTR-type constructions in adult speech. Kuczaj suggests that once a minimally sufficient amount of exposure to a particular construction has occurred, additional exposure is not necessarily helpful to the child's acquisition of it. Some forms of input are more helpful to the child than are others, e.g. repetitions and expansions;
3. *intake:* what the child *does* with the input is crucial to language acquisition. The child may be selective in *what* they use from the adult input and *when* they use it. The intention behind the particular construction of speech used is equally important. For example, a child is more likely to *attend* to BTR that is meant to praise or to encourage rather than to chide or scold.

This view seems to account for the striking similarities seen among children in their early use of language. All children share the same 'pre-programmed' set of rules, and most children are exposed to very similar input from the people around them.

activity

Observing language development in adult–child interaction:
Observe a one-to-one relationship between a mother and her young child under 4 years old. Choose an appropriate context such as bath-time, story-time or meal-time. Ask permission to make an audio tape of the language used, and try to observe also the non-verbal communication used.
After the Activity:

- make a transcript of the tape; do not use more than 5 minutes of the tape as transcripts take a long time to make
- analyse the transcript: write down the child's language and the mother's language, referring to the sections below on stages in language development and the above Baby Talk Register information
- evaluate the language development of the child; note also the features of BTR used by the mother

Stages in language development

1 The stage of emerging language

Often called the **prelinguistic stage**, this is the stage *before* the first word that is used with meaning – including crying, cooing, babbling, pointing and smiling.

0–8 weeks: basic biological noises

Expression: over the first few weeks of life, a baby's vocal sounds directly reflect their biological state and activities. States of hunger, pain or discomfort that cause fussing and crying are known as **reflexive noises**. Bodily actions which are concerned with survival – breathing, eating and excreting – give rise to a wide range of **vegetative noises** such as sucking, swallowing, coughing and burping. It is often difficult to determine the nature of a baby's cries during this period.

Reception: the baby will turn their head to regard a nearby speaker and react appropriately to meaningful sounds, e.g. when their meal is being prepared. Just as very young infants show a preference for human faces, so they are able to distinguish and show a preference for listening to human speech.

8–20 weeks: cooing and laughing

Expression: cooing sounds develop alongside crying, but are produced when the baby is in a settled state. These cooing sounds are quieter, lower-pitched and more musical than crying. They usually consist of a short, vowel-like sound preceded by a consonant-like sound made toward the back of the mouth. Later in this period, cooing sounds are strung together – often 10 or more at a time. Some of these sequences (such as 'ga' and 'gu') begin to resemble the syllables of later speech. At around 4 months, the first throaty chuckles and laughs come out.

Reception: the baby can now **localise** sounds, and pays interested attention to nearby meaningful sounds, particularly familiar voices.

20–30 weeks: vocal play

Expression: there is a lot of variation in the sounds produced during vocal play. The sounds are much steadier and longer than those of cooing. Most voice sequences last over one second and are usually at a high pitch level. They consist of consonant + vowel-like sequences that are often repeated. There seems to be a strong element of practice in the vocal activities of this period.

Reception: the baby now begins to respond in a discriminating way to emotional overtones in the speech of familiar adults (i.e. soothing or annoyed).

25–50 weeks: babbling

Expression: a similar set of sounds is used in babbling, but the sounds are much less varied. Sequences such as 'bababa' are common and are termed **reduplicated babbling** because of the repeated use of the same consonant sound. This later develops into **variegated babbling** in which consonants and vowels change from one syllable to the next (e.g. 'adu'). Whilst babbling appears to have no meaning, the rhythm and syllable length often resemble the words of later speech.

Reception: the baby becomes increasingly competent at localising sounds from greater distances. Towards the end of this period, babies imitate adult's playful sounds, including occasional word forms. Babies now know and turn to their own name.

9–18 months: melodic utterances, holophrastic speech

Expression: towards the end of the child's first year, variations in melody, rhythm and tone of voice become a major feature of speech. Individual syllables are increasingly used with a fixed melody or intonation, producing **proto-words** where the sounds are clear but the meaning is often unclear. These are the first real signs of language development, and children growing up in different language environments begin to sound increasingly unlike each other. At around 15 months, the child will spontaneously use single words in the correct context, and often points to familiar objects or to things that they want. Often, one word is used to mean different things; this is called **holophrase**, e.g. 'car' may mean 'give me the car' or 'look at the car'. By 18 months, the child may echo the last words spoken by an adult – this is called **echolalia** – and may use **pivot words**: words which have a fixed position in the child's speech – e.g. 'Mummy *gone*, 'car *gone*', '*more* milk', '*more* biscuit'. Children also often use **jargoning**, which is babbling with the sound of adult speech. This is also sometimes called **scribble talk**, and to the listener it sounds as if the child is having a conversation.

Reception: the child now turns to another's voice appropriately, and may obey simple instructions. At this stage, children will also recognise words for several common objects and activities.

2 The stage of symbolic development

This stage is also called **language explosion**.

18 months to 4 years

During this period, language and the ability to communicate develop so rapidly that it almost seems to explode.

Expression: at about 18 months to 3 years, children begin to use:

- *telegraphic speech:* this is when a sentence is abbreviated, with certain 'function' words missed out, e.g. 'Daddy kick', 'shut door', 'him got car', or 'where mummy going?'
- *inflections:* these are grammatical 'markers' such as plurals, possessives and past tenses. A 2 year old will begin to use plurals, past tenses and auxiliary verbs, as in 'I am not going'
- *overextensions:* a form of mislabelling in which many members of a category are referred to by a single term that adults use to label only one of them; e.g. 'doggie' is used by a child to describe other animals also, such as cats, cows, sheep etc.
- *increased vocabulary:* towards the end of their second year, the child may have a vocabulary of several hundred words; and they will also now refer to themselves by name
- *virtuous errors:* children make **virtuous** (or **logical**) **errors** in the way that they pronounce (articulate) things, and in the way that they use grammar (syntax): e.g. 'I goed there' instead of 'I went there', and 'mouses gone'
- *sentences with clauses:* towards the end of their second year, the child's speech will become more creative. They will use sentences with clauses, often joined

by 'and', e.g. 'Daddy have breaked the spade all up and ... and ... and it broken ... and ... he did hurt his hand on it and ... and ... it's gone all sore and ...' Other words are also used, but less frequently: 'so', ''cause', 'after', 'if' and 'what' – as in 'I won't go 'cause I tired'
- *questions:* the child will ask simple questions in a set format, particularly 'What's that?'

Between 3 and 4 years, children will use:

- *problem-solving and hypothesis making:* they will ask why, when and how questions as they become fascinated by cause and effect
- *overregularisation:* this is the tendency that young children have to make the language regular, or to make it fit the grammatical rules, e.g. 'wented', 'goed', 'taked'
- *a larger vocabulary:* children now possess a vocabulary of about 1,000 words, and their grammar increasingly resembles that of adults. Pronunciation is also more accurate
- *past, present and future tenses:* this is because they are now able to think back and forward more easily, and can occasionally think about things from someone else's point of view.
- *metalinguistics:* children love to make up both nonsense words and jokes using words
- *longer sentences:* children now use six- or seven-word sentences; and they still ask lots of questions

Reception: between 3 and 4 years, children develop a liking for complicated stories. Their thinking proceeds faster than their ability to say what is in their mind, and this sometimes causes them to stutter and become frustrated when their attempts to communicate are thwarted.

3 The growth of communication skills

From 4 to 8 years

Further developments in the use of language mainly consist of consolidating what is already known and enhancing skills. Sentences are more complex, and in general children use or display:

- *correct irregular forms:* children learn to use the correct forms for irregular nouns and verbs, e.g. 'mice', 'went' and 'took'
- *an increasingly large vocabulary:* this can contain between 8,000 and 14,000 words
- *semantic integration:* this is the ability to infer meaning not directly expressed in statements, such as an understanding of sarcasm
- *metalinguistic awareness:* this is an understanding of language itself, and is a useful tool in learning how to read and write
- *referential communication skills:* children become skilled at inferring what information a listener may need to understand a message. Children also become better at *listening*, and are more likely to ask for clarification of an ambiguous message

Interactional synchrony

W. S. Condon and Adam Kendon (1974) studied the movements of newborn babies (or **neonates**) to discover whether they were synchronised with speech sounds in the same way that adults' movements appear to be. They characterised their method as a 'frame-by-frame microanalysis of sound films' whereby very brief sequences of audio-visual records are inspected in great detail. The results of the study showed that the movement of neonates *was* synchronised with adult speech sounds: changes in the direction and speed of moving body parts occurred precisely in coordination with the speech segments that the researchers had identified. Moreover, the synchronisation appeared to be just as strong when an unfamiliar language was played. Much lower levels of synchronisation of movement, however, were noted with ordinary rhythmic tapping sounds and with disjointed vowel sounds. This seems to suggest that babies, at birth, are somehow **tuned into** the sounds and structure of normal adult speech. They also observed that the synchronies appear between speech and movement *when the baby is already moving*. This suggests that the speech sounds are not 'causing' the baby to move; rather, they show that there is a kind of interactional ballet between the adults and the babies.

Taking account of the listener

Some interesting research by Rochel Gelman and Marilyn Shatz (1977) demonstrates the ability of children as young as 4 years old to take account of the listener and to adapt their language in form and content to different listeners. The researchers tape-recorded 4 year olds introducing younger children and then adults to a new toy. They found that when explaining the toy to a 2 year old, the older child would speak more slowly, use shorter sentences and simplify both their grammar and their vocabulary to make it easier for the younger child to understand. When speaking to adults, the 4-year-old children adjusted their language accordingly: they used longer sentences with more complex grammar.

The interrelated components of language development

There are many different kinds of communication. Language does not have to be oral, i.e. spoken. Language can also be:

- *receptive:* the ability to receive and understand what is being said
- *expressive:* the activity of talking and communicating, including the use of signs and symbols, i.e. in:
  - British Sign Language (BSL)
  - American Sign Language (ASL)

    These combine gestures and agreed and shared signs with finger spelling

activity

Conversational strategies:
Ask a 4-year-old child to introduce a new toy to (i) a 2-year-old child and (ii) an adult (the toy could be a construction toy, a matching game, a jigsaw puzzle or any other appropriate toy). Observe the differences in the use of language in:

- the style of introducing the toy
- the length and complexity of sentences
- the speed of speech and variations in vocabulary

Relate your observation to the findings of Gelman and Shatz.

- drawing and painting
- making music
- writing
- dancing
- making sculptures
- using mathematical notations, e.g. in algebra and geometry

In all these components of language, the child is using **symbols**, both to *receive* language – through reading – and to *express* language – through all the methods listed above. **Symbolic behaviour** is about making one thing stand for another. Once at school, the child soon learns to represent language in its written form, both as reading and writing.

LANGUAGE AND LITERACY

Literacy is the ability to read and write. Writing is putting language into a **code** and reading is the **decoding** of what has been written. Apart from the fulfilment and enjoyment that being able to read and write provides, literacy is necessary in order to:

- seek, give and record information
- keep contact with other people
- help in remembering things and events
- help in planning for the future
- share feelings, thoughts and ideas

Reading plays a fundamental role in promoting children's critical and imaginative thinking, and thus their cognitive and emotional development. There are many approaches to the teaching of reading, including:

- *breakthrough to literacy* – involving word- and sentence-maker cards
- *phonics* – based on the principle of identifying the regular sound–letter relationships in a writing system
- *look-and-say (whole-word approach)* – based on the principle of recognising individual words as wholes
- *paired reading* – individualised programmes where children select their own reading based on interests and ability
- *'basal reading' programmes* – a system of graded readers and work books

As in the development of cognitive skills, research has found that reading skills are more easily learnt if they take place in a context that makes 'human sense' to the child.

WAYS OF PROMOTING LITERACY

At the same time that language begins to develop, young children spontaneously begin to make marks and to develop symbols. They show an interest in the words they hear and the symbols they see around them. Most young children in the USA and even in the UK will recognise the symbol which stands for MacDonald's restaurants, and will learn from an early age about traffic lights and other road signs. The following activities would all help to develop the skills needed when beginning to read:

- *reading books, telling stories and conversations*
- *sorting activities, games like Snap and Lotto:* these help in visual discrimination – noticing similarities and differences
- *rhymes, games like 'I Spy', 'O'Grady Says' and Sound Lotto:* these help in auditory discrimination – developing listening skills
- *following a line from left to right, e.g. when reading:* this helps to encourage the movement of eyes from left to right
- *using pencils, scissors, brushes, threading*

activity

Promoting the development of literacy:

1 Find out which method or combination of methods is used to teach reading to children in an infant class. Look at the books used and evaluate them in the following terms:

- the illustrations: how helpful are they as word pictures?
- the story-line: does it capture the imagination?
- the characters: are they interesting?
- the vocabulary and structure of the language.

2 Try reading one or two of the books you have evaluated with a child of the appropriate age. Write an observation of your reading session, using an audio tape as a prompt, and state the learning outcomes for the child and for yourself.

3 Make a book for use with a group of children who are just beginning to learn to read. You could plan to write and illustrate the book yourself, or incorporate the children's own drawings and stories. When completed, use the book with the children and write an evaluation of the activity.

beads: these help to develop hand–eye coordination

- *setting out picture cards of a story in the correct sequence:* this activity and other similar sequencing tasks, such as copying a rhythm pattern, help to organise thought into a logical time pattern
- *telling stories with repetitive phrases:* e.g. Gingerbread Man, learning rhymes, playing Kim's game etc. – these activities help to develop memory
- *talking, listening, thinking and doing:* children need a variety of experiences inside and outside the home in order to have plenty to talk about and to increase their vocabulary

LANGUAGE AND DEPRIVATION

If exposure to language were the crucial element in language acquisition, then children who are born deaf should be unable to acquire language, and this is clearly not the case. Similarly, children who have suffered extreme forms of deprivation (often called 'feral' or 'wild' children) show how much the same **sequence** of language development as children reared normally – once they have been placed in a more caring and stimulating environment. One such case is that of Genie:

CASE STUDY

GENIE

In 1970, a child called Genie was admitted to a children's hospital in Los Angeles. She was 13 years old and, for more than 11 years, had been locked alone in a darkened room. She was kept tied to a potty chair (commode) during the daytime and tied up in a sleeping bag at night. Although she had been fed, no-one had spoken to her, and she was beaten by her father if she made a sound. When he came to tie her in at night or to deliver food, her father used animal-like growls and scratched her with his fingernails. There had been no radio or television, and Genie's mother was forbidden to spend more than a few minutes with the child to feed her. When Genie finally escaped from this pitiful existence, her mother, who was partially blind and completely dominated by Genie's father, escaped with her. Genie then weighed only 59 lb and was only 1.35 m tall. She was unable to walk normally; instead, she shuffled her feet and swayed from side to side. A series of psychological tests revealed that although Genie could hardly speak, and spent much of her time spitting and salivating, she had an uncanny ability to perceive and think about spatial relationships.

Susan Curtiss, a graduate of linguistics at the time, worked closely with Genie and documented her progress in acquiring language. Genie's first utterances were very similar to the vocabulary of 12–18-month-olds, e.g. 'no', 'no more', 'sorry'. She showed great interest in language, and was even able to use words to describe her experience of deprivation and neglect; Curtiss records Genie as saying 'Father hit arm. Big wood. Genie cry.' However, Genie never asked questions, she never learned to use pronouns and the telegraphic speech did not lead on to more complex sentences. Genie was in fact more inclined to use gestures to get her message across.

Curtiss provides a detailed record of Genie's speech and language development, and theorised that Genie was using the *right* hemisphere of the brain for language use – not the *left* as is usual. If this is a correct explanation for Genie's unusual language development, then it supports the **critical period** hypothesis (see page 143 above). If language is not acquired at the right time, the cortical tissue normally committed for language and related abilities may functionally **atrophy** – or waste away.

All research into Genie's development ceased after one year as Genie's mother was awarded guardianship by the law courts, having filed a lawsuit claiming that Curtiss and others had used Genie for their own personal gain.

(Source: Curtiss 1977)

activity

The sad case of Genie is just one of similar case studies of early deprivation. Find out about some other cases of severe deprivation, e.g. Koluchova's study of identical twin boys in Czechoslovakia (1972), or Douglas and Sutton's study of two sisters called Alice and Beth (1978). (For these two studies, see the Gross and Hayes entries in the 'References and resources' section at the end of this chapter.) Discuss the differences between these cases in terms of their later recovery.

Language disabilities

About 40% of **language disability** cases can be related to a physical cause. Examples are:

- *damage to the brain before or at the time of birth:* any such damage may cause a degree of mental or physical disability, which often results in the impairment of linguistic skills;
- *deafness:*
  1. About 1 in 1,000 children have a hearing loss that is present at birth, or acquired soon after, caused by pathology of the **inner ear** and its relationship to the **auditory nerve**. Causes include maternal **rubella** (**German measles**), **meningitis** and several other diseases;
  2. Acquired hearing loss during early childhood is usually the result of problems in the middle ear, often caused by repeated infections and/or 'glue ear';
  3. Acquired hearing loss in adulthood is caused by old age or regular exposure to loud noise (e.g. at discos and raves, and at work).
- *aphasia:* **aphasia** is an impairment of language function due to localised cerebral damage which leads to difficulty in understanding and/or producing linguistic forms. The most common cause of aphasia is a **stroke** (or **CVA** – **cerebro-vascular accident**); other causes include traumatic head injuries through violence or accidents.

  The following symptoms often accompany aphasia:

  - *agnosia:* a difficulty in recognising familiar sensory stimuli. When this relates to sounds, it is termed **auditory agnosia**. When it relates to shapes or pictures, it is termed **visual agnosia**;
  - *dyspraxia:* an often severe difficulty in controlling voluntary movements of limbs or vocal organs; the *intention* to communicate is present, but the person cannot carry it out;
  - *dysarthria:* difficulty in articulating speech. The effects range from mild to severe – from a slight slurring to total unintelligibility;
- *dyslexia:* difficulty in developing literacy skills. By age 9 or so, spoken language ability is apparently normal, but children face difficulties in reading and writing. This can severely damage their ability and motivation to learn. The causes of dyslexia are not known.

References and resources

Bee, H. (1992) *The Developing Child*, New York: HarperCollins Publishers.

Brierley, J. (1994) *Give Me a Child Until He Is Seven: Brain Studies and Early Childhood Education*, 2nd edn. London: The Falmer Press.

Bruner, J. S. (1963) *The Process of Education*, New York: Vintage Books.

Cole, M. and Cole, S. R. (1993) *The Development of Children*, New York: Scientific American Books.

Condon, W. S. and Kendon, A. (1974) 'Neonate movement is synchronized with adult speech: interactional participation and language acquisition', *Science* 183: 99–101.

Curtiss, S. (1977) *Genie: a Psycholinguistic Study of a Modern-day 'Wild Child'*, New York: Academic Press.

Fantz, R. L. (1961) 'The origins of form perception', *Scientific American*, 204: 66–72.

Gelman, R. and Shatz, M. (1977) 'Appropriate speech adjustments: the operation of conversational constraints on talk to two-year-olds', in Lewis, M. and Rosenblum, L. A. (eds) *Interaction, Conversation and the Development of Language*, New York: Wiley.

Gregory, R. L. (1963) 'Distortion of visual space as inappropriate constancy scaling', *Nature* 119: 678.

Gross, R. (1996) *Psychology: the Science of Mind and Behaviour*, edn. London: Hodder & Stoughton.

Hayes, N. (1994) *Foundations of Psychology: an Introductory Text*, London: Routledge.

Horn, J. L. and Donaldson, G. (1980) 'Cognitive development in adulthood', in Brim, O. G. and Kagan, J. (eds) *Constancy and Change in Human Development*, Cambridge (Mass.): Harvard University Press.

James, W. (1890) *Principles of Psychology* (2 vols). New York: Holt.

Keating, D. (1980) 'Thinking processes in adolescence', in Adelson, J. (ed.) *Handbook of Adolescent Psychology*, New York: Wiley.

Kuczaj, S. A. (ed.) (1982) *Language Developments. Vol. 1: Syntax and Semantics*, New Jersey: Erlbaum.

Lee, V. and Das Gupta, P. (ed.) (1995) *Children's Cognitive and Language Development*, Oxford: Blackwell.

McShane, J. (1991) *Cognitive Development: an Information Processing Approach*, Oxford: Blackwell.

Nelson, K. (1988) 'Constraints on word learning', *Cognitive Development* 3: 221–246.

Oates, J. (ed.) (1994) *The Foundations of Child Development*, Oxford: Blackwell.

Richardson, K. and Sheldon, S. (eds) (1988) *Cognitive Development to Adolescence*, East Sussex: Lawrence Erlbaum Associates Ltd.

Rosch, E., Mervis, C. B., Gray, W. D., Johnson, D. M. and Boyes-Braem, P. (1976) 'Basic objects in natural categories', *Cognitive Psychology* 8: 382–439.

Siegal, M. (1991) Knowing Children: *Experiments in conversation and cognition*, Hillsdale, NJ: Erlbaum.

Smith, P. K. and Cowie, H. (1991) *Understanding Children's Development*, Oxford: Blackwell.

Vygotsky, L. (1986) *Thought and Language*, Cambridge (Mass.): MIT.

Walton, G., Bower, N. J. A. and Bower, T. G. R. (1992) 'Recognition of familiar faces by newborns', *Infant Behaviour and Development*

Watson, J. B. (1930) *Behaviourism*, Chicago: Chicago University Press.

Wittgenstein, L. (trans. Anscombe, E.) (1967) *Philosophical Investigations*, Oxford: Blackwell.

PART

III

Emotional and Social Development

CHAPTER 6

Emotional *and* Social Development *from* Birth *to* Late Childhood

Psychodynamic theories of emotional and social development focus on the importance of unconscious motives; in this approach the relationship of the child with 'significant others' and the quality of **attachment**, particularly in early childhood, is seen as critical.

Bowlby's theory of maternal deprivation was influential in shaping the provision of child care in day nurseries; his work also led to much research into the effects of bonding and patterns of attachment on later behaviour.

Temperament may be seen as the precursor to personality. How a baby or child behaves will be affected by individual temperament as well as by the responsiveness of those with whom he interacts.

A self-concept, or sense of personal identity, develops during the first year of life. Self-esteem is the evaluative part of the self-concept. Margaret Donaldson argues that children can only develop a strong self-concept when they feel that they are effective, competent and independent.

Prosocial behaviour includes altruism, cooperation and empathy; even very young children show an ability to empathise with others. The development of social cognition, (or the way in which we see others) and of empathy may be seen to progress through definite stages.

Play has a crucial role in emotional and social development. It helps children to develop their self-concept, to come to terms with emotional tensions, to explore ideas about morality and to experience a sense of belonging to various social groups.

Moral development is concerned with how we understand ideas of right and wrong and matters of conscience. Piaget, Kohlberg and Eisenberg developed theories about the development of moral reasoning; the stages of moral development are closely connected to the stages in cognitive development, and are particularly related to *social* cognition.

What is emotional and social development?

Emotional development involves the development of **self-image** and **identity**, of the ways in which children make sense of emotions in themselves, and of feelings towards other people. **Social development** involves the growth of the child's relationship with others, the development of social skills and **socialisation**. It is impossible to isolate emotional and social development from any other areas of development: both these aspects of human development are inextricably bound up with the other aspects of cognitive, language, spiritual and moral development.

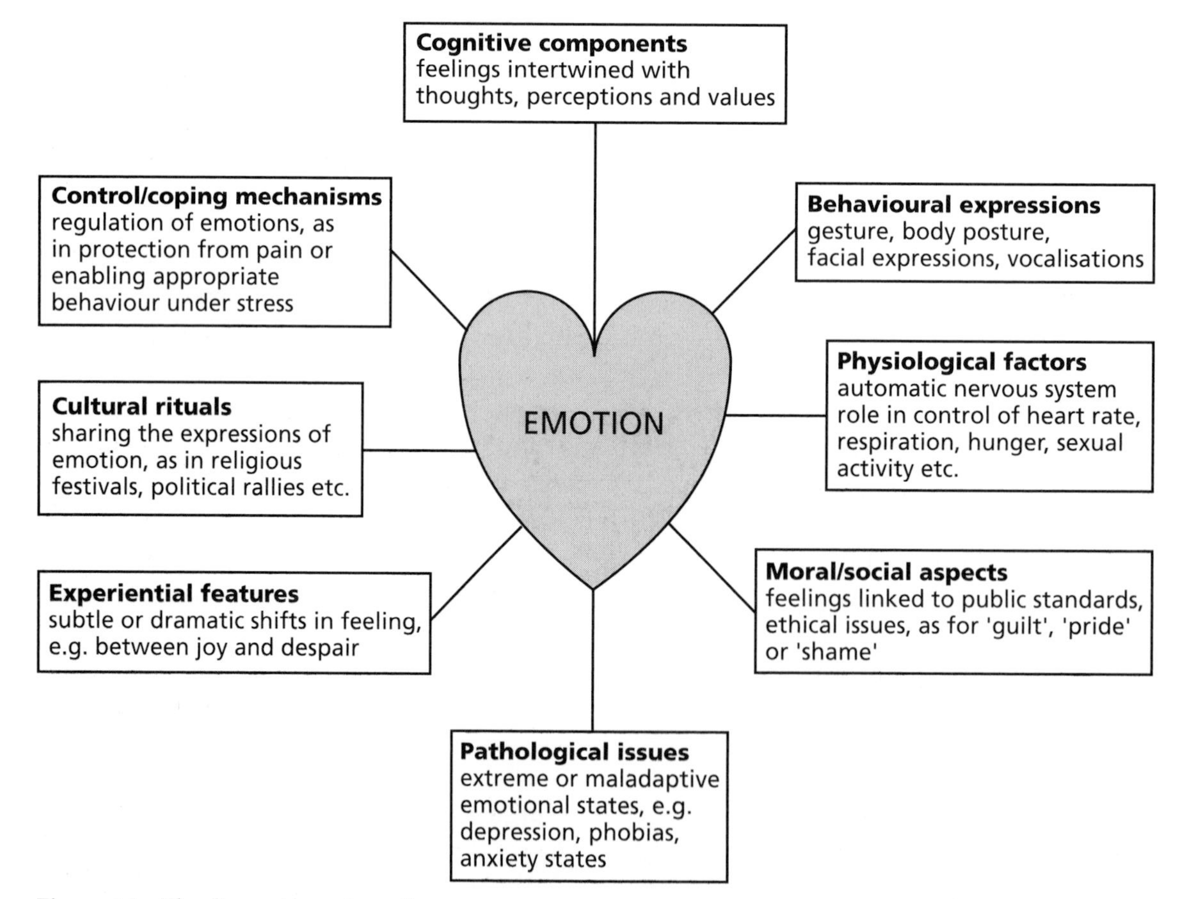

Figure 6.1 The dimensions of emotion

For the purposes of understanding the 'whole child', it is useful to study these aspects of development in manageable sections and from the viewpoint of the relevant theoretical perspectives.

The emergence of emotions

Babies have feelings and emotions from the moment they are born. The word 'emotion' derives from a Latin verb meaning 'to move, excite, agitate'. Emotion is often referred to as 'affect' by psychologists, and is an important part of human psychological behaviour. By expressing emotions, we can:

- **communicate** to other people how we are responding to certain situations.
  Example: a newborn baby will cry to express hunger or discomfort;
- **motivate ourselves** – our emotions alert us to particular information in the environment, and prepare us to respond in certain ways.
  Example: the 'fight or flight' reaction to a perceived threat enables us to cope effectively.

The behaviourist John B. Watson, writing in 1930, described three primary emotions felt by newborn infants: fear, anger and love. Fear is aroused by threatening stimuli, and the baby's response is shown by crying and clutching; anger is provoked by the blocking of the baby's activities, and they respond by stiffening their body and holding their breath; love is aroused by soothing stimulation, e.g. cooing, and the baby responds by smiling. Not all psychologists, however, agree that newborn babies feel such emotions. Although facial expressions have universal meanings for adults, young babies lack the maturity of higher brain mechanisms to be able to convey these meanings through their own facial expressions.

THE NATURE–NURTURE DEBATE

As with cognitive and language development, theorists of emotional and social development tend to emphasise either **nature** (the idea that personalities are fixed from the moment of birth) or **nurture** (the idea that emotional and social behaviour is learnt). In this area of study, there are three main approaches:

1. *Nature.* This includes:
   - **psychodynamic theories** (Sigmund Freud, E. H. Erikson, John Bowlby)
2. *Nurture.* This includes:
   - **behaviourism** (B. F. Skinner)
   - **socialisation theory**
   - **social learning theory** (Albert Bandura)
3. *A combination of nature and nurture:*
   - **social evolution theory** (R. Dawkins)
   - **social constructivist theory** (C. Trevarthen, Judy Dunn, Lev Vygotsky)

Theories about emotional and social development

PSYCHODYNAMIC THEORIES

Psychodynamic theories hold that we are all born with a set of 'dependency' needs, e.g. love, affection and security. These needs emerge at different ages and stages of childhood, and children can only remain healthy if all these needs are met. All psychodynamic – or **psychoanalytic** – theories rely heavily on the idea of an

unconscious mind and emphasise the dynamic inner forces which regulate and control behaviour. These theories are based to varying degrees on the theory of Sigmund Freud.

Sigmund Freud (1856–1939)

Sigmund Freud trained as a doctor in Vienna and specialised in the treatment of nervous disorders. He noted that many neurotic symptoms exhibited by his patients seemed to stem from earlier traumatic experiences rather than from physical disorders. According to Freud, a young child has only one of the *three* basic personality components that they will eventually have as an adult:

1 The **id** is the primitive, impulsive part of the personality which makes 'I want' demands. This part of the personality works on what Freud described as the **pleasure principle**, that is to say, it seeks to obtain pleasure and avoid pain. The id is mainly concerned with things which ensure that the person survives, and with things that give pleasure, such as food, shelter, comfort and avoidance of pain. In the newborn infant, all mental processes are id processes.
2 As the child grows older, reality intervenes and the **ego** develops. The ego is the part of the mind which operates according to the **reality principle**, trying to balance the demands of the unconscious with what is possible or practical. The ego is rational and logical and allows the child to learn that negotiating, asking and explaining is a more effective way of satisfying demands than through the id's 'I want'. For example, the young child learns that hunger will only be satisfied when someone is available to provide food.
3 At around the age of 4 to 6, the child comes into contact with authority, and the **superego** emerges. This is the part of the unconscious mind which acts as society, or as a strict parent*, incorporating ideas of duty, obligation and conscience. The superego relies on the **morality principle**, acting as a censor and conscience by telling us what is right and wrong. The superego has two parts: the **ego-ideal** and the **conscience**. The ego-ideal is concerned with what is right and proper; it represents the individual's idea of the sort of virtuous behaviour that would be rewarded by others, initially the parents. The conscience intercepts and censors immoral impulses from the id and stops them from entering the consciousness of the ego.

(*The context in which Freud lived and worked was that of middle-class late-19th-century Austria, when the father was seen as a remote figure who exerted firm discipline in all areas of the child's life.)

According to Freud, the ego maintained a state of **dynamic equilibrium** between the conflicting pressures of the id and the superego. When the ego listens to the id more than the superego, the person is said to be **egocentric** (self-centred). When the ego listens to the superego more than to the id, the person is said to be **conformist**. When the needs of the id and the superego are well-balanced (i.e. in a state of dynamic equilibrium), the person is said to be **well-grounded**.

Freud believed that human beings, like other animals, are largely motivated by biological drives; e.g. hunger and thirst are states of arousal which urge the person to obtain the food and water necessary for survival. As the basic need is satisfied and the drive thereby reduced, pleasure is felt and so, in turn, the pursuit of pleasure becomes a basic principle of existence. Freud also argued that development through the first few years followed a par-

The oral stage (0–1 year)	The mouth is the primary focus of pleasure. Babies gain satisfaction from putting things into their mouth and sucking. The earliest attachment is usually to the mother as providing oral gratification; thumb-sucking is defined as **fantasy gratification** as no milk or food is delivered via the thumb. For normal development, the infant needs an optimum amount of oral stimulation – neither too much nor too little. Babies who have not received this optimum amount of stimulation (perhaps through being weaned too early or too late) become **fixated**.
Behaviour in adulthood if fixated at this stage	Smoking, nail-biting, over-eating, passivity.
The anal stage (1–3 years)	The anus is the primary focus of pleasure. The child becomes capable of more control over their bowels and derives great pleasure from the retention and expulsion of faeces. Parents and carers place great emphasis on potty training; those who adopt too strict an approach to potty training may cause the child to become fixated at the anal stage.
Behaviour in adulthood if fixated at this stage	Could become an **anal-retentive** personality – very concerned with orderliness, tidiness and cleanliness, and maybe miserly; if parents were too lenient, could become **anal-expulsive** – overly generous and giving.
The phallic stage (3–6 years)	The genitals are the primary focus of pleasure. Children start to develop an interest in their own genitals and in their parent's genitals. Unconsciously, the boy's love for his mother increases to the extent that he wants to possess her sexually; the father is seen as a rival for his mother's love – this is called the **Oedipus Complex**. In order to escape this complex and the fear of castration by his father, the boy will unconsciously go through the process of **identification** – he takes on the characteristics of his father, becoming as like him as possible. Girls go through a similar process, called the **Electra Complex**, which results in identification with the mother. Absence of the 'appropriate' parent at this stage could lead to the child becoming fixated.
Behaviour in adulthood if fixated at this stage	Vanity and recklessness, and their opposites – modesty or cautiousness.
The latency stage (6–12 years)	There is no specific focus of pleasure. During this stage, sexual desires are suppressed; sexual energy is channelled into the acquisition of technical skills that will be needed in adulthood. Identification with the same-sex parent is now extended to others of the same sex; children tend to play exclusively with members of the same sex and often develop 'crushes' on same-sex adults. Fixation does not normally occur at this stage.
The genital stage (12–18 and adulthood)	The genitals are the primary focus of pleasure. The sex organs are maturing in shape and functioning, and hormonal changes occur. At around puberty, children begin to develop an interest in relationships with members of the opposite sex and during this stage reach mature sexual intimacy.
Behaviour in adulthood if fixated at this stage	Difficulty in relating to people of the opposite sex, shyness and immaturity.

Table 6.1 Freud's psychosexual stages – a summary

ticular pattern for all children – his was therefore a **stage theory**. He also believed that all the main outlines of human personality are determined by experiences within the family before the age of 4 years. The pattern of development takes the form of distinct **psychosexual stages**: **oral**, **anal**, **phallic**, **latency** and **genital** – see Table 6.1.

Criticisms of Freud's theory of personality development

Freud's theories have provoked strong criticisms ever since they were first proposed in the early 20th century. There have been many attempts to verify his theories, but none has managed either to prove or to disprove them. However, they remain influential because they were the result of years of clinical investigation, and they provide an explanation for behaviour in terms of the unconscious mind.

Some criticisms are that:

- *Freud's theory is unscientific:* to be truly scientific, a theory must make hypotheses which are testable in such a way that if the hypothesis proves false the theory would be discarded. (On the other hand, there are also many other aspects of the human condition that are not able to be proved scientifically either – e.g. the existence of a Higher Being or God.) Furthermore, Freud used no quantitative data or statistical analysis in support of his theories.
- *Freud views the child as passive and helpless:* Freud emphasises the biological roots of behaviour to the neglect of social and cultural influences. However, most theorists now recognise that children are much more active in their own socialisation.
- *Freud uses very limited samples from a narrow social context:* Freud based his theory on a very limited sample of women and of just one child. His evidence of the stages of personality development are drawn from the dreams and spoken memories of a small, mainly middle-class group of people who already had some personality problems.
- *Freud's theory is essentially about what people think, feel and dream, rather than about how they behave:* Freud had to rely on his patients' ability to report their own thoughts and dreams, and on the skill of the psychoanalyst in interpreting them. The available data is thus open to **bias**, first by the subject and then by the interpreter.

Defence mechanisms

During the development of his theory, Freud described a number of **defence**

activity

1 How could a carer of children (in either a hospital or a day nursery) help to ensure that a child does not become fixated at (a) the oral stage and (b) the anal stage?

2 Try to identify some examples of behaviour among children at junior school (ages 6–12 years) which might show that they are fixated in one of the early stages.

mechanisms, which were later elaborated by his daughter Anna Freud. Defence mechanisms are mental processes which are automatically triggered when anxiety occurs. They are unconscious strategies which are used by individuals to protect themselves from stress or guilt. The short-term use of these defences is thought to be a healthy way of coping with life's stresses. On the other hand, where they are used to excess or on a long-term basis, they are thought to be dangerous and unhealthy.

Repression	Forcing painful or frightening memories and feelings out of conscious awareness and into the unconscious. Freud saw this as the most important and basic defence. *Example:* a child who has been abused – in any way – may force the memory of that abuse into the unconscious.
Regression	Reverting to an earlier time of life when faced with a threat or unsafe situation. *Example:* **enuresis** (bedwetting) as a response to a major life change, such as starting school or the birth of a sibling.
Denial	Refusing to accept reality; this is the most primitive defence and plays an important part in the grieving process. *Example:* refusing to believe that a partner is being unfaithful, or that we have a serious illness.
Displacement	Redirecting feelings or impulses towards a substitute object or person because you cannot direct them towards their real target. *Example:* a child may be annoyed by her father but direct her feelings towards 'safer objects' such as toys.
Projection	Attributing your own unacceptable feelings or impulses to someone else. *Example:* saying 'He hates me' when your real feeling is 'I hate him'. The extreme case is that of the paranoid individual who feels continually threatened by everyone with whom they come into contact.
Sublimation	This is a type of displacement where totally unacceptable behaviours are sublimated (or redirected) into a substitute activity; this is considered to be a positive and beneficial mechanism. *Example:* violent impulses may be sublimated into sporting activities, particularly contact sports.
Rationalisation	Justifying our actions to ourselves when we do or think something that makes us feel guilty. *Example:* when we desperately want something but fail to obtain it and then disparage its value (known as 'sour grapes')

Table 6.2 A summary of defence mechanisms

activity

Match the statement with the appropriate defence mechanism as shown in Table 6.2:

1 A man is locked in a traffic jam on his way home from work and has a furious row with his wife when he eventually reaches home.
2 A teenager cries when his parents refuse to let him go to a night club.
3 A mother beats her child repeatedly and is convinced that it is 'for the child's own good'.
4 A young mother refuses to believe the doctor who tells her that she has a serious illness.
5 A young man with a short temper works out regularly in a gym and always feels calmer after a session.
6 A mature man repeatedly 'forgot' to keep an appointment with his dentist. He always found dental surgeries to be frightening places.

Erik Erikson (1902–79)

Erikson, like Freud, proposed a 'stage' theory of **psychosocial** development to explain the development of the personality. Erikson describes eight stages, each of which is dominated by a crisis or conflict which has to be resolved (see Table 6.3).

Stage 1: the first year of life

The psychosocial crisis or conflict characteristic of this stage is to gain a balance between trusting people and risking being let down, or being mistrustful and therefore suspicious of others. This corresponds to Freud's oral stage. If the mother or

Stage and approximate age	Psychosocial crisis (name of stage)	Psychosocial relationship
1: birth to 1 year	Basic trust vs basic mistrust	Principal caregiver (usually mother)
2: 1 to 2 years	Autonomy vs shame and doubt	The parents
3: 3 to 5 years	Initiative vs guilt	The family
4: 6 years to puberty	Industry vs inferiority	Neighbourhood and school
5: adolescence (12–18)	Identity vs role confusion	Peers
6: young adulthood (20s)	Intimacy vs isolation	Sexual partners, colleagues
7: mature adulthood (late 20s–50s)	Generativity vs stagnation	Shared household and society
8: old age (50s and beyond)	Integrity vs despair	'Humankind', 'my kind'

Table 6.3 Erikson's eight psychosocial stages

principal caregiver meets the baby's needs for hunger and comfort, then the baby will learn to trust. Erikson is not saying that there should be *total* trust, as the child needs to develop a healthy mistrust to learn about dangerous situations. However, the position on the 'trust–mistrust' continuum should be much nearer to trust than to mistrust.

Favourable outcome: hopes for the future and trust in the environment.

Unfavourable outcome: fear of the future, insecurity and suspicion.

Stage 2: the second year of life

As children develop physically and experience wider choices, they need to assert their independence. This stage corresponds to Freud's anal stage. The child needs to be carefully guided by their parents and not made to feel ridiculous or a failure if thwarted in their efforts towards independence – e.g. in toilet training or in feeding themselves. Again, there needs to be a balance between autonomy and doubt, as the child needs to know which sorts of behaviour are socially acceptable and safe. However, the ideal does lie on the autonomy end of the continuum.

Favourable outcome: a sense of independence and self-esteem.

Unfavourable outcome: a feeling of shame, and doubt about one's own capacity for self-control.

Stage 3: 3 to 5 years

Further development and mastery of physical skills leads to children learning to **initiate** their own activities and to engage in purposeful activity. This stage relates to Freud's phallic stage. The child begins to recognise the differences between the sexes, and will express a desire to marry the opposite-sex parent. Children will enjoy their accomplishments and try out their new cognitive and creative abilities. Parents and caregivers may perceive the child's use of initiative as aggression or forcefulness and seek to restrict and punish the child. The child will then feel guilt and will be inhibited in their creativity and use of initiative. There needs to be *some* sense of guilt, however, since without it there will be no conscience or self-control.

Favourable outcome: the ability to initiate activities and to enjoy carrying them out.

Unfavourable outcome: guilt about one's own feelings, and fear of being punished.

Stage 4: 6 years to puberty

This stage is centred around school and the learning of skills. It corresponds to Freud's latency stage. Children need to become competent in certain areas that are important within the school context and valued by adults and peers, e.g. reading and early mathematics. If they are continually rejected and criticised by their teachers, parents or peers, then they will feel inferior and have a sense of failure. However, if they are praised and encouraged in their achievements, they will be spurred on to further industry. Again, there needs to be a balance here as too much emphasis on competence leads to a 'hot-house' approach to schooling: some failure is necessary so that the child can develop some humility.

Favourable outcome: confidence in one's own ability to make and do things; a sense of achievement.

Unfavourable outcome: feelings of inferiority and inadequacy resulting from unfavourable reactions from others.

Stage 5: adolescence

The main focus in this stage is the development of **identity**. For Erikson, both sexual and occupational identity are important during this crisis. This stage corresponds to Freud's genital stage. Adolescents are faced with many role changes, and this can produce conflict and stress. During adolescence, the individual needs to develop a sense of identity by integrating all the images they have of themselves as son/daughter, brother/sister, student, friend, and by reflecting on past experiences, thoughts and feelings. Those who have emerged positively from the earlier stages of development are more likely to achieve an **integrated psychosocial identity** at adolescence.

Favourable outcome: the ability to see oneself as an integrated person with a strong personal identity.

Unfavourable outcome: fear of the future, insecurity and suspicion.

Stage 6: young adulthood (20s)

The main focus of this stage is the formation of social relationships. Erikson sees a great difference between Intimacy with a capital I, and intimacy, by which he means sexual activity. Erikson defines Intimacy thus: 'Real Intimacy includes the capacity to commit yourself to relationships that may demand sacrifice and compromise; the ego strength of young adulthood is love – a mutual, mature devotion' (cited in Hall 1983). In extreme cases, it is quite possible to have a very full and active sex life and yet still feel a terrible sense of isolation, because there is no feeling of **mutuality**, and because the partner is never perceived as a person. If the adolescent has been successful in the formation of their identity, then this will be tested in early adulthood, mainly from an occupational and relationship viewpoint.

Favourable outcome: the ability to experience love and commitment to others.

Unfavourable outcome: superficial relationships with others and isolation.

Stage 7: mature adulthood (late 20s–50s)

The focus of this stage is generativity, which is composed of three related activities: procreation, productivity and creativity. Erikson believed that there is an instinctive wish to have children – a procreative drive which can be sublimated into productivity and creativity. Productivity is the inborn desire to make society better for one's children, and creativity involves learning the new rather than rigidly trying to maintain things as they used to be. Failure to establish a sense of generativity results in a state of stagnation and self-absorption: the individual becomes preoccupied with their own personal needs and comforts and tends to self-indulgence.

Favourable outcome: the capacity for being concerned and caring about others in the wider sense.

Unfavourable outcome: boredom, lack of personal growth and self-absorption.

Stage 8: old age (50s and beyond)

The major task of old age is to reflect on one's life and to assess how fulfilling and worthwhile it has been. If older people remain active, and if they still relate directly to society, they can integrate all of life's experiences and thus achieve **ego integrity**. The individual who has achieved this stage of ego integrity will face the prospect of death philosophically and with a sense of inevitability. The individual who has failed to solve most of their earlier crises may succumb to feelings of despair at the futility of existence.

Favourable outcome: a sense of satisfaction with one's life and its achievements; an acceptance of death.

Unfavourable outcome: regret over omissions and missed opportunities; fear of death.

An evaluation of Erikson's theory

Erikson's extension of his theory to include young, middle and late adulthood is a useful addition to psychodynamic theories on development. In general, his theories are highly regarded not only in psychology but also in the fields of education and psychiatry. The choice of identity as the central theme of adolescence has, however, been criticised as having a *male bias*, at least in Western society: men are encouraged to develop identity at the expense of intimacy, and for women this is reversed. Another criticism is that Erikson's theory does not apply universally to people in different cultures and societies. For example, stage 4, industry vs. inferiority, may only be applicable to cultures, such as ours, which emphasise competitiveness and which disapprove of children who do not succeed at the appropriate times.

activity

1. In a group, describe the various youth cultures that have existed in the past 40 years (e.g. teddy boys, mods and rockers, hippies, punks etc.) in terms of (a) their common interest, (b) their musical style and (c) their clothes and hairstyles.
2. How do these youth cultures fit in with Erikson's theory of psychosocial development?
3. What do you see as the predominant youth cultures in the UK today?

John Bowlby (1907–90)

John Bowlby trained as a child psychiatrist and favoured the psychodynamic approach. He used the **case-study method** and many of the ideas from psychodynamics to form his basic theory. However, he also believed that the psychodynamic approach put too much emphasis on the child's fantasy world and not nearly enough on actual events.

Bowlby was also influenced by **ethology** – particularly Konrad Lorenz's theory of **imprinting**.

Maternal deprivation and attachment

In 1951, John Bowlby wrote a paper for the World Health Organization which suggested that maternal deprivation could be a major cause of many emotional, social and intellectual disorders. He wrote: 'Mother-love in infancy and childhood is as important for mental health as are vitamins and proteins for physical health.' Bowlby's research was to have an enormous impact on the delivery of care both to mothers in post-natal wards and to children in institutions.

The main principles of the theory are that:

- the first five years of life are the most important in a person's development. (This had already been proposed by Freud and other psychodynamic theorists)
- a child's relationship with their parents (in particular with the mother) has an enormous effect on the child's overall development
- separation from a parent, particularly from the mother, is a major cause of psychological distress or trauma
- such separation and consequent psychological trauma in childhood has long-lasting effects on the overall development of the child
- the attachment bond is **monotropic**. This means that it is established between the infant and one other person. Other relationships may be formed, but these differ in quality from the one between the infant and the primary caregiver and do not have the same impact on later social and emotional development
- attachment is a highly evolved system of regulation that normally develops during the first year of life to produce a **dynamic equilibrium** between the mother–child pair
- there is a **critical** (or **sensitive**) **period** for attachment formation: Bowlby thought that the period between 6 months and 3 years was critical for attachment formation
- if children are deprived of a mother or mother-surrogate, then they are far more likely to show delinquent behaviour in later life

Bowlby did *not* say that the most important attachment figure must be the natural mother. He did stress, however, that babies need one central person who is the mother figure. There are obvious ethical considerations which make it difficult to conduct experiments on the effects of maternal deprivation on young human infants, although James and Joyce Robertson made a series of films in the

Figure 6.2 A still from 'Young Children in Brief Separation', a video diary of children who were separated from their parents during a spell in hospital, in the 1950s.

1950s which showed Bowlby's theory in action. One film was of young children who were separated from their parents during a brief stay in hospital. The film showed that children separated from their families went through various stages in their loss and grief:

1 They **protested**. They cried out – but were able to be comforted.
2 They **despaired** about what was happening – and were inconsolable.
3 They showed **denial** and became detached in the way that they related to others. They seemed superficially unconcerned at the separation, but denied any affection or response to the mother when eventually reunited.

Defining attachment

What is believed to be essential for mental health is that the infant and young child should experience a warm, intimate and continuous relationship with his mother (or permanent mother substitute) in which both find satisfaction and enjoyment.

(Bowlby 1975)

Children who did not benefit from a mother's 'warm, intimate and continuous relationship' were considered by Bowlby to be suffering from **maternal deprivation**. He asserted that a child can be deprived even when living at home if their mother fails to provide the necessary loving care. On the other hand, a person other than the child's mother, and whom the child knows and trusts, can act as a substitute. In either of these scenarios, a child is considered to suffer **partial deprivation**. A child with no close, secure relationship at all suffers what Bowlby called **complete deprivation**. (Note: this deprivation is not the same as **privation** – see page 177).

Bowlby noted three factors which influence the effects of deprivation:

1 the age at which a child loses a mother;
2 the length of time that a child is separated from a mother;
3 the degree of deprivation that a child experiences.

Mary Ainsworth, who worked closely with John Bowlby, offers the following definitions of terms (1989).

- *affectional bond:* a relatively long enduring tie in which the partner is important as a unique individual and is interchangeable with none other. There is a desire to maintain closeness to the partner.
- *attachment:* a sub-variety of affectional bond in which the central figure is experienced as a safe base from which to explore the world.
- *attachment behaviours:* the collection of (probably) instinctive behaviours of one person towards another that brings about or maintains proximity and caregiving. These behaviours can be shown by both adult and child, and could include smiling, making eye contact, touching, clinging, calling out etc. It is not the *frequency* of such behaviours that demonstrates the attachment but the *pattern*.

Bonding

Donald Winnicott, a British psychologist, called the effect of the hormonal changes in late pregnancy 'primary maternal preoccupation'. He described it as a 'state of heightened sensitivity, almost an illness' (1958) which made the mother ready to fall in love with her baby, thus creating a mother–infant 'bond'. It used to be thought that this **bonding** happens rapidly in the first few days (or even hours) after the baby's birth, and a lack of early bonding meant problems in the future. It is now recognised that a bond of attachment is established over a period of time, and that it is the *quality* of the time the child spends with people which determines whether or not the child becomes attached to them.

Separation anxiety

Showing anxiety or distress when separated from an adult is a sign that the baby is **attached**. A firmly attached baby will resist anyone else who tries to comfort them, and if the separation is prolonged, the baby may go through the three stages of loss and grief as shown in the Robertsons' films. The adverse effects of long-term maternal separation were confirmed by research carried out with rhesus monkeys in the USA. Harry and Margaret Harlow conducted a series of experiments to determine the source of attachment and the effects of maternal separation. In one of these studies, they separated infant monkeys from their natural mothers at a very early age and placed them in individual cages with two inanimate surrogate

Figure 6.3 Harlow's monkey: 'he jumps up and down to register his happiness at seeing her'

(meaning 'substitute') mothers. The surrogates were dummies made to look something like real monkeys. One surrogate was made from wire mesh, the other was padded with foam and covered with terry cloth (see Figure 6.3). The surrogate made of wire mesh contained the food bottle, whilst the soft padded surrogate did not provide any food. The monkeys showed a clear preference for the soft padded mother even if they were always fed from a bottle attached to the wire mesh mother: they would only go to the wire mesh dummy to feed, and would then go back and cling to the terry-cloth mother. In other experiments, the monkeys had access to the wire mesh dummy only. These monkeys showed more signs of emotional disturbance – rocking, clutching and failing to explore – than the monkeys raised with the padded mother. The Harlows' research refuted the behaviourist (conditioning) theory that attachment develops because the parent feeds the child and that affectionate behaviour is **reinforced** by food. Results from the many Harlow experiments consistently showed that a warm, comfortable area to which to cling was more likely to promote attachment than a mere source of food.

Recent research on the effects of separation of animals from their mothers has been conducted in the Netherlands:

> Infant rats separated from their mothers for just a single day are marked for life, Dutch researchers at the University of Njimegen have found. When these rats are examined a few months after the one-day separation, their adrenal glands are larger, the concentration of corticosteroid hormones in their blood is higher, their immune response is reduced, and their reactions to stress last longer. Such early experiences may therefore increase the risks of stress-related disorders in some individuals, the researchers believe. The evidence is that, in rats at least, early separation stimulates the adrenal gland – almost inactive when the mother is present – into producing high levels of corticosteroid hormones which then activate certain genes and create permanent changes in brain function. Interestingly, the same changes do not occur when brief daily separations occur. Then the infant rats appear better able to cope with stress until an advanced age, and better able to learn.
>
> *(The Times, 2 September 1996)*

The impact of attachment is not only negative (i.e. a fear of strangers or of being deserted): attachment also has a positive consequence, in giving the baby a safe base from which to explore the world (see Figure 6.4). The more the baby is attached, the freer they feel to explore the social and physical worlds. The attached baby may crawl away from their parents for minutes at a time, but they always keep them within a safe range and never stray beyond a radius of about a hundred feet. As Annette Karmiloff-Smith writes, 'it is as if she were joined to the parents by an invisible thread' and this is delightfully demonstrated in the film which accompanies her book *Baby it's you*.

Figure 6.4 With her mother close by, Emily confidently explores a new environment

THE STRANGE SITUATION

Mary Ainsworth devised a research procedure in the 1960s called the **strange situation** to study the way in which infants are attached to their mothers. The basic purpose of the procedure is to observe how different infants (aged between 12 and 24 months) respond to a stranger when they are with their mothers, when they are left alone and when they are reunited with their mothers. This method is now widely used:

- A mother and her baby are brought into a strange room, well supplied with toys. The baby is given the opportunity to play with the toys and to explore the room while mother is watching
- After a few minutes, an unfamiliar person enters and engages the mother in conversation
- The stranger moves closer to the baby, and after a minute the mother leaves as unobtrusively as possible

activity

The use of animals in psychological research:

Some psychologists believe that the study of animals can tell us a lot about human behaviour, whilst others think that we can learn very little about people from such animal studies.

1. Discuss the advantages and disadvantages of animal research in terms of its contribution to pyschological knowledge. Illustrate your answer with two detailed animal-research studies. Two such interesting studies were carried out by Gardner and Gardner (refer to Davenport) and by Overmeir and Seligman (refer to Hayes 1994).
2. Find out about the main guidelines for using animals in psychological research (provided by the British Psychological Society – see the 'Useful address' section at the end of Part III on page 227).
   - How do these guidelines differ from the ethical guidelines for research with *human* subjects?
   - Discuss the ethical issues raised by animal research

- The baby is left in the room with the stranger, who joins in with the baby's activities, e.g. accepting a toy when proffered etc. (if the baby became very anxious and distressed, the session was concluded)
- After a few more minutes, the mother returns to comfort her baby and to settle her down to play
- When she leaves the room again, she waves goodbye, drawing attention to her departure

Hundreds of infants have been observed using this technique and variations of the strange situation. The typical reaction of the child on entering the new room with their mother is to stay close to her, at first physically touching her. Later, the child moves away to explore, but looks back from time to time – as if to check that mother is still there. When a stranger enters the room, the child tends to rush back to mother and will only play with the unfamiliar person after some time. If the mother leaves the room, most children tend to cry and to stop playing.

Ainsworth and her colleagues identified three types of **attachment relationship**:

Figure 6.5 The strange situation

1. Type A – *anxious-avoidant*: before being separated from the mother, the child pays her relatively little attention and is not particularly distressed when she leaves the room. The child does not react very anxiously to the stranger and either ignores the mother when she returns or greets her tentatively.
2. Type B – *Securely attached*: before the mother leaves the room, the child plays quite happily and reacts positively to the stranger. After the mother leaves the room, the child becomes distressed and plays much less. Any distress shown during the separation period was clearly related to the mother's absence. When the mother returns, the child is quickly consoled and settled and resumes playing.
3. Type C – *anxious-ambivalent*: before the mother leaves the room, the infant is fussy and wary, showing a mixture of emotions. Often, the child is clingy before separation but does not always show any signs of welcome when the mother returns, and does not resume play easily. The child also resists comfort from the stranger and seems to be torn between seeking and resisting contact with the mother.

Type B – securely attached – was the most common attachment noted by Ainsworth and others, although there is some variation between cultures. Mothers also influence the development of particular attachment relationships by the extent of their responsiveness to the child's behaviour. Ainsworth identified four **dimensions of maternal behaviour** that correspond to the type of attachment the child has:

1. *sensitive–insensitive:* sensitive parents who were positive and encouraged close physical contact. These parents were able to see things from the child's point of view

2 *accepting–rejecting:* accepting parents are tolerant of the restrictions imposed by having a baby, and regard it as a positive change to their lives
3 *cooperating–interfering:* cooperating parents see the relationship with their child as a valuable interaction. They try not to impose their own wishes on the child.
4 *accessible–ignoring:* accessible parents are more 'there' for their child. They take more notice of the child and of their needs and wishes.

The mothers of securely attached infants (Type B) tended to be more sensitive, accepting, cooperating and accessible. The mothers of Type A (anxious-avoidant) children tended to be rejecting and insensitive. The mothers of Type C (anxious-ambivalent) children tended to be rejecting, interfering and ignoring.

CROSS-CULTURAL RESEARCH

Mary Ainsworth studied the process of infant–mother attachment in the Ganda community of Uganda. Babies aged from 15 weeks to 2 years of age were observed by **naturalistic observation** and interviews in the family home (with the aid of an interpreter). Ainsworth noted that the babies stopped crying when lifted by their mothers, but not when lifted by anyone else. Babies in the Ganda tribe sleep with their mothers and are breastfed until they are about 2 years old. The mothers kept their babies close by them, usually in a cotton sling, when working in the house, but often left them for three or more hours when working in the garden. Ainsworth compared this group of infants with a group of American infants in Baltimore,

activity

Observing attachment:

1 *Naturalistic observation.* Arrange to visit a home where there is a small child (aged between 3 months and 3 years). Explain that you want to observe the child's reaction to an unfamiliar situation as part of your study into children's emotional and social development. Ask if you can pick up the child, play with her and be alone with her for a short while. Act in a friendly, natural way. Then record what happened as soon as possible afterwards.

- Did the child appear friendly of cautious?
- Did the child display a mixture of emotions? Try to build up an accurate picture of the child's emotions by describing facial expressions, vocalisations, gesture and body language.

Write an evaluation of the observation which includes your own personal learning about the nature of attachment and of mother–child separation.

2 *Research into attachment in childhood.* Different patterns of attachment or bonding occur in different parts of the world. Choose a different culture to research, e.g. Japanese society, the kibbutzim in Israel, China or Africa. Find out about the different child-rearing practices in the culture and relate these to the theories on attachment and personality.

USA. The American mothers tended to leave their babies in one room while they moved around the house working, popping in and out to check on them. The Ganda infants were much more upset when their mothers left the room than were the American infants. Ainsworth concluded that babies in different cultures might react differently to their mothers leaving them, depending upon their previous experiences of separation.

ATTACHMENT, CAREGIVERS AND INSTITUTIONS

Multiple attachments

Research shows that although the *strongest* attachment is to the mother, early attachments are usually multiple in nature, including relationships with the father, siblings and grandparents. In general, attachments are formed to *responsive, sensitive* people who interact and play a lot with the infant. A study of 1 and 2 year olds in an Israeli kibbutz used the 'strange situation' technique (Fox 1977). The infants spent the majority of their waking hours in the communal nursery, looked after by a trained children's nurse, or **metapelet**. In spite of the reduced amount of time spent with the parents – usually about two hours every evening – these infants were found to be more attached to their parents than to the metapelet. The significant factor would seem to be the *intensity* of the interaction.

The role of the father

The strength of the attachment that children have to their fathers depends (just as with any attachment) upon the *quality* of the relationship. Father and child will be securely attached when the father:

- is sensitive to the baby's signals
- spends a lot of his time with the infant in face-to-face interaction
- engages in play with the baby

In general, infants prefer either the father or mother to a stranger, but when frightened or in distress, babies are more likely to turn to the mother than to the father. Fathers have become more involved with their babies over the last two decades, and many now attend the births of their babies to offer practical and emotional support to the mother.

Siblings

In many traditional societies with large families, older siblings often act in a caregiver role to younger ones. It is characteristic of older siblings that they show tolerance for them, although jealousy of the new baby is also very common amongst firstborns. Judy Dunn and her colleagues conducted a study of siblings and their significance in psychological development. Dunn and Kendrick (1982) started making observations in the homes of 40 firstborn children living with both parents in or near Cambridge, England. They used a combination of observations and interviews to find out about the nature of sibling relationships after the birth of a second child. The researchers made four visits to the homes in the sample:

1. At the first visit, a new sibling was expected in a month or two, and the first child was generally approaching their second birthday.
2. The next visit was made after the birth of the sibling, when the second child was about one month old.
3. The third visit was eight months after the birth of the baby.

4 The fourth visit was when the baby was about 14 months old.

Overall, Dunn and Kendrick noted that the sibling relationship is one which promotes strong emotions – both of love and of envy. From an early age, often as young as 2 years old, siblings are learning how to understand and to influence others – to tease, placate, comfort or to get their own way with their brother and sister. Young children do not automatically form good relationships with their siblings shortly after birth, and the study showed that it may take some while for children to become **attached** to their siblings. Sibling relationships are often ambivalent: it is not possible to distinguish them as either consistently friendly or consistently hostile.

Figure 6.6 Siblings often get on very well with each other

Some examples of older siblings' views of the new baby

Mother: 'He's generally more depressed, more quiet, more touchy. I'm expecting him to play more on his own than he used to – I'm not giving him so much attention.'

Girl to baby: 'All right, baby' (caressing him). (To mother:) 'Smack him.'

Boy (while the baby is playing with a balloon): 'He's going to pop it in a minute. And he'll cry. And he'll be frightened of me too. I *like* the pop.'

Child: 'Baby, baby' (caressing her). 'Monster, monster.'
Mother: 'She's not a monster.'
Child: 'Monster.'

Mother: 'He asks where she is first thing in the morning. He's happy when he can see her.'

Mother: 'He wants to play with her but he's so rough. Lies on top of her. Then she cries. He wants to roll all over her. I have to keep her away from him 'cause I can't let her be bashed about yet.'

Mother: 'There's a new independence. She's started talking to people in the shops, which she never used to.'

Grandparents

The Cambridge study revealed the extent to which grandparents featured in the lives of the families as attachment figures. Grandparents can often act as surrogate parents to young grandchildren – for example, by looking after them whilst the parents are at work. This role is even more important in lone-parent families, where poverty may be a significant factor. Half of the children in Dunn's study saw their maternal grandmother at least once or twice a week, and their father's mother was also a regular if somewhat less frequent visitor. Apart from being important attachment figures themselves, grandparents can serve a supportive role in promoting and maintaining children's attachments to their primary caregivers.

Care outside the family

In the United Kingdom, most young children are looked after at home by their mothers until they are old enough to attend school, although many attend some sort of play school or nursery school from about the age of 2 or 3 years. There are various alternative options for the working parent/s to consider, and these are described in Chapter 8 on page 240.

Difficulties in forming attachments

There are certain circumstances when communication difficulties make attachment more difficult. Some reasons for these difficulties may be:

- *if the birth has caused mother and baby to be separated:* there is much greater awareness in maternity units and amongst the midwifery profession generally of the importance of early and prolonged contact between parents and their baby. If the baby is very ill or in need of specialised treatment (e.g. in an incubator in a Special Care Baby Unit – SCBU), the parents are usually given a photo of the baby taken straight after birth and allowed as much access to their baby as possible.
- *if the baby is visually impaired and eye contact is absent:* Selma Fraiberg (1975) studied a group of blind babies and found that, when compared with sighted babies of the same age, they:
  - smiled less often and less intensely
  - did not enter into mutual gaze
  - generally showed impassive or sober facial expressions.

  Most of the mothers of the blind babies studied gradually withdrew from their infants. However, they were helped to form a strong bond with their baby by being shown how to 'read' the baby's *other* signals; e.g. the child may *stop* moving when the mother enters the room, showing that they are listening to her footsteps, or they may move their hands when they hear their mother's voice, rather than smiling as a sighted child would. The *mutuality* of the relationship is the foundation for the formation of attachments.
- *if the child is hearing-impaired and does not turn to the parent's voice:* establishing eye contact may be harder because the baby will not turn to the direction of sound. Introducing sign language early is therefore useful.
- *if the child has severe learning difficulties:* a child who has difficulty expressing their emotions may need many experiences of the person before bonding can become stable.

Temperament and attachment

Temperament is the term used to describe the different styles of behaviour in infancy, and it interacts with experience to produce personality. Temperament, indeed, can be thought of as a precursor to personality. The individual child's temperament may contribute to the quality of their attachments. Thomas and Chess

(1977) conducted research into the variations in behavioural characteristics of young children, and identified nine main dimensions of temperament: see Table 6.4. On the basis of these dimensions of temperament, Thomas and Chess distinguished three main types of baby:

1 *easy babies:* positive in mood, regular and predictable in behaviour, moderate in their activity and reaction, and highly adaptable to changes.
2 *difficult babies:* negative in mood, irregular in behaviour and slow to adapt.
3 *'slow to warm up' babies:* inactive, withdrawn and slow to adapt.

Babies who fit into the latter two categories are more of a challenge for parents to cope with and seem to be more at risk for later behaviour problems. As the research was based on interviews with the mothers (or caregivers) of young children, it could be as much a reflection of the mother's own psychological state and of her understanding of the child's behaviour as it is a description of the innate characteristics of babies.

Dimensions of temperament	Description
Activity level	The amount of physical activity during sleep, feeding, dressing, play etc.
Regularity	In bodily functions – sleep, feeding patterns, bowel movements etc.
Adaptability to change in routine	The ease or difficulty with which initial responses can be modified in socially desirable ways
Response to new situations	Initial reaction to anything new – food, people, stimuli, places, toys, activities etc.
Level of sensory threshold	The amount of external stimulation, such as sounds or changes in food or people, necessary to produce a response in the child
Intensity of response	The energy content of the responses regardless of their quality
Positive or negative mood	The amount of pleasant or unpleasant behaviour throughout the day
Distractibility	The effectiveness of external stimuli (sounds, toys, people, etc.) interfering with ongoing behaviour
Persistence and attention span	The duration of maintaining specific activities with or without external obstacles

Table 6.4 Dimensions of temperament in young babies

TEMPERAMENT AND INTERACTION

Temperament, like personality, tends to be *continuous* but varies in interaction with different members of the family. It is difficult, if not impossible, to determine the *extent* to which the baby's temperament affects the responsiveness of the caregiver and thus the quality of the attachment. A mother who is unresponsive and shows little sensitivity to her baby will undoubtedly affect the baby's behaviour.

Examples: a baby who likes to be cuddled and generally strives for plenty of contact with their caregiver tends to be more placid and easy to look after. A baby who actively resists being hugged or held tight even when ill or tired tends to be much more active and restless generally.

These observations fit in well with the three categories 'easy', 'difficult' and 'slow to warm up'. Although it is important to understand about differences in temperament and about how personality and temperament 'clashes' occur, we should always be wary of applying **labels** to children (and adults) as this leads to stereotyping and loss of self-esteem. It is very important that adults working with young children do not favour those with 'easy' temperaments; and it is equally important that children with 'difficult' temperaments not be scapegoated.

activity

1 *Promoting emotional and social development.* Looking at the dimensions of temperament, try to think of ways in which you could provide a stimulating environment for babies and children with 'difficult' or 'slow to warm up' temperaments. For each activity, list the benefits to the child in terms of self-esteem.

2 *Labels* Working in groups, make a list of the labels you remember from your own childhood. Examples are 'cry baby', 'fatty', 'four-eyes', 'titch', 'clever clogs', 'dumbo' etc. Try to describe the feelings that you had when you were labelled. How would you respond if children at your nursery or school were 'labelled'?

ATTACHMENT AND THE EFFECTS OF PRIVATION

Bowlby talked about maternal **deprivation** as the loss, through separation, of the mother-figure. The effects are usually short-term and can be defined as **distress**. **Privation** is more serious in its effects on emotional and social development, as it refers to the *absence* of any attachment. There have been various studies made of children who have suffered extreme privation and isolation; one such study was that of Genie (see page 151 above). Privation also takes place when a baby has multiple changes of caregiver, or if the child is in the kind of institution where there is a rapid turnover of staff and where attachments are discouraged. Bowlby believes that a child may then suffer from **affectionless psychopathy**. This is characterised by:

- a phase of very clingy, dependent behaviour, followed by
- attention-seeking behaviour and indiscriminate friendliness, and finally
- a personality which shows no feelings of guilt, is unable to keep rules and is incapable of forming lasting relationships.

Attachment reassessed

Michael Rutter (1981) conducted a major review of maternal-deprivation research and found – unlike Bowlby – that there is *not* a direct causal link between early experiences of separation from parents and later emotional distress. Rutter believed that:

- a distinction should be made between **disruption** of affectional bonds, (i.e. where there *has* been a bond established, but where that maternal care is lost, and between **privation** of affectional bonds, where children growing up in institutionalised care are denied the opportunity of establishing such bonds;
- a distinction should be made between the **disruption** of affectional bonds (e.g. if the mother has died) and the **distortion** of relationships within the family, brought about by separation or divorce (when the mother is still physically present);
- the *quality* of family relationships affects the child more than the actual fact of separation or divorce. For example, children separated because of discord between their parents are more likely to show the sort of 'deprivation reaction' which Bowlby described than are children separated by the death of a parent;
- the separation of the child from the parents is not itself as significant as the quality of **sensitive support** given to the child during the experience of separation;
- **multiple attachments** can be formed with various people without harm, as long as there is not an *extreme* form of shared care, e.g. with tens of adults involved;
- children often appear to be extremely resilient to situations of deprivation. Other factors – such as understimulation and minimal social contact – play an unquantifiable part in the overall picture of deprivation.

Barbara Tizard

Barbara Tizard researched the development of children who had been adopted after spending their early years in residential institutions. In particular, she looked at the relationships formed between the children and their adoptive parents. Most adoption agencies in the UK follow the principle, based on Bowlby's work, that children should not be placed for adoption when they are older than 5 years, because the first five years of a child's life are thought to be particularly sensitive in relation to the ability to form genuine attachments. Barbara Tizard's (1977) findings, however, dispute this idea of a sensitive period:

- Most of the children studied had become very attached to their adoptive parents
- The children who were living with adoptive parents showed better-adjusted behaviour later on than did the children who were returned to their own families
- The long-term effects of separation were probably offset by the fact that the adoptive parents worked harder at

being parents than did the biological parents

Studies such as Tizard's suggest that we may have seriously underestimated the **adaptability** of the developing child. Children who have been deprived of the continuity of individualised comfort and attention in the first two years of life are still capable of forming deep and lasting attachments when provided with an opportunity later on. It is now widely accepted that emotional and social development are affected by attachment, and that how children interact with their parents or caregivers has a significant effect upon how their parents or caregivers behave towards them.

activity

Separation and transition:
Working, if possible, in groups, design and produce an information pack for use with children and parents who are new to a caregiver or care environment – e.g. a playgroup, a childminder, a day nursery or a family centre. The rationale for the pack is to reduce parent and child anxiety at a time of separation and transition, and it should therefore aim to give as much information as possible about such matters as the physical environment, daily routines and the people who work in the environment. The pack could be in one of various formats:

- an illustrated booklet
- a video or audio tape
- a display
- a strip cartoon, perhaps with a fictional 'welcome' character

Evaluate each other's packs according to previously agreed criteria, and if possible, arrange to test the packs out in the *real* care situation.

Developing a personal identity

Children develop a sense of identity and a **self-concept** during the first year of life. A self-concept is one's idea or image of oneself, and it involves an awareness of a sense of separateness and an increasing sense of self-awareness. The concept of **object permanence** (see Chapter 4, page 106 above) is closely linked to the concept of **person permanence**, that is, to the infant's ability to recognise 'particular others' and to search for them when that person disappears from view. Both object permanence and person permanence are achieved during the **sensorimotor period** (that is, before the age of 18 months).

The self can be divided into two main steps or tasks:

- *Step 1: the existential self – the understanding of 'I'.* The child's first task is to recognise that she **exists**, and that she is separate from others. This realisation that she is a separate being occurs within the first two or three months of life.

  Examples: when a baby touches a

mobile, it moves; when they cry, someone responds; when they close their eyes, the world goes dark.

- *Step 2: the categorical self – the understanding of 'Me'.* The child's second task is to understand themselves as an agent. Having achieved the awareness that the 'I' exists, the child must then understand themselves to be an *object* (or 'Me') in the world, with certain qualities and properties. This process is known as the **categorical self** because it takes the form of placing oneself in an ever-increasing number of **categories** – such as size, age and gender.

  Examples: the child understands that they have a name, a gender and – later – other qualities such as clumsiness, shyness or adventurousness.

Studies in self-awareness

1. *The 'mirror' technique.* Lewis and Brooks-Gunn (1979) placed infants aged between 9 and 12 months in front of a mirror. After allowing the infants time for free exploration – during which they typically looked at their own images or tried to interact with the infant in the mirror – the experimenter secretly put a spot of rouge on the infant's nose and then let them look again in the mirror. The crucial test of self-awareness was whether the infant would reach for the spot on their *own* nose and not the nose on the face in the mirror. None of the infants aged 9–12 months touched their own noses; see Figure 6.7. When the experiment was repeated with infants aged 21 months, 75% of infants touched their own noses.
2. *The 'photo' technique.* Lewis and Brooks-Gunn (1979) showed infants of 9–12 months a photo of themselves and noted that they smiled more and looked longer at pictures of themselves than at pictures of other same-age babies. They also found that, between 15 and 18 months, infants would use verbal labels such as 'baby', and by about 22 months most babies used their own names to distinguish pictures of themselves and others. By the age of 3, they could refer to themselves by use of the pronoun 'me'.

The development of the self-concept

Michael Argyle proposes four factors which play an important part in the development of the self-concept:

1. *the reactions of other people to us:* it is through interaction with others that we gain knowledge of ourselves. Children

Figure 6.7 At 9 months old, Emily reaches for the red spot on the face in the mirror, rather than her own face.

incorporate the opinions and reactions of others into their self-concept – a process known as **introjection**. This can give rise to a **self-fulfilling prophecy**.

Examples:

- A child who is repeatedly described by their parents as 'very shy' will assimilate this opinion into their self-concept, and it then forms part of their **self-attribution**. In other words, they may begin to use 'shy' as a term to describe themselves.
- A nurse in uniform for the first few weeks will adjust his/her behaviour according to the reactions and expectations of their patients; and they may display more self-confidence and self-esteem than before.

2 *Comparing ourselves with others:* many self-concepts are comparative terms, that is, they can only be seen in relation to others.

Examples: the terms 'tall', 'poor' and 'intelligent' can only be used if one person is being compared with others who are shorter, richer and less intelligent.

3 *The past, present and future roles that we play:* young children use mainly physical characteristics when asked to describe themselves – 'I am 7. I have brown hair' etc. Older children and adults incorporate more **roles** into their self-concept, and become increasingly focused on **social roles**.

Example: Montemayor and Eisen (1977) used the Twenty Statements Test on about 50 young people, made up of groups of people in the ages 10, 12, 14, 16 and 18. Each person was asked to describe themselves in just 20 statements. Most of the changes between age groups were from a more concrete to a more abstract way of describing oneself. Responses in terms of occupational or social roles and ideological beliefs also increased with age. The following two samples from the study illustrate some of the trends:

Boy nearly 10: 'My name is Bruce C. I have brown eyes. I have brown hair. I love! Sports. I have seven people in my family. I have great! Eyesight. I have lots! Of friends. I live at Pinecrest Dr. I'm going on 10 in September ... I have an uncle who is almost 7 feet tall. My teacher is Mrs. V. I play hockey! I'm almost the smartest boy in the class. I love! Food. I love fresh air. I love! School.'

Girl, nearly 18: 'I am a human being. I am a girl. I am an individual. I don't know who I am. I am a Pisces. I am a moody person. I am an indecisive person. I am a very curious person. I am not an individual. I am a loner. I am an American (God help me). I am a Democrat. I am a liberal person. I am a radical. I am a conservative. I am a pseudoliberal. I am an atheist. I am not a classifiable person (i.e. I don't want to be).'

(Montemayor and Eisen 1977)

4 *identification with models:* this involves incorporating the characteristics of another person into the self-concept, and can be done either consciously or unconsciously. From early childhood, we all model ourselves on people that we would wish to be like.

Four mechanisms of **identification** are apparent, namely identification as:

- a process of differentiating oneself
- a process of empathy and attachment
- resulting from observation and imita-

tion of powerful others, and from the rewards gained by appropriate behaviours
- resulting from the cognitive ability to recognise oneself as belonging to a social category

The early ability to **identify** oneself as a girl or boy does not depend on any anatomical knowledge of sex differences. Research has shown that it is not until about age 4 that girls and boys fully understand that gender is a permanent characteristic.

Example: boys and girls in early childhood tend to choose same-sex parents with whom to identify.

activity

1 *Exploring the self-concept.* Try the Twenty Statements Test on yourself, on your peers and on children of various ages. Classify the responses into different categories, and compare the results with those of Montemayor and Eisen (1977). Refer to Table 6.5.

	Age and % figures				
Category	***10***	***12***	***14***	***16***	***18***
Address/citizenship	48	16	21	13	11
Possessions	53	22	24	14	8
Physical self	87	57	46	49	16
Occupational	4	12	29	28	44
Ideological	4	14	24	24	39
Self-determination	5	8	26	45	49
Interpersonal style	42	76	91	86	93
Name	50	10	8	11	31
Judgements, likes	69	65	80	45	31

Table 6.5 The Twenty Statements Test 1
The table shows the percentage of participants in each age group who used each category at least once in the Twenty Statements Test

2 *Promoting the self-concept.* It is the start of a new school year, and you are helping the reception class teacher to prepare the classroom for the new intake of 5 year olds. The teacher has listed some ideas that will help promote a sense of separate identity for the children, and has asked you for any additional suggestions.

- Use a child's photo to mark their clothes peg
- List the name and birthday of the child alongside their photo
- Encourage the children to draw or paint a picture of themselves, and display all the pictures in a prominent position
- Refer to children by name whenever possible
- Tell a story or sing a song in which the children's' names are mentioned. Ask them to indicate when they hear their own name. (If there are two or more children with the same name, refer to the full name)

Try to think of at least five more ideas for displays or activities which will help to encourage a sense of identity and so enhance self-esteem.

DEVELOPING SELF-ESTEEM

Self-esteem is the evaluative part of the self-concept. It is the regard people have for themselves. Our feelings of self-worth or self-esteem can strongly influence our moods and our behaviour. It is difficult to mark exactly how we arrive at a sense of self-esteem; such measurements are subjective and often bear no resemblance to the opinions that others hold about our own worth. Even before a child can understand spoken words, parents and caregivers can show approval, disappointment, anger or pleasure by the tone of their voice, their facial expressions and general body language. Having **high self-esteem** increases self-confidence and possibly enables an individual to cope more easily with conflict and aggression than can those with low self-esteem. High self-esteem during childhood has been linked to contentment and happiness in later life. On the other hand, a child with **low self-esteem** tends to be lacking in confidence and is more likely to be easily 'led' by other children. Low self-esteem during childhood has been linked to anxiety, depression and maladjustment both in school and in social relationships.

Studies in self-esteem

Stanley Coopersmith (1967) conducted a longitudinal study of hundreds of boys aged between 10 and 12. He used a questionnaire, called the Self-Esteem Inventory, and teacher's ratings to investigate the development of self-esteem and its relation to personality and to child-rearing patterns. Coopersmith's questionnaire used 58 statements which covered how the boys saw themselves in relation to their peers, their parents, school and hobbies. Boys were categorised as being high, medium or low in self-esteem:

- Boys with high self-esteem were self-confident, academically successful and popular
- Boys with low self-esteem were isolated, self-conscious, underachieving and very sensitive to criticism

The study also found three parental characteristics which combine to produce high self-esteem in late childhood:

- *acceptance of their children:* the mothers of the boys with high self-esteem had closer, more affectionate relationships with their children than the mothers of boys with low self-esteem
- *clearly defined boundaries:* the parents of boys with high self-esteem were consistent in their discipline techniques, being firm but fair in their setting of limits for their children's activities
- *respect for individuality:* the parents of boys with high self-esteem encouraged two-way communication, involving their children in family decisions and taking their points of view into account. Within the boundaries set by the parents' sense of standards and social values, their children were allowed a good deal of individual self-expression

Coopersmith's data was criticised by some researchers for being too *broad* in the sense of measuring self-esteem as an overall quality rather than a multi-faceted quality. Others thought that the questionnaire encouraged certain socially desirable responses, and that generalisations from his findings either to girls or to different socioeconomic groups were not valid.

A study by Susan Harter (1985) looked at five different areas of self-evaluation and devised a profile of self-perception (see Figure 6.8). These areas were:

1 *cognitive competence:* how able the child feels in schoolwork;

Really true for me	Sort of true for me				Sort of true for me	Really true for me
1	2	Some kids often forget what they learn	BUT	Other kids can remember things easily	3	4
1	2	Other kids are not very popular	BUT	Some kids are popular with others their age	3	4
1	2	Others don't feel that they are very good when it comes to sports	BUT	Some kids do very well at all kinds of sports	3	4
1	2	Some kids usually get into trouble because of the things that they do	BUT	Other kids usually don't do things that get them into trouble	3	4
1	2	Some kids wish their physical appearance was different	BUT	Other kids like their physical appearance the way it is	3	4

Figure 6.8 Sample items from Harter's self-perception profile for children. Adapted from Harter (1985) Manual for the Self-Perception Profile for Children, University of Denver

2 *social acceptance:* how popular the child feels with peers;
3 *athletic competence:* how well the child does in sports and games;
4 *behavioural conduct:* the extent to which the child feels that they behave in an appropriate and acceptable manner;
5 *physical appearance:* how attractive the child feels, and how much they like various physical characteristics.

Self-concept and children with special needs

Margaret Donaldson, a psychologist with a particular interest in the development of children's minds, argues that a child can only develop a strong **self-concept** when they feel that they are effective, competent and independent. A child with special needs may have weaknesses in these areas, and this may result in a lowering of self-esteem. Within the confines of the family environment, the child will probably have a good self-image as they have been encouraged in their all-round development to use the skills they possess.

However, when the child starts playgroup, nursery or school, they will come into contact with other children and adults who are not as supportive as their parents. They may find that they are stared at, or that people avoid them, or they may be asked lots of questions about their difficulties. Other factors which can affect a child's self-concept are:

- *comparisons with other children:* it is a natural part of development for children to judge their own abilities and strengths in comparison with their peers;
- *the need to fulfil untypical childhood roles:* a child with special needs may have to adapt to a role not normally associated with childhood, or to roles that require normal development, e.g. the roles of 'someone needing extra help with reading', or of 'someone who sits out of PE classes';
- *physical appearance:* children with special needs have the same system of values about attractiveness and physical appearance as do all children. If asked to draw a self-portrait, a child with a physical disability may draw a picture in which the disability is completely ignored (i.e. they draw themselves without the disability) or hidden (e.g. they may draw themselves behind a wall so that only their head shows) or even exaggerated (e.g. their wheelchair may be drawn as disproportionately large);
- *identification:* feelings of self-esteem are influenced by the process of identifying firstly with her parents and later with other adults and friends. Parental attitudes about the way the child's difficulties are managed directly affect the child's self-concept;
- *the self-fulfilling prophecy:* our expectations of people's personalities or skills may influence the way that we actually treat them, and this in turn may influence their behaviour in such a way that our expectation is then confirmed. Children with special needs are best served by people having higher expectations in all areas of development. This approach, combined with a realistic appraisal of their capabilities, will help children towards independence and an improved self-concept.

The development of pro-social behaviour

Pro-social behaviour has been defined as 'actions that are intended to aid or benefit another person or group of people without the actor's anticipation of external rewards. Such actions often entail some cost, self-sacrifice or risk on the part of the actor' (Mussen and Eisenberg-Berg 1977). Pro-social behaviour includes altruism, helping, cooperation, comforting and empathy.

Empathy – or the sharing of another's emotions and feelings – is widely believed to provide the emotional foundations of pro-social behaviour. Martin Hoffman (1982) proposed four stages in the development of empathy:

- *Stage 1: global empathy.* This stage occurs during the first year of life. Babies as young as 2 days old cry at the sound of another infant's cries, a phenomenon Nancy Eisenberg terms **emotional contagion**. These early sympathy cries are like innate reflexes, since such young infants cannot yet have developed an understanding of the feelings of others.
- *Stage 2: egocentric empathy.* During the second year of life, children begin to become aware of themselves as distinct individuals. When confronted by some-

one who is distressed, they realise that it is someone else who is upset, not themselves. They may attempt to comfort the other person in a way that *they themselves* would find most comforting; for example, they may offer their daddy a favourite teddy or 'transitional' object (see page 136 in Chapter 2).

- *Stage 3: empathy for another's feelings.* During the period from 2 to 5 or 6 years of age, children note others' feelings and respond to their distress in *non-egocentric ways*. As their command of language and other symbols increases, they are better equipped to empathise with a range of feelings that require more subtlety to express. Television, books and pictures all enable children to empathise with people whom they have never met.

Figure 6.9 A show of empathy: a young boy feels the pain of his cat, who needs help urgently

- *Stage 4: empathy for another's life condition.* In late childhood or adolescence, children begin to be concerned about the general situation or plights of others. They are able to discriminate between momentary problems and a more 'chronic' condition such as poverty, illness or oppression, and are capable of empathising with groups of people.

Hoffman's stage theory of the development of empathy closely parallels Piaget's stages of cognitive development. However, although the child may be able to perceive or *understand* another person's distress, it does not necessarily mean that the child will always act in an altruistic or comforting manner. Judy Dunn (1988) noted that children's powers of empathy can be driven by motives of self-interest as well as by altruism. Children show from a very early age (18 months) that they can recognise the emotional expressions of their siblings and are able to respond in a variety of ways which will either reduce or amplify their sibling's emotional state. Dunn also found that children develop a wide range of strategies to evoke an emotional response from their siblings, commonly known as 'teasing'. Teasing strategies include: (a) taking away a sibling's comfort object, (b) hiding a favourite toy or (c) taunting them with something they knew they disliked.

Studies in how children see others

Carl Barenboim (1981) studied the development of **social cognition**, or the way in which children see others. He asked children ranging in age from 6 to 16 years to describe three people. From their replies, Barenboim found that they varied in type according to the age of the child:

- *behavioural comparisons:* descriptions that involved comparing a child's behaviours or physical features with another child, or with a norm.

  Examples: 'Jenny runs a lot faster than Maria', and 'She draws the best in our whole class.'
- *psychological constructs:* statements that involved some internal personality construct.

  Examples: 'Fatima is so kind' or 'He's a real idiot.'
- *organising relationships:* descriptions that included qualifiers, exceptions, explanations or references to changes in character.

  Examples: 'Usually, he's nice to me, but sometimes he can be quite mean', or 'She's only shy when she meets someone new.'

Barenboim found that behavioural comparisons were used most at the age of 8 to 9, psychological constructs were used mostly at about age 14, and organising relationships appeared at age 10 and were still increasing at age 16.

activity

Describing others:
Try the same exercise as above on children ranging in age from 6 to 16, and see if the results are similar to the findings in the Barenboim study.

Play and the development of social competence

There is no single satisfactory definition of **play**, although many different types of play have been identified. Mildred Parten (1932) identified five different kinds of play.

1. *solitary play:* children play on their own and are largely unaware of other children;
2. *onlooker (or spectator) play:* the child watches other children, and may react to what they are doing, but doesn't actually join in with them;
3. *parallel play:* two children play side by side but not looking at each other or talking very much about what they do.

   Example: two children playing independently at the water tray;
4. *associative play:* children interact with each other, often in a common activity, but they might keep their own ideas separate from each other. Each child acts as they wish, without any subordination of interests to that of the group. Problems may occur when one child's play 'agenda' conflicts with another child's agenda.

   Example: when two children are playing in the home area at a nursery – one child is pretending to lay the table for tea, the other child is cooking at the table, and neither wants to give way to the other.
5. *co-operative play:* when children interact together in complementary ways.

   Example: one child gets the blocks out

of a box and hands them to another child, who builds the tower.

It is important not to view these categories of play merely as a simple-to-complex ladder of activity as some stage theorists would: babies as young as 6 months enjoy 'peek-a-boo' games, which are an early kind of cooperative play. Children are sometimes solitary, and sometimes they interact with others in parallel, associatively or cooperatively.

THE TWELVE FEATURES OF PLAY

Tina Bruce (1996) describes 12 features of play:

1. Children cannot play at a quality level unless they have had previous first-hand experiences of people, objects and materials. They can then use these experiences in their play. Some of these experiences will have been enjoyable. Some might have been frightening or painful.
2. When children play, they make up their own rules. These help them to keep control as they play. When the play fades, the rules fade too. Feeling in control is an important part of play.
3. When children represent (keep hold of) their experiences, they may do so by drawing a cat or making a model of a bus. Sometimes what they make becomes a **play prop** which is used in their play.
4. No-one can *make* a child play. A child has to *want* to play.
5. During play, children often rehearse what they will be able to do without any help from adults later on. This is often called **role play**: they pretend to be other people, and they take on adult roles.
6. Children can **pretend** when they play. They can pretend a lump of dough is a cake. They can pretend they are someone else.
7. Children sometimes play alone.
8. Children sometimes play in a pair, in parallel or in a group with other children.
9. Adults who join children in their play need to remember that each person playing has their own play ideas. The adult's play ideas are not more important than the child's play ideas. Play ideas are sometimes called the **play agenda** or **play script**.
10. When children play, they wallow in their feelings, ideas and relationships. They move about and are physically active. They are deeply involved in their play.
11. When children play, they try out what they have been learning. They show their skills and competencies.
12. Play helps children to coordinate what they learn. This means that play brings together all the different aspects of a child's development. The result is that the child is a grounded, centred, together and whole person. Play is thus a *holistic* kind of learning.

(Taken from Bruce and Meggitt 1996)

FREE-FLOW PLAY

Bruce uses the term **free-flow play** to describe play which involves these 12 features. Free-flow play 'is where the child learns at the highest level, using ideas, feelings and relationships that have been experienced, and applies these to what they know and understand with control, mastery and competence'. Free-flow play includes:

1 *symbolic play:* this involves pretend play, socio-dramatic play, role play and imaginative play:

- *pretend play (or ludic play):* when an object or an action is given a symbolic meaning which is different from real life.
  Example: a stick is used as a gun; a cardboard box becomes a car.
- *role play:* when pretend symbols are used together.
  Example: a child pretends to be a doctor by putting on a white coat, using a toy stethoscope and listening to a teddy's heartbeat.
- *socio-dramatic play:* when several children role-play and pretend-play together.
- *imaginative play:* when children use their own real-life experiences to express ideas and feelings.
- *fantasy play:* when children role-play situations they do not know about but which might happen to them one day.
  Example: getting married, going to hospital, travelling in space.
- *phantasy play:* when children role-play *unreal* events from cartoons on TV – Superman, Power Rangers. War play dominates this kind of play. Because it is not rooted in real experience, it is difficult to help children to use this kind of experience for their benefit.

2 *manipulative play:* this play is concerned with what children can do, not with what they are struggling to do.
Example: when children use and celebrate physical prowess, such as when riding a two-wheeler bicycle or playing on a skateboard with competence.

3 *play using props:* this is sometimes called **constructive play**, and it involves children making their own props and using them to pretend-play.
Example: making a car from a box and using a plate as a wheel, then driving off to work.

4 *rough-and-tumble play:* this usually involves one or more of the following activities: chasing, catching, pillow fights, pretend fights. It often occurs at bedtime, and is difficult to incorporate into an early-childhood setting as it can be overwhelming for those not taking part.

PLAY THERAPY

Play therapists may be qualified nursery nurses, psychotherapists or qualified hospital play specialists. Their role is to use **therapeutic play** with one child or a group of children to enable them to feel more secure emotionally in potentially threatening situations. Play therapy involves:

- the provision of activities and toys which satisfy the needs of children with fears and anxieties
- enabling children to gain some measure of control over their lives and what is happening around them
- establishing a good relationship with the children
- providing activities that will promote normal development

Toys and activities can often be categorised as either **therapeutic** or **diversional**. Therapeutic toys let children 'play out' their anxieties, and include clay, sand, hammer toys, medical kits and puppets, and anatomically correct dolls. Diversional toys divert children's attention away from their illness or problems by promoting creativity and the enjoyment of developing new skills; these include board games, video games, paint, puppets, mobiles and rattles.

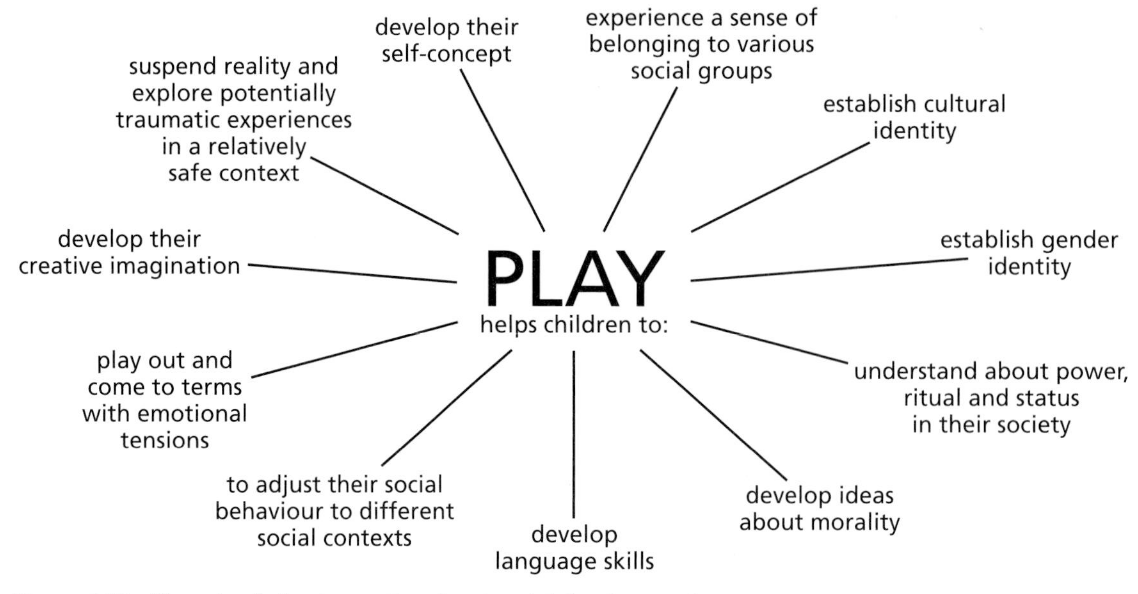

Figure 6.10 The role of play in emotional and social development

activity

Observing children's play:
Observe a small group of children in a playgroup or nursery setting and try to categorise the different types of play. Using a time sample technique, assess the amount of time spent in each type of play. For each type of play observed, list the benefits to the children in terms of their holistic development.

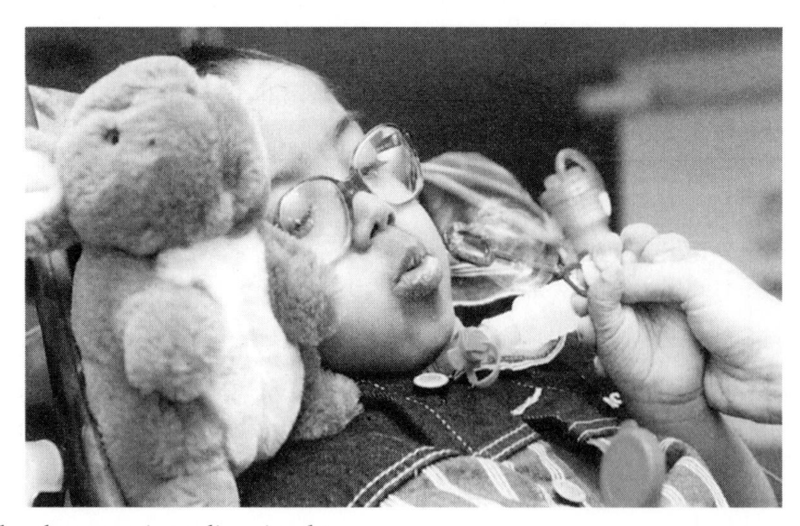

Figure 6.11 Play therapy using a diversional toy

Moral development

Moral development is concerned with how children understand ideas of right and wrong and matters of **conscience**. A conscience is a set of moral principles that each individual develops and tries to live by. Psychologists who have studied the development of moral reasoning in children have asked the following questions:

- How do children understand notions of right and wrong?
- Do children understand the world in the same (albeit less developed) way, or are there *qualitative* differences between the thought of children and of adults?
- If there are such differences, what stages do children go through in their moral reasoning as they grow to adulthood?

THEORIES OF MORAL DEVELOPMENT

Piaget's theory

Piaget developed his theory of moral development from the observation of a relatively small number of children. He was concerned with: (a) the child's ideas about rules, (b) how a child decides what is right and what is wrong, and (c) the child's ideas about punishment and justice. Piaget proposed that moral behaviour and moral reasoning develop in two identifiable stages:

1 the stage of **heteronomous morality** (sometimes called **moral realism**)
2 the stage of **autonomous morality** (or **subjective realism**).

1 The stage of heteronomous morality

In this stage, characteristic of children aged 3 to 7 or 8 years, children believe that all rules are fixed and unchallengeable. They can see the difference between *intentional* and *unintentional* actions, but base their judgement on the severity of an outcome.

Piaget presented children with several pairs of short stories which posed a problem of moral judgement. One pair is as follows:

- A little boy who was called John was in his room. He was called to dinner. He went into the dining room. But behind the door there was a chair, and on the chair there was a tray with 15 cups on it. John couldn't have known that there was all this behind the door. He went in, the door knocked against the tray, bang go the 15 cups and they all got broken!
- Once there was a little boy called Henry. One day when his mother was out he tried to get some jam out of the cupboard. He climbed onto the chair and stretched out his arm. But the jam was too high up and he couldn't reach it and have any. But while he was trying to get it he knocked over a cup. The cup fell down and broke.

Piaget would tell a child this pair of stories and ask them to repeat each one to ensure that they remembered them. Next, he asked them to make a judgement as to which child was the naughtiest. Some sample answers are given on page 192.

In the stage of heteronomous morality, children judge by the objective amount of damage, and tend to view punishment as inevitable and retributive. Children are unable to understand alternative

1 From a child aged 6:

Piaget:	Are those children both naughty, or is one not so naughty as the other?
Child:	Both just as naughty.
Piaget:	Would you punish them the same?
Child:	No. The one who broke 15 cups.
Piaget:	And would you punish the other one more, or less?
Child:	The first broke a lot of things, the other one fewer.
Piaget:	How would you punish them?
Child:	The one who broke 15 cups: two slaps. The other one, one slap.

2 From a child aged 9 years:

Child:	Well, the one who broke them as he was coming in isn't naughty, 'cos he didn't know there was any cups. The other one wanted to take the jam and caught his arm on a cup.
Piaget:	Which one is the naughtiest?
Child:	The one who wanted to take the jam.
Piaget:	How many cups did he break?
Child:	One.
Piaget:	And the other boy?
Child:	15.
Piaget:	Which one would you punish the most?
Child:	The boy who wanted to take the jam. He knew, he did it on purpose.

interpretations which take motives or intentions into account.

2 The stage of autonomous morality

In this stage, characteristic of children aged 8 years and above, children begin to learn that rules can be changed by experiment and trial and error. The motive or intention is taken into account, and the punishment is viewed more as a lesson suited to the offence.

Piaget's theories of moral development correspond to his theories of cognitive development (see Chapter 2, page 107). The child in the pre-operational stage uses moral ideas that are imposed on it from the outside. The child in the operational stage is able to invent their own rules and to change their own ideas of what is right and what is wrong.

Evaluation of Piaget's theory

Various criticisms of Piaget's theory have been put forward:

- that he presented children with poorly designed stories which tempt them to ignore motive or intention
- that he assumed that moral development is complete by about 12 years of age, whereas subsequent research has shown that our ideas about morality continue to develop and change throughout adolescence and adulthood
- that his theory may not be relevant to other (non-European) cultures
- that he underestimated the nature and extent of parental influence in shaping children's moral development
- that he had a 'romantic' view of childhood which is not supported by the opposite 'problem' view which emphasises the effects on children of negative

playground behaviours such as bullying, taunting and aggression

In spite of these criticisms, many researchers have agreed that children do pass through similar stages of moral reasoning, and some have used similar techniques to develop their own theories.

Kohlberg's theory

Kohlberg carried out work on moral reasoning over a 12-year period in the late 1950s and 1960s. He drew substantially on Piaget's research into moral development, but extended the scope of study right through to middle adulthood. Kohlberg studied children from the USA over a period of 12 years and compared them with children from Taiwan, Mexico, Turkey and Yucatan. Unlike Piaget's, his research was thus both longitudinal and cross-cultural. Kohlberg proposed a six-stage theory of moral development which was sub-divided into three levels: see Table 6.6.

Some examples from Kohlberg's research

Kohlberg posed the same question to the same individual when he was 10 years old, when he was 17, and again when he was 24:

To Joe, aged 10 years:

Kohlberg: Why shouldn't you steal from a store?
Joe: It's not good to steal from a store. It's against the law. Someone could see you and call the police.

To Joe, now aged 17 years:

Kohlberg: Why shouldn't you steal from a store?
Joe: It's a matter of law. It's one of our rules that we're trying to help protect everyone, protect property, not just to protect a store. It's something that's needed in our society. If we didn't have these laws, people would steal, they wouldn't have to work for a living, and our whole society would get out of kilter.

To Joe, now aged 24:

Kohlberg: Why shouldn't you steal from a store?
Joe: It's violating another person's rights, in this case to property.
Kohlberg: Does the law enter in?
Joe: Well, the law in most cases is based on what is morally right so it's not a separate subject, it's a consideration.
Kohlberg: What does 'morality' or 'morally right' mean to you?
Joe: Recognising the rights of other individuals, first to life and then to do as he pleases as long as it doesn't interfere with somebody else's rights.

Level	Age	Stage	Characteristics
1 Pre-conventional	6–13	1	**Punishment and obedience orientation** Something is wrong if it is punished or punishable. The physical consequences of an action regardless of its human meaning or value determine its goodness or badness.
		2	**Instrumental hedonism** People conform to rules and laws to gain rewards, or to have a favour they have done to somebody returned. Right is what's fair, a deal or an equal exchange.
2 Conventional	13–16	3	**Good boy–good girl orientation** Good behaviour is that which pleases or helps others and is approved by them. Behaviour is often judged by intention – 'He means well' becomes important for the first time.
		4	**Law and order orientation** What is right is doing one's duty, showing respect for authority and maintaining the given social order for its own sake. Society's laws should only be disobeyed in extreme circumstances.
3 Postconventional	16–20+	5	**Social contract orientation** Whilst laws should be upheld, they can be changed by agreement. Right action tends to be defined in terms of non-relative values and rights like life and liberty. The result is an emphasis upon the 'legal point of view'.
		6	**Universal ethical principles** Following self-chosen ethical principles. Most laws conform to these principles, but where they do not, one acts in accordance with the principle. These principles are abstract and ethical; they are universal principles of justice, equality of human rights and respect for the dignity of human beings as individual persons.

Table 6.6 Kohlberg's stages of moral development (Kohlberg, 1968)

These three responses correspond to the three levels of morality (see again Table 6.6).

The most famous **moral dilemma** posed by Kohlberg is that of Heinz and the druggist. In Europe, a woman was near death from a special kind of cancer. There was one drug that the doctor thought might save her: it was a form of radium that a druggist in the same town had recently discovered. The drug was expensive to manufacture, and the druggist was charging 10 times what the drug cost him to make: $2,000 for a small dose. The sick woman's husband, Heinz, went to everyone he knew to borrow the money, but he could only raise about $1,000, which is half of what it cost. He told the druggist that his wife was dying, and asked him to sell it cheaper or to let him pay later. But the druggist said: 'No, I discovered the drug and I'm going to make money from it.' So Heinz got desperate and broke into the man's store to steal the drug for his wife.

Should Heinz have done that? If so, why? Or if not, why *not*?

Characteristic responses from children in the different levels of morality were:

- level 1: 'Heinz must not steal the medicine because he will be put in jail'
- level 2: 'Heinz should steal the drug because one day he might have cancer and would want someone to steal it for him'
- level 3: 'If I was Heinz, I would have stolen the drug for my wife. You can't put a price on love, no amount of gifts make love. You can't put a price on life either'

Evaluation of Kohlberg's theory

Kohlberg hypothesised that in all societies, individuals would progress upwards through these three levels in sequence – neither missing out a stage nor regressing. He also thought that an individual would be attracted towards reasoning just above their own level on the scale, but would not be able to understand reasoning more than one stage above.

Some criticisms of Kohlberg's approach are:

- that Kohlberg's research was biased towards males, as his original participants were all male. Carol Gilligan (1982) conducted research into the very real moral dilemma faced by women attending an abortion and pregnancy counselling service. Gilligan found that women put people before principles, rather than principles before people (the latter she believed to be a 'male' characteristic). Instead of using abstract, principled judgements which are universally applicable, the women used an alternative ethic of care and responsibility;
- that the dilemmas posed by Kohlberg were unrealistic and did not represent the actual moral debates which children engage in;
- that the method of research was subjective, and that the scale used was unreliable;
- that the very few teenagers or adults seem to reason at the postconventional level (i.e. Stages 5 or 6);
- that Kohlberg has not really addressed the issue of *moral* reasoning. Rather, he is concerned with the development of reasoning about justice and fairness;
- that Kohlberg's Level 3 (Stages 5 and 6) is significantly culturally biased as it reflects the individualistic capitalistic orientation of middle-class Western urban society. Critics here point out that other religions and societies may put less value on individual life and more emphasis on collectivist values.

Kohlberg's theory developed a more detailed sequence of stages than Piaget's theory. Both theories, however, focus more on what children *say* than on what they actually *do*.

Eisenberg's theory of pro-social reasoning

Nancy Eisenberg and her colleagues developed a model of moral development which focuses on sensitivity to others. They also proposed a set of moral dilemmas to children, but instead of exploring the 'wrongdoing and punishment' aspect of moral reasoning (as both Piaget and Kohlberg had done), Eisenberg set **self-interest** against the possibility of helping someone else. Every two years, Eisenberg asked the same group of children what a person should do when confronted with each of a series of moral dilemmas about doing good. One of Eisenberg's dilemmas is as follows. A child is walking to a friend's birthday party. On the way, they come across another child who has fallen and hurt themselves. If the party-bound child stops to help, they will probably miss the cake and ice-cream. What should they do? On the basis of the children's answers, Eisenberg proposed a model of pro-social reasoning, with five stages or levels: see Table 6.7. By classifying the answers to such dilemmas, Eisenberg showed that hedonistic reasoning falls steadily by the age of 7 and 8, while needs-oriented reasoning rises to high levels at the same age.

activity

Models of moral development:

1 Group work:

- Invent some moral dilemmas which would be appropriate for children aged 3–4 years, children aged 7–8 years and children aged 10–11 years; then read the 'stories' to children in each age group and record their answers.
- Check the answers against both Kohlberg's stages of moral development and Eisenberg's levels of pro-social reasoning.
- Evaluate the application of each of the two models.

2 Find out about:

- the learning theory
- the social learning theory

Write some brief comments on each theory, outlining the advantages of moral development and limitations for your understanding of moral reasoning.

Promoting moral development in children

Understanding the way in which children develop the capacity to make moral judgements will help adults to decide how best to 'manage young children'. Children need a secure framework of rules which they can understand in order to learn consideration for others and how to behave in a socially acceptable manner. Some methods of promoting the development of

Level	Description
Level 1 Hedonistic, self-focused orientation	The child is more concerned with self-oriented consequences than with moral considerations. *Examples:* 'I'd help because she'd help me next time'; 'I won't help because I'd miss the party.' Seen in: pre-school and infant-school children.
Level 2 Needs-oriented orientation	The child expresses concern for the other person's need rather directly, even if the other's needs conflict with the child's. There is no clear evidence here of sympathy, reflectiveness about the other's role or internalised values. *Examples:* 'She's hurt'; 'She'd feel better if I helped.' Seen in: some pre-school and most primary-school children.
Level 3 Approval and interpersonal orientation	The child does good things because others will like them if they do, because it is expected of them or because there is a social rule. *Examples:* 'They'd like her if she helped'; 'It's nice to help.' Seen in: some primary- and some secondary-school children.
Level 4a Self-reflective empathic orientation	The young person shows evidence of some sympathetic response or explicit role-taking. *Examples:* 'I'd feel sorry for her', or 'I'm trying to put myself into her shoes.' Not usually seen until secondary school age.
Level 4b Transitional level	Justifications for helping or doing good are based on internalised norms, duties or responsibilities, but these ideas are not yet strongly stated. *Example:* 'I'd feel good if I helped.' Seen in some secondary-school students and some adults.
Level 5 Strongly internalised stage	Justifications for helping are stated in terms of clear values, such as belief in the dignity or rights of individuals, or maintaining self-respect. *Example:* 'I'd feel a responsibility to help because of my values', or 'If everyone helped, society would be a lot better.' Never seen in primary-school children, and only rarely in secondary-school students.

Table 6.7 Eisenberg's levels of pro-social reasoning (Eisenberg, 1989)

moral reasoning and pro-social behaviour are:

- *setting boundaries:* although young children may not understand why certain rules are necessary, even when an adult explains, they will find it easier to accept rules if they are applied fairly and consistently;
- *showing unconditional love and acceptance:* children should be accepted and loved for themselves and not just for behaving well;
- *using discipline appropriately:* discipline should focus on the unwanted behaviour, *not* on the child by saying 'That is a dangerous or an unkind thing to do' rather than – e.g. 'You're a very naughty girl';
- *never scapegoating a child:* some children are used as scapegoats because they seem to suffer a permanent sense of guilt and often take the blame when they are not in the wrong. Often, one child is the scapegoat in the family, and this feeling of guilt carries over into all their relationships;
- *encouraging children to empathise with others:* if someone has done something wrong, i.e. broken a rule, adults should encourage children to consider what their own actions might have been and to try to put themselves in the rule-breaker's shoes;
- *encouraging decision-making:* children learn to think issues through effectively if they are given the necessary information and responsibility for making choices, when appropriate. Children develop greater social responsibility when they are included in family discussions.

The development of aggression

Aggression is a term often used very loosely, but generally it describes negative or hostile behaviour or feelings towards others. The causes of aggression in children may be summarised as follows:

- a physiological or neurological disorder, e.g. brain damage;
- frustration: children become very irritated when they are prevented from achieving their goal because of limited competence – e.g. a child may throw a jigsaw across the room because they are unable to find all the pieces;
- when demands are made upon a child which exceed their level of understanding;
- when the child is in an unfamiliar situation and does not know what the 'rules' are, or what is the 'proper' way to behave;
- when aggressive behaviour is directly and immediately **reinforced**; e.g. when a boy's punching and kicking of another child in order to obtain a toy is praised and urged on by his friends; in other words, when behaving in an aggressive manner has been amply rewarded;
- observing that aggressive behaviour by others frequently achieves results, namely either an increase in adult's attention or (as above) obtaining the wanted toy;
- people tend to behave consistently with their self-concept (see page 178 above). A child who is used to being told off for aggressive behaviour may enjoy the sense of continuity if they continue that behaviour, thus fulfilling others' expectations of them.

Aggression is common in children of nursery-school age. It usually decreases in the primary school but increases again during early adolescence, declining again during late adolescence.

Managing problem behaviour

Not all problem behaviours centre around aggression: children may also lie, steal, bully and swear. **Bullying**, in particular, has received a great deal of attention in the media and in schools. Psychologists now emphasise three aspects of bullying:

1. *the physical aspect:* fighting, punching, pushing and kicking
2. *mental subordination:* the 'put-downs', taunting and name-calling
3. *social exclusion:* ignoring someone, deliberately avoiding someone or excluding someone from one's company.

Labelling a child as a 'bully' is a negative response to the problem.

Certain general principles underpin good practice when working with children:

- *containment:* a term used by psychologists to describe the act of 'containing' a child's anger in a safe way so that the child does not feel out of control. This needs to be practised by someone who has a good relationship with the child. It may take the form of quietly holding the child or simply 'being there' for them;
- *discussion:* with older children at least, sensitive issues can be discussed;
- *language:* it is important to give children all the language they need to express themselves. This includes eye contact, body language and gestures;
- *praising and rewarding positive behaviour:* a child who is disrupting the group will be seeking attention. Children are best helped if they realise that they will have warm positive attention when they are cooperative;
- *teaching children to be assertive,* rather than aggressive or timid;
- *remembering the needs of all children:* personal space, friends, one-to-one attention, to feel secure and to feel part of the group;
- *distracting,* not confronting, young children;
- *providing activities and equipment* through which children can play out their strong emotions;
- *being a good role model.*

TECHNIQUES USED IN MANAGING CHILDREN'S BEHAVIOUR

ABC analysis of behaviour

All behaviours, whether problematic or not, follow the same pattern, known as **the ABC of behaviours**:

- *A for Antecedents:* observable events that occur *immediately* before the problem behaviour occurs
- *B for Behaviour:* the resulting behaviour, either acceptable or unacceptable
- *C for Consequences:* the observable things that happen to the child *immediately* after the problem behaviour occurs

Problem behaviours (B) are examined for regularly occurring antecedents (A) and consequences (C). Careful observation is necessary: by anticipating the antecedents to behaviour, adults can encourage children to change their behaviour and thus minimise conflict. It is not useful in this context to consider causes of, or antecedents to, the problem behaviour that happened a long time ago; this is partly because we would be unable to change these in order to alter the behavioural consequence.

Example:

- Antecedents: Patrick (aged 3) demands something; his parents deny it
- Behaviour: Patrick starts screaming
- Consequence: his parents give him what he wants

In this example, it would be easier to alter the **consequence** of the behaviour, by using reinforcers/punishers.

Behaviour modification

As in the field of cognitive development, B. F. Skinner and other behaviourists thought that adults *shape* children's behaviour and that they rehearse adult life through role play. Such shaping is achieved through the use of **positive and negative reinforcements**, and is used to ensure that the child conforms to the social expectations and customs of the culture in which they grow up. This use of reinforcements needs to be consistent and effective in inducing the desired behaviour.

Some examples of positive reinforcements (rewards):

- 3-year-old Sasha rarely spoke and was generally very quiet at nursery school. The teacher decided to praise Sasha every time she spoke to her, hoping that this would encourage communication. Unfortunately, the idea backfired and Sasha communicated *less* often in response to the 'reward'. For Sasha, the praise acted as a negative reinforcement or 'punisher'.
- A group of children in a reception class were given 'smiley face' stickers for work that had been very carefully completed. Most of the children tried very hard to earn these stickers but soon became discouraged if they never received a reward for their efforts. Teachers are very aware of the need to reward *effort* rather than mere performance.
- Every day that 7-year-old David practised the piano for 30 minutes, his mother gave him 30 pence. David liked seeing the money build up, and each week would buy sweets and comics. The novelty, however, soon wore off, and David's mother then resorted to pleading and nagging to induce the desired behaviour.

Some examples of negative reinforcements (punishments):

- Tommy was a very active and energetic 4 year old who continually left his place during story-time, and his behaviour distracted all the other children. At first, the nursery teacher gently asked him to sit down, and this method worked for a while. When Tommy began to leave his place again, the teacher spoke very harshly to him in a scolding way. Tommy's behaviour then became much worse. In this case, the 'punishment' turned out to be an effective reward.
- Six-year-old Sheena showed hostility towards most of the children she came into contact with at school; she frequently pulled their hair or pinched them. At first, she responded to teachers' requests to stop this behaviour, but soon she began to lash out again. Her class teacher decided to try the negative reinforcement of 'Time Out'. This strategy involves the removal of the child

from a situation, other children, an activity or toys, and should never be used for a prolonged period. In this case, Sheena's teacher explained what behaviour was expected to allow her to rejoin the other children and then removed her to a classroom where she could be monitored but where nobody would communicate with her. After three 10-minute sessions of 'Time Out', Sheena rejoined her classmates at playtime, and no further aggressive tendencies were observed.

Play therapy

See page 189 above.

Play tutoring

Play tutoring is where adults become involved with children's play. It can take many forms: extending children's ideas in imaginative play; providing praise and reward; offering a disturbed child a good deal of personal attention.

Other methods used to teach children desirable behaviour are: **contingent reinforcement**, **response competition**, **modelling**, **token economy** and **shaping**.

activity

Children's behaviour:

1. Think about your own childhood experiences, and discuss in a group any positive and negative reinforcements that were used on you.
2. Find out about the famous experiments conducted by Albert Bandura and his colleagues (1963) in which pre-school children imitated the behaviour of adults who were acting aggressively towards a 'Bobo' doll.
3. How do children become aggressive? Think about the strategies *you* would employ to cope with aggression in a child.
4. What greater variety of rewards and punishments can be used on an older child which would not be effective with a younger child?
5. Find out about the techniques of: contingent reinforcement, response competition, modelling, token economy and shaping. Write a brief description of each method. Apply the ABC analysis of behaviour, and decide both what sorts of behaviour and which age groups each technique is suited to.

CHAPTER 7

Emotional *and* Social Development *from* Adolescence *to* Adulthood

Adolescence is a period when most young people are striving towards independence. Erikson views it as a time of stress and confusion, and states that resolving such an 'identity crisis' is an important step towards becoming a healthy adult. James Marcia describes four patterns of coping with the task of identity formation: identity diffusion, foreclosure, moratorium and identity achievement. Coleman does not view adolescence as being significantly different from any other period of development; rather, different issues and problems come into focus at different times, and more problems require to be resolved within a shorter time span.

The development of self-esteem during adolescence depends mainly upon attractiveness and peer acceptance. Most studies confirm that young people are more self-conscious and more self-critical during early adolescence than before.

There are four main theories of the development of personality in adulthood: (1) Psychodynamic theory; (2) Trait theory and type theory; (3) Humanistic theories; and (4) Social learning theory. There is both continuity and change in personality during adult life.

Michael Argyle describes eight social motivations which cause us to interact socially. Argyle's work on social interaction has led to the development of training techniques to improve individuals' social skills.

Antisocial behaviour in adolescence is the result of a wide range of factors, such as genetic predisposition, coercive family environments and response to frustration.

Daniel Levinson described a stage theory of adult development which recognised the importance of family and work roles. Other studies have focused on the importance of life events and stress levels in adulthood.

Theories of ageing include Erikson's psychosocial theory and Cumming and Henry's social disengagement theory; this theory describes two important social changes: (1) society withdraws from the individual; and (2) the individual withdraws from society.

Adolescence and self-esteem

Adolescence is a period when, for most young people, the struggle for their own independence begins. Young people want to make their own decisions, test the limits of authority and express their own individuality. It is also a time when peer pressure is at its highest and conforming to the peer norms in matters of fashion and music assumes great importance.

G. Stanley Hall was one of the first psychologists to develop a theory of adolescence, and he saw the period of life between 12 and 25 years as a time of 'storm and stress' (1904). Hall was particularly influenced by the idea of **recapitulation**, which is the idea that human development mirrors that of society, that is, from primitivism through periods of savagery to civilisation. Erikson also views adolescence as a time of stress and confusion; and he suggests that those who *do not* suffer an 'identity crisis' as adolescents are less mature and healthy as adults than those who *do* have a crisis and who manage to resolve it successfully. (See Erikson's stages of psychosocial development in Chapter 6 on page 162.) Most studies of adolescence confirm that during the early part of adolescence young people are more self-conscious and more self-critical than before. Attributes associated with high self-esteem in adolescence are the same ones that are attributed to popular peers. These are:

- attractiveness
- peer acceptance

All other attributes, such as being good at sports or good at academic subjects, trail behind these two during adolescence. Girls in particular place great emphasis on attractiveness, while often believing themselves to be unattractive. This often leads to girls having a lower sense of self-esteem than boys.

ESTABLISHING A SENSE OF IDENTITY

James Marcia (1966) developed a semi-structured interview technique to assess 'identity status' in certain areas:

- the choice of an occupation
- decisions about religious belief
- decisions about political belief
- sexual orientation
- attitudes towards sexual behaviour

Marcia asked questions such as 'Have you ever had any doubts about your religious beliefs?' and identified four forms of **identity status** or patterns of coping with the task of identity formation:

1 *identity diffusion:* a state in which the young person has not thought seriously about the issue and has not made any commitment. An answer to the question above may be: 'I don't really know. I guess so. Everyone goes through some sort of stage like that. But it doesn't really bother me much.'
2 *foreclosure:* a state in which the young person has made a commitment and would defend it strongly, but shows no signs of having explored or questioned the alternatives. This pattern of identity is usually adopted from their parents. An answer to the question above here may be: 'No, not really. Our family is pretty much in agreement on these things.'
3 *moratorium:* a state of 'identity crisis', as described by Erikson, in which the young person is struggling with the issues and trying to make a commit-

ment. An answer here to the question above may be: 'Yes, I guess I'm going through that now. I really don't see how there can be a god with so much evil in the world . . .'

4 *identity achievement:* a state of having explored alternative options and entered into a commitment. The young person is now actively pursuing their own goals. An answer here to the question above may be: 'Yes, I even started wondering whether or not there was a god. I've pretty much resolved that now, though. The way it seems to me is . . .'

Waterman, in a (1982) review of many similar studies, reported that **diffusion** and **foreclosure** statuses were more frequent in the teenage years of 11–17, and that the level of **identity achievement** varies with the area in question: it is considerably lower for political beliefs than for vocational choice.

Adolescence in a different culture

The turmoil and identity crises associated with adolescence may have been overstated by psychoanalytic theorists and those engaged in clinical practice, partly because these individuals are more likely to see 'problem' adolescents in the course of their work. The anthropologist Margaret Mead (1901–78), in her book *Coming of Age in Samoa*, supports a different view of adolescence – namely as a tranquil and conflict-free period. Mead observed that young people in Samoa have less conflict and stresses during adolescence, partly because of the relaxed attitude towards sexual relationships and partly because of the general lack of competitiveness and ambition. Mead believed that the adolescent experience was entirely a matter of social structure and cultural pressures, and contrasted the Samoan culture with that in Western Europe and the USA. She concluded that it is the wide variety of conflicting attitudes and choices that confront young people in industrialised society which create stress. She also recommended that we do not try to remove these pressures, but that we prepare young people better. Both Mead's methods of study and her interpretations have often been criticised, but they remain very influential in focusing attention on the cultural and social factors related to adolescence.

The focal theory of adolescence

John Coleman also challenged the traditional view that adolescence is a time of conflict and turmoil. Coleman conducted a study of 800 young people in the UK in which girls and boys aged 11, 13, 15 and 17 completed various identical tests devised to investigate their self-image, friendships and parental relationships. Although crises *do* occur during adolescence, Coleman found that the process of adaptation is spread over the years and that problems are dealt with one at a time. He called this the **focal model** because relationship patterns and other issues come into *focus* at different times. In this way, adolescence may be seen as not significantly different from any other period of development; the only exception is that there are *more* problems to be resolved within a shorter time span during adolescence.

Coleman also emphasised the role of the adolescent as an active agent in shaping the course of an individual's life:

In any one day a teenager may choose to confront a parent over the breakfast table, to argue with a sibling, to accept the suggestion of a best friend. To stand up to an authoritarian teacher, to conform to peer group pressure, to resist the persuasion of a girlfriend or boyfriend, and so on. Every one of these situations offers the young person a choice, and all may well have a bearing on the interpersonal issues with which the focal model is concerned.

Different problems, different relationship issues come into focus and are tackled at different stages, so that the stresses resulting from the need to adapt to new modes of behaviour are rarely concentrated all at one time. It follows from this that it is precisely in those who, for whatever reason, do have more than one issue to cope with at a time that problems are most likely to occur.

(Coleman and Hendry 1990)

It would seem from recent studies of adolescence that Coleman's theory fits the evidence better than theories which emphasise the 'storm and stress' aspect. Most adolescents appear to like, respect and feel close to their parents, and arguments are usually about minor issues of dress, musical taste and so on. Where families *do* show marked alienation and conflict between parents and their adolescent children, it was found that, in the great majority of cases, these problems had been present for some time previously; in other words, they were not a true problem of adolescence.

ANTI-SOCIAL BEHAVIOUR IN ADOLESCENCE

The majority of adolescents are law-abiding most of the time and have developed a strong sense of right and wrong. The small minority of adolescents who engage repeatedly in serious anti-social conduct, such as muggings, knifings, rapes and armed robberies, are not necessarily incapable of the conventional moral reasoning described on page 194.

Studies into the nature of delinquency and aggressive behaviour point to a wide range of contributory factors:

- *genetic predisposition:* twin studies show that some individuals are genetically predisposed to have hostile, touchy temperaments and to engage in aggressive and delinquent behaviour;
- *the conflict between the life and death instincts:* psychodynamic theorists (e.g. Freud) argue that all human beings are 'driven' by two instincts: the *life instincts* which aim for survival, and the *death instincts* which are destructive forces. Destructive tendencies can be displaced as aggression towards others or sublimated into sport or some other physical activity;
- *the specific cultural context:* inner-city areas and areas where poverty is rife are more likely to foster aggression. The USA leads all industrialised countries in the incidence of rapes and murders;
- *coercive family environments:* highly anti-social adolescents often come from families whose members are locked in power struggles, each trying to control the others by coercive tactics, e.g. threatening, shouting and hitting. In such families, parents gradually lose control over their children's behaviour, with sanctions and physical punishment having increasingly little effect;
- *a response to frustration:* some psychologists believe that frustration always

leads to aggression and that aggression is always caused by frustration. Others argue that not all frustration leads to aggression: frustration leads to aggression because it causes general arousal, but this arousal is only expressed as aggression if the appropriate environmental cues are in place;

- *reinforcement and observation of aggressive behaviour:* social learning theorists (e.g. Bandura) argue that in many societies male aggression is respected. They also place great emphasis on the power of the mass media (especially television) to influence behaviour;
- *de-individuation:* this is a loss of personal identity in which the individual surrenders their own independence and conscience and simply merges anonymously into the crowd; **de-individuation** can be liberating in its release of inhibitions, as well as encouraging anti-social behaviour.

VISUAL IMPAIRMENT AND ADOLESCENCE

It is often at adolescence that the full impact of visual impairment is felt, and young people have to face the fact that they are visually impaired for life. Sometimes, this emotional trauma results in a period of mourning over the lost or absent vision.

The main problems associated with visual impairment are:

- *restricted mobility:* at a time when many of their sighted friends are able to drive a car, this can be a major cause of stress
- *restricted social opportunities:* unless they have had a full programme of mobility training, visually impaired adolescents will be dependent upon fully-sighted people to take them out
- *reliance on others for choice of dress style:* those with severe visual impairment may never have been able to choose their own clothes and may have been guided by adult tastes rather than by their peers
- *the skills of eating appropriately:* eating in a group situation is fraught with difficulty if you can't see clearly, and many young people may always ask for the same meal which they know is relatively easy to manage

It is important for the development of **self-esteem** that young people with a visual impairment receive **personal counselling** to help them to come to terms with their particular impairment, together with **specialist training** in the important areas of self-presentation skills, communication, the manner of dressing and the skills of eating appropriately.

ADOLESCENCE AND DISABILITY

Most of the limitations imposed by disability will become more pronounced during adolescence. The child who was the focus of attention at nursery school age may find it hard to accept the change in attitude of those around them when they reach adolescence. A physical disability will be more noticeable, especially if the young person is confined to a wheelchair. Difficulties in communication will also be more pronounced as the child becomes older. The onset of puberty may exacerbate any feelings of self-doubt and unattractiveness, and lead to a lowering of self-esteem. Problems associated with sexuality and the social barriers which all people with disabilities face may all cause stress and anxiety, and it is important that carers be aware of the issues, and that they attempt to equip themselves with the strategies to cope in a sensitive and caring manner.

Eating disorders in childhood and adolescence

The most common eating disorders affecting children and adolescents are **obesity**, **anorexia nervosa** and **bulimia nervosa**. All three have profound implications for the successful development of the individual's self-concept and resulting self-esteem.

- *Obesity:* obesity or fatness results from taking in more energy from the diet than is used up by the body. Some children appear to inherit a tendency to put on weight very easily, and some parents and carers offer more high-calorie food than children need. Obesity can lead to emotional and social problems as well as the physical problem of being more prone to infections. An obese child is often the target for bullying, and if severely obese, the child will be unable to participate in the same vigorous play as their peers;
- *Anorexia nervosa:* anorexia nervosa is popularly, but wrongly, called 'the slimmer's disease'. Those affected are predominantly adolescent girls from the higher social classes in the developed world, but recent evidence points to problems in children as young as 7 years old, with a slight increase in the number of boys affected.

  Features of the disorder are:

  - weight loss
  - overactivity and obsessive exercising
  - tiredness and weakness
  - extreme choosiness over food
  - lanugo (baby-like hair on the body; thinning of hair on the head).

  There are various theories on the causes of anorexia. These include the following:

  - Affected individuals do not wish to grow up and are trying to keep their childhood shapes. In part, this may be influenced by the media obsession with achieving the 'perfect' (i.e. slim) body, and also by the desire to defer the 'storm and stress' of adolescence;
  - Those affected see anorexia as a way of taking control over their lives;
  - Some specialists see it as a true **phobia** about putting on weight;
  - It may be due to an attempt to avoid adult sexual feelings and behaviours;
  - The affected individual is over-involved in their own family, so that when they enter adolescence there is a confrontation between the peer group and the family;
  - It may be a physical illness caused in part by **hormonal** changes or a disorder of the **hypothalamus** (the part of the brain concerned with hunger, thirst and sexual development);
  - It is caused by depression, a personality disorder or, rarely, schizophrenia.
- *Bulimia nervosa:* bulimia is often, but not always, a variant of anorexia nervosa. Again, the majority of individuals affected are female, but recently there has been a rise in the number of males affected. Bulimia nervosa is characterised by episodes of compulsive overeating usually followed by self-induced vomiting. Features of the disorder include the following:

  - The individual may be of normal weight or only slightly underweight;
  - Bingeing and vomiting may occur

once or several times a day;
- The individual may become clinically depressed or even suicidal;
- In severe cases, repeated vomiting leads to dehydration and loss of the body's vital salts, especially potassium; this may result in weakness and cramps;
- The acid present in gastric (stomach) juices may damage tooth enamel.

As with anorexia, there is no single cause to account for the disorder. Many of the theories advanced are linked closely to those put forward to explain anorexia nervosa, and include:

- a morbid fear of fatness;
- a constant craving for food developed after months or years of fasting.

activity

Group work on adolescence:

1 *Research into relationships.* Working in a group, devise and administer a simple questionnaire to find out about the relationships between adolescents, their families and their peer groups. You may wish to focus on these areas:

- how much leisure time is spent with (a) the peer group, (b) the parents and (c) alone;
- the nature and frequency of disagreements between subjects and their parents;

Compare your group's findings with the findings of the following research studies:

- the 'Isle of Wight' study – Rutter *et al.* 1976 – and
- the relationship between parent–adolescent conflict and the amount of time adolescents spend alone and with parents and peers – Raymond Montemayor (1982).

Both these studies are described in Smith and Cowie 1991 (see the 'References and resources' section at the end of this chapter on page 227).

2 *Eating disorders in childhood and adolescence.*

- Discuss the prevalence of slim role models in the media – on film, in television and in magazines. In particular, try to collect articles and advertisements in which photos of slim models are used, and evaluate the effectiveness of the appeal to adolescents.
- 'Teenage dolls (such as Sindy and Barbie) promote an idealised role model which is unhealthy and can damage the self-concept of the child.' Discuss this statement.

3 *Variations from the norm.* Individually, choose a topic to research from the following:

- giftedness
- Attention Deficit Hyperactivity Disorder (ADHD)
- depression in adolescence
- autism (see Chapter 1, page 59).

Find out as much as possible about the chosen topic, and present your findings in written form. It may help to structure your research by using the following headings: definition, incidence and possible causes, description with examples, impact on the family and on the individual, programmes of therapy and treatment, and a bibliography.

Emotional and social development in adulthood

Adulthood is usually viewed as the period that starts at the end of adolescence and ends with 'old age' at about 65. Turner and Helms (1989) define adulthood in terms of **maturity**, as 'a state that promotes physical and psychological well-being'. The mature individual possesses the following attributes:

- a well-developed value system
- a stable emotional behaviour
- an accurate self-concept
- intellectual insight
- satisfying relationships
- a realistic estimation of future goals

Erikson defines adulthood in terms of the successful achievement of the developmental tasks which relate to that period (see again Chapter 6, page 164 above). He believed that the attainment of **identity** by the end of adolescence was an essential task for the ability to share with and care about another person – a characteristic that he called **intimacy**. Intimacy does not just imply sexuality: it can describe the relationship between friends as much as that between sexual partners. Erikson further states that if a sense of intimacy is not established, then the result is a sense of **isolation**, of being alone with no-one to care for or share with.

THE DEVELOPMENT OF PERSONALITY IN ADULTHOOD

Personality is the characteristic patterns of thought, emotion and behaviour which define an individual's personal style and influence their interactions with the environment. The earliest visible manifestations of personality are **temperamental traits** (see page 175). As children develop, their initial ways of responding to their environment (temperament) have to be adjusted in accordance with their developing cognitive and emotional understanding (personality). Relationships are the prime source of childhood **socialisation**, and the kinds of relationships that we have shape our personality.

There are four main theories of personality:

1. *psychodynamic theory:* this theory, proposed by Freud, emphasises the effects of early experiences on the shaping of adult personality. (The psychodynamic theories have been discussed in Chapter 6.)
2. *trait theory and type theory:* these theories attempt to describe individuals by a set of characterising attributes.
3. *humanistic theories:* these theories emphasise self-determinism (or free will) and personal growth; they view all individuals as innately good.
4. *social learning theory:* this theory is sometimes called the **behavioural-cognitive theory**; it asserts that people behave in a particular way because of the situation they are in or have been in on previous occasions.

Trait and type theories

The trait theories of personality describe individuals in terms of quantities of selected **traits**. A trait is a specific facet of personality, which is sometimes seen as a merely descriptive category but which may be a predisposition to behave in a certain way. In order to assess personality by these means, theorists first devise a **taxonomy** – or system of classification. R. B. Cattell and Hans Eysenck used a statistical method known as **factor analysis**: by analysing the **correlations** between certain personality characteristics, they reduced the vast list of adjectives used to describe aspects of personality to more manageable lists of basic traits.

Cattell's trait theory

Cattell identified two kinds of personality trait:

1 *surface traits:* aspects of the personality which could be easily identified by others, by observing what the person says and does – e.g. assertive, ambitious;
2 *source traits:* aspects of the personality which lie behind the surface traits and are not readily observable by others – e.g. self-assured or dominant.

Cattell also developed a comprehensive questionnaire, the 16PF (16 Personality Factor) Test (see Figure 7.1), to identify where on each personality continuum an individual is placed. Cattell argued that while the 16PF test provided a personality profile, every individual also shows some *unique* traits which cannot be measured by means of personality tests. Any such profile should therefore be accompanied by an individual description of the person's unique traits.

1	Reserved	Outgoing
2	Less intelligent	More intelligent
3	Affected by feelings	Emotionally stable
4	Submissive	Dominant
5	Serious	Happy-go-lucky
6	Expedient	Conscientious
7	Timid	Venturesome
8	Tough-minded	Sensitive
9	Trusting	Suspicious
10	Practical	Imaginative
11	Forthright	Shrewd
12	Self-assured	Apprehensive
13	Conservative	Experimenting
14	Group-dependent	Self-sufficient
15	Undisciplined self-conflict	Self-disciplined
16	Relaxed	Tense

Figure 7.1 Cattell's 16 personality traits

Eysenck's type theory

Eysenck saw personality as arising largely from inherited physiological tendencies, with environmental influences playing a secondary part. Eysenck's types fall into two bipolar dimensions (although he added a third dimension, psychoticism versus normality, in later years):

1 *introversion–extraversion:* this occurs as a result of inherited individual differences in the **reticular formation**, which is part of the brain stem. In extraverts, the reticular formation strongly inhibits incoming sensations, resulting in the need to seek stimulation. In introverts, the reticular formation augments incoming sensations, so that they seek less stimulation;
2 *neuroticism–stability:* this dimension also depends upon the inherited type of **autonomic nervous system (ANS)**. The ANS is concerned with the body's reaction to stressful or threatening events. The neurotic individual has an easily activated ANS and will therefore react very readily to stressful stimuli. The

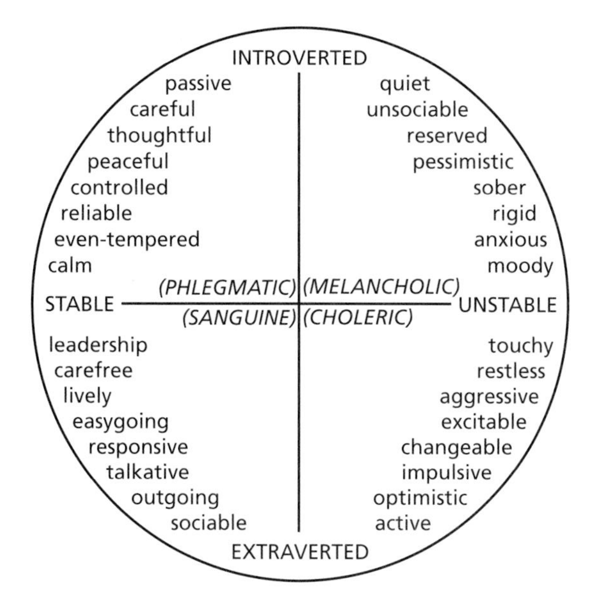

Figure 7.2 Eysenck's dimensions related to personality traits

stable personality takes longer to react to such stimuli, and will not react as strongly.

Eysenck linked his theory to those of the ancient Greek physician-philosophers who proposed that every individual's well-being and behaviour is influenced by a balance of four body fluids or 'humours':

- Yellow bile causes a **choleric** temperament – irritable and excitable
- Blood causes a **sanguine** temperament – optimistic and cheerful
- Black bile causes a **melancholic** temperament – pessimistic and sad
- Phlegm causes a **phlegmatic** temperament – calm and apathetic

The four types of personality proposed by Eysenck correspond to these early theories (see Figure 7.2). Eysenck believed that every individual could be placed somewhere on the **continuum**, even if they did not fit neatly within one of the quadrants.

The 'big five' personality dimensions

Many researchers attempting to reach a consensus on personality traits have used Cattell's 16PF test and Eysenck's Personality Inventory. McCrae and Costa also used factor analysis to identify five basic traits which underlie all others:

1. extraversion vs. introversion
2. agreeableness vs. disagreeableness
3. conscientiousness vs. irresponsibility
4. emotional stability vs. neuroticism (emotional instability)
5. openness to experience vs. being closed to experience

Occupational psychologists have used this model to assess the suitability of individuals for certain jobs, for example by using questionnaires.

The concept of stable personality traits has been challenged by critics who argue that people do not behave with such consistency and predictability. For example, an individual may behave in a way which conflicts with their basic trait in certain social situations; a person who is normally reserved and unsociable may become animated and talkative after a few alcoholic drinks. It may be more useful to look at underlying temperaments and then examine individual behaviour in the wider context of social experience, while also taking into account the expectations of other people.

Humanistic theories

Humanistic psychology emerged in the 1950s and 1960s as an alternative to the two major forces of psychodynamics and behaviourism, both of which relied on scientific generalisations. Abraham Maslow

activity

Group exercise on personality traits:

1 Choose either Cattell's 16PF traits or Eysenck's dimensions to conduct your own research into personality traits. Work with one partner whom you know fairly well and decide where on each continuum they could be placed. Then repeat the exercise on yourself. Compare the results.

2 Devise a questionnaire to use when interviewing candidates for a job in health and social care. What sort of personality traits would the ideal candidate have? How could you structure the questions to encourage honesty and openness?

called the humanistic approach the 'third force'. Its central principles are:

- the uniqueness of the human individual
- the importance of individual freedom and choice
- the development of the self-concept

Humanistic theories make no attempt to predict how people will behave in any situation, and unlike psychodynamic theories, they ignore the unconscious.

Carl Rogers: self-image and positive regard

Carl Rogers (1902–87) developed his theory from his work in clinical practice with emotionally troubled people. He argued that all human beings have two basic needs:

1 *the need for self-actualisation:* this may be seen as an active striving for personal development, and manifests itself in perfecting physical skills, educating oneself or realising one's own potential. Rogers believed that all people are born with the actualising tendency. At the lowest level, it entails basic needs for physical requirements such as food, water, shelter and comfort. At a higher level, it involves the need for **self-fulfilment** in terms of independence and creativity;
2 *the need for positive regard:* healthy personal development occurs through forming relationships which provide us with affection, love or respect from others. Such positive regard is **unconditional** in that it does not matter how badly we behave, we are still loved just for being ourselves. The individual also needs positive regard from themselves; and where a person experiences unconditional positive regard, positive self-regard will also be unconditional.

If either of these two basic needs are not met, Rogers argued that psychological problems result. Parents who give love **conditionally**, perhaps only showing affection when their child is well behaved or fits with their own 'ideal' image, inflict severe psychological damage on the child. A failure to show unconditional love prevents the child from feeling free to explore their own potential and thus achieve self-actualisation. As the child grows to adulthood, they will constantly seek approval from others. In humanistic terms, the **ideal self** and the **self-concept** are mismatched. Good psychological health exists where the perceived self, or self-concept, and the ideal self are reasonably compatible. Rogers believed that we each need relationships characterised by genuineness, **empathy** and unconditional positive regard, and he advocated the use of 'encounter groups' in which a trained therapist provides such a relationship in an atmosphere of acceptance and trust.

Maslow's hierarchy of needs

Abraham Maslow (1908–70) evolved a hierarchy of needs from which arise all our motivations. These needs are usually represented in pyramid form, starting with the most basic physiological needs at its base and ending with the highest need – for self-actualisation – at its apex (see Figure 7.3). Maslow's theory is similar to Rogers' in that he believed that there is an innate tendency to move up the hierarchy of needs in the individual's search for personal fulfilment. The needs at one level must be at least partially satisfied before those at the next level start to motivate behaviour. The highest motive, self-actualisation, involves the emergence of the following qualities:

- perception of reality
- toleration of uncertainty
- creativity and an expansion of spiritual and aesthetic experiences
- an acceptance of what our human nature is like, in self and in others
- an appreciation of basic life experiences
- a concern for humanity

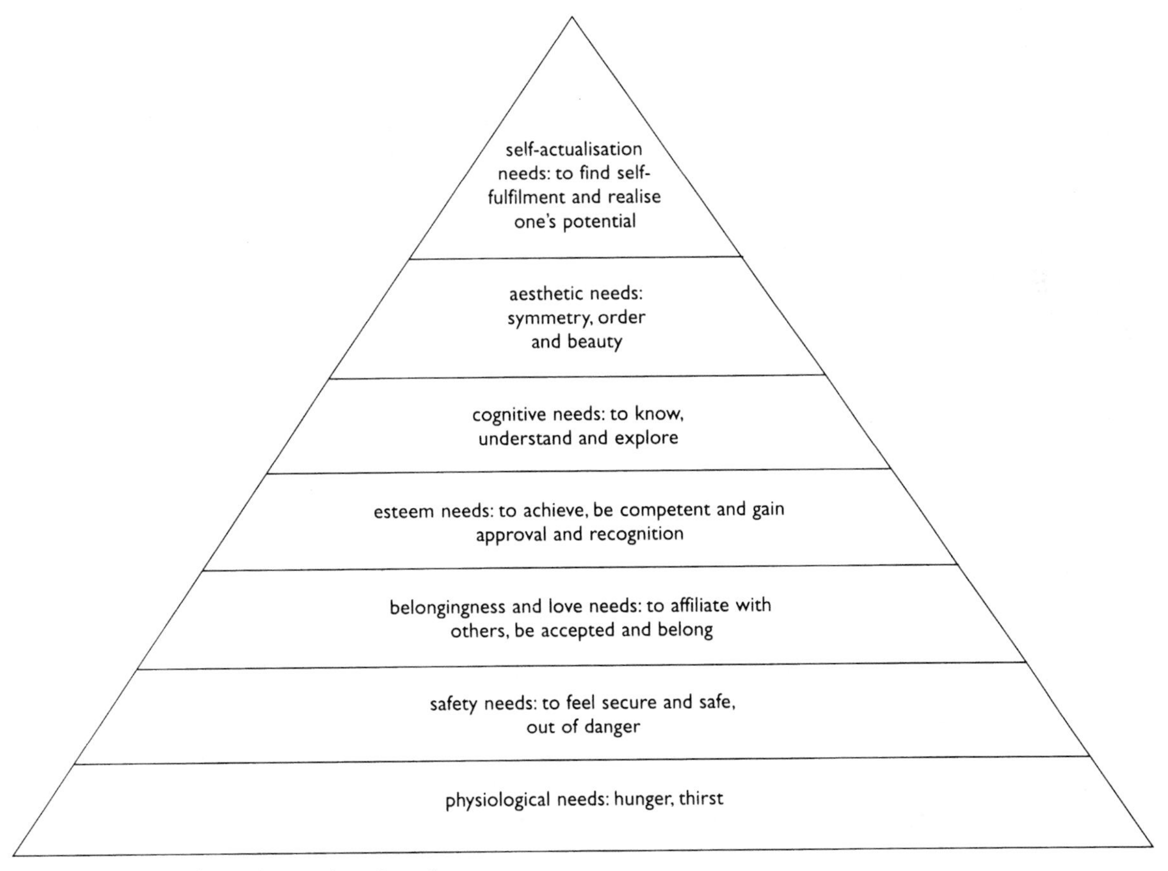

Figure 7.3 Maslow's hierarchy of needs

Maslow's hierarchy of needs is more a framework of motivation than a theory of personality. It is widely used on training courses in business management and health and social care, as it focuses attention on the motives which underlie people's behaviour.

Kelly's Personal Construct Theory

George Kelly (1905–66) believed that people are scientists in that they are continually making and testing out **hypotheses** about what the world is like. The unique view of the world formed by each person becomes an individual framework which is used to control their behaviour and to make sense of further experiences and events. People interpret or **construe** the world rather than observing it directly; and people need to be able to predict in order to control. Every individual develops a whole set of personal theories about what the world is like, which is used as a guide for behaviour. These theories are called **personal constructs**. Personal constructs may be seen as:

- statements of **opposing dimensions** which individuals use to describe and make sense of the people and events they encounter.

  Examples: intelligent–dull; reserved–outgoing; kind–cruel; honest–dishonest.
- *unique to each individual:* the same word may have different meanings for anyone else.

  Example: one person may see others in terms of the construct 'intelligent–dull', while another person may use the construct 'reserved–outgoing'.
- the key to *problem-solving:* as they enable us to predict and control our behaviour. If a construct makes a prediction which doesn't come true, then it is invalidated and we have to search for an alternative explanation.

  Example: if someone we would describe as 'honest' is later discovered to be a thief, we would then have to reject the initial construct and seek an alternative construct.

Kelly believed that a person's constructs could be elicited in conversation or by asking for a written self-characterisation, in the third person, like a character in a play. He also developed the **repertory-grid** as a means of eliciting personal constructs.

The repertory grid

This is the basic method of eliciting personal constructs. A person is given a list of roles, such as employer, teacher, close friend or parent, and then asked to supply the name of someone who fits the role. The roles played by these 'significant others' are listed across the top of the grid. The person then fills in the actual names of the people who fit these roles in that person's life – these are called the **elements** of the grid. They are then asked to consider the similarities and differences between these elements, which are always presented in sets of three.

In the example in Figure 7.4, a fictitious student, Marcia, is asked to consider the ways in which her mother, father and brother are alike or different in the 'caring–not caring' construct. She thought of her mother and father as being alike in that they are both caring, and her brother as different in that he is not caring. Marcia then repeats the comparisons with other elements (or people in given roles) until a rating is arrived at for each of the elements against each of the constructs. When Marcia has completed the grid, it should be possible to obtain a mixed list of constructs and to assess the predominant tone, focus and range of descriptive categories used.

ELEMENTS					CONSTRUCTS
Mother	Father	Brother	Boyfriend	College tutor	
✓	✓	✗	✓	✗	Caring ✓ Not caring ✗
					Gentle ✓ Aggressive ✗
					Generous ✓ Not generous ✗
					Intelligent ✓ Unintelligent ✗

Figure 7.4 An example of a repetory grid

Kelly's theory has been criticised for failing to deal adequately with the possible effect of strong emotions such as love or hostility on an individual's construct system. Kelly argues that certain specific constructs, such as anxiety, hostility, guilt, fear and aggressiveness, *do* fit into his theory but should be defined as aspects of construct systems *in a state of change*. He developed the idea of a **circumspection–pre-emption–control cycle (CPC cycle)**:

1 Initially, we **circumspect** the field – by dreaming, imagining and speculating;
2 This is done in order to **pre-empt** – to select out certain issues as crucial and to decide what kind of situation we are in;
3 Finally, we move to **control** – we make active choices by deciding what construct will cover the situation and which pole of that construct will provide us with the best anticipatory base for action.

activity

Working with personal constructs:

1 Select eight people from different areas of your life as 'elements' and represent them by the letters A to H. Consider these individuals in any combinations of three at a time (i.e. ABC, DEF, GHA, CFA, GHB or other combinations) and write down the constructs that come to mind as you compare them. Write each result from these comparisons as a statement: 'A and B are.........., but C is..........'
2 Arrange your constructs in repertory-grid form, as shown in Figure 7.4.
3 Outline Kelly's personal construct theory, and state its importance to an understanding of an individual's personality.

Social learning theory

Social learning theory was proposed by Bandura, and is discussed in Chapter 4. Personality is here seen as being the product of the individual's unique experiences and learning, and develops through:

- classical and operant conditioning
- imitation and **identification**

In this approach, the main determinants of an individual's behaviour are not any consistent internal traits they may possess but what happens to that individual in the environment, through observing the behaviour of others and receiving patterns of reinforcement.

Personality and change in adulthood

There is both continuity and change in personality during adult life. Many social psychologists argue that personality is expressed in and partly determined by the social roles occupied. For example, a person may be cruel and dominant in his role as prison officer, yet kind and submissive when at home with his family; or a woman may be a loving mother at home, yet behave in a harsh, authoritarian way in her occupational role as a teacher. Studies using the 'big five' personality traits (see above, page 211) show that personalities are still fairly unsettled in adolescence and early adulthood but then become more firmly established by the time adults are in their 30s.

Bernice Neugarten and her colleagues have studied personality in adults and noted that older adults, as a group, *do* have different personalities from younger adults: elderly men and women were more introverted, introspective and in touch with inner feelings than were middle-aged adults.

Personality and social behaviour

Michael Argyle (1925–) proposes eight roots of social behaviour, in the form of **social motivations** which cause us to interact socially:

1 *biological needs:* these basic needs of eating, drinking, warmth and bodily comfort are an important source of motivation and influence on our behaviour;
2 *dependent behaviour:* dependence is at the core of early attachment. It extends from the satisfaction of feeding needs to a lessening of anxiety brought about by the feeling of security when one begins to trust others. At the other end of the scale is **dominance**: alternating styles of submissive behaviour to those in authority and dominance of those of lower rank are the distinguishing features of an **authoritarian personality**;
3 *affiliation:* the capacity and need for friendship which arises out of the fulfilment of dependency needs by the mother. Affiliative behaviour makes cooperation easier and inhibits aggression;
4 *dominance:* the desire to be influential in decision-making, to talk a lot and to have one's ideas attended to. There may also be a need for power, status and recognition. Dominant behaviour may have elements of both **generativity** and unconscious inferiority, encouraging the dependence or submissiveness of others, and sometimes despising them for it;
5 *sex:* the motivation for certain kinds of social interaction and bodily contact usually, but not always, directed towards members of the opposite sex. Human sexual motivation is a continual drive to seek social interaction which extends beyond our affiliation needs;

6 *aggression:* an innate response to frustration and attack, rather than an intention to harm. Aggression is restrained and controlled by social rules. Aggressive behaviour increases as a result of:

- a lack of warmth or rejection in childhood
- inconsistent behaviour of 'significant others'
- physical punishment
- parental and social modelling, including media models
- actual encouragement to aggressive attitudes and behaviour by parents, peers and cult propaganda

7 *self-esteem and ego identity:* this starts with the acceptance of early parental evaluation and continues with the seeking of experience and evaluations that are consistent with this sense of self-worth. It is only when we feel insecure that we rely heavily on the reactions of others to confirm our self-esteem. Social behaviour may be adapted in an attempt to get other people to accept and to bolster our self-esteem. Argyle has researched the social skills involved in the way in which we present ourselves, particularly the use of eye contact, facial expression and general posture;

8 *other motivations:* these are the motivations which go beyond the purely biological needs but are closely linked with them:

- achievement, attributed to high levels of independence – most often found in firstborn children and in those with achieving parents
- intellectual and recreational interests
- the pursuit of idealistic values

The above **achievement motivation** is not like a drive that can be satisfied, for Argyle explains that when we have achieved our goals, we continually revise our targets upwards – as does a high jumper.

Argyle's work on social interaction has led to the development of training techniques to improve individuals' social skills.

Social interaction and motivation:

1 Select examples of social interaction, and describe the motivations of the participants according to Argyle's eight 'roots'. Evaluate the categories in the light of your own observations. Can you think of any other motivations for social behaviour?

2 How useful do you think Argyle's roots of social motivation are in explaining social behaviour?

LEVINSON'S THEORY OF ADULT DEVELOPMENT

Daniel Levinson described six 'seasons of a man's life' (see Table 7.1). Levinson proposed that adults go through a recurring process of building life structures and revising them. Movement from one stage to the next is the product of both external events (e.g. success or failure in a job, marriage, divorce) and internal ones (e.g.

Stage	Age	Major tasks
Early adult transition	17–22	Make the transition from adolescence to early adulthood; establish independence from parents and explore possibilities for an adult identity.
Entering the adult world	22–28	Create a first major life structure, usually by making and testing out a career choice and getting married. Find people who can support your development (i.e. a mentor or advisor).
Age-30 transition	28–33	Work on imperfections of first life structure: is this what you really want? Make adjustments or plan a more major life change – e.g. career change, divorce.
Settling down	33–40	Create a major new life structure, more stable than the first. Become your own person – outgrow the need for a mentor. Be ambitious, task-oriented and unreflective.
Mid-life transition	40–45	Confront the facts of ageing; consider making major changes – re-examine settling-down structure and modify it.
Entering middle adulthood	45–50	Create a new life structure. Focus is on new relationships with children, a deeper concern for your family and a capacity for mentoring younger colleagues. (Compare with Erikson's generativity.)

Table 7.1 Daniel Levinson's stages of adult development
Source: *The Seasons of a Man's Life*, D. J. Levinson, New York: Alfred A. Knopf, 1978

satisfaction or dissatisfaction with the life structure one has created). Central to the life structures are family and work roles. Levinson's theory focused exclusively on male development; and although studies of women reveal and very similar situation with respect to career choices and marriage, Levinson's theory obviously does not describe a unique conflict faced by women – that is, the decision between career and motherhood.

According to Levinson, the **transition period** (age 40–45) is a developmentally significant time of **mid-life crisis**.

Mid-life crisis

Gail Sheehy describes a shift in the mid-life stage when women begin to become more assertive and ambitious (more 'masculine') and men begin to become more caring and intimate (more 'feminine'). The tension produced by this shift produces a certain amount of insecurity: the entire life structure is questioned, including the choice of career. The individual comes to terms with the reality of growing old and perhaps reviews the progress of their life so far.

LIFE EVENTS IN EARLY ADULTHOOD

It is difficult to identify a single pattern for adult development, as the particular pattern of life events varies in accordance with gender, social class, culture and historical period. Any 'life-span' approach to charting emotional and social development in adulthood can never be regarded as universal. The chronological age at which a person leaves home to find employment or to marry will vary according to their economic and cultural circumstances. Similarly, the concept of retirement in old age is unique to industrialised societies.

FORMING RELATIONSHIPS

The psychiatrist Harry Stack Sullivan (1953) believed that the experience of friendship during middle childhood (8–12 years) is an essential precursor to adult intimacy. The tendency of children to select one or a few other children with whom they feel a special affinity is the first sign of the need for interpersonal intimacy – which is called love when it is encountered again in adolescence. Many other researchers have noted that children who have failed to form close friendships in childhood experience certain difficulties in forming relationships in their adult life; and these difficulties may result in failure to complete school, delinquency or anti-social behaviour. However, children's relationships with their parents or main caregivers continue to play an important role in emotional and social development.

THE SOCIAL-READJUSTMENT RATING SCALE

Holmes and Rahe (1967) developed a **Social Readjustment Rating Scale (SRRS)** which looks at the stresses caused by major life events (i.e. the kind of events that we experience as difficult to handle). It is based on earlier research which had found that some social events that required a change in lifestyle were associated with the onset of illness. They first identified 43 events which seemed particularly stressful, and then, after further research, assigned each a value of 'life change units' dependent on the degree of adjustment it took. (See Table 7.2.) To use this scale, you simply tick each event that has happened to you during the last year and add up the re-adjustment values.

Some criticisms of the major-life-changes approach are:

- Some of the items on the scale are vague or ambiguous
- Some events become more stressful if the person is *already* ill or depressed
- Some of the items on the scale will have greater value for some people in society rather than others. For example, an unmarried 15-year-old schoolgirl will almost certainly view pregnancy very differently from the way it is viewed by a 30-year-old married woman
- Some people are better able to cope with stressful events than others
- The amount of support from friends and others can significantly alter the effect of major life changes

The SRRS provides a relatively straightforward method of measuring stress, and has generated much research. Some other researchers have argued that the minor stressors and pleasures of everyday life have a more significant effect on health

Rank	Life event	Mean value
1	Death of spouse	100
2	Divorce	73
3	Marital separation	65
4	Jail term	63
5	Death of close family member	63
6	Personal injury or illness	53
7	Marriage	50
8	Fired at work	47
9	Marital reconciliation	45
10	Retirement	45
11	Change in health of family member	44
12	Pregnancy	40
13	Sex difficulties	39
14	Gain of new family member	39
15	Business re-adjustment	39
16	Change in financial state	38
17	Death of a close friend	37
18	Change to different line of work	36
19	Change in number of arguments with spouse	35
20	Mortgage over $10,000	31
21	Foreclosure of mortgage or loan	30
22	Change in responsibilities at work	29
23	Son or daughter leaving home	29
24	Trouble with in-laws	29
25	Outstanding personal achievement	28
26	Spouse begins or stops work	26
27	Begin or end school	26
28	Change in living conditions	25
29	Revision of personal habits	24
30	Trouble with boss	23
31	Change in work hours or conditions	20
32	Change in residence	20
33	Change in schools	20
34	Change in recreation	19
35	Change in church activities	19
36	Change in social activities	18
37	Mortgage or loan less than $10,000	17
38	Change in sleeping habits	16
39	Change in number of family get-togethers	15
40	Change in eating habits	15
41	Vacation	13
42	Christmas	12
43	Minor violations of the law	11

Table 7.2 The Social Readjustment Rating Scale
Source: Holmes & Rahe (1967)

than the big, traumatic events assessed by the SRRS. For example, Kanner *et al.* (1981) devised a scale called the **Hassles and Uplifts Scale**. (Hassles may be described as everyday frustrations and irritations which interfere with the smooth running of everyday routines. These include bad weather, traffic jams or losing one's keys.) The Hassles scale in particular was found to be a better predictor of psychological problems than life-event scores, both at the time and later.

activity

Examine Table 7.2.

1 Work out your own score and see if you agree with the weighting given to the various life events.
2 This scale was devised in 1967 in the USA. What differences would you expect if you made up a similar scale today?
3 Identify three items in the scale that are likely to have different values for *men* and *women*, and explain why. Repeat the exercise for people of different *ages*.
4 Draw up a personal list of 'hassles' and rank them in order of levels of stress they induce. Compare your list with someone else's list. Try to account for any similarities and differences between the two lists.

LOSS AND BEREAVEMENT

Loss is experienced in many ways, and does not necessarily involve the death of a loved one. For example, growing up involves the loss of all the infancy support networks; going to school involves temporary separation from parents; and changing school involves the loss of familiar surroundings. There are obviously corresponding 'gains' here as well; for example, the child will gain new friends and experiences with each change in circumstances. Other life events which involve loss are:

- new siblings (i.e. the loss of parental attention)
- the death of a sibling
- bereavement, as grandparents grow older and die
- the loss of a parent through separation, divorce or death
- ending or changing relationships
- unemployment (either the parent's, the sibling's or one's own)
- miscarriage, termination of pregnancy or stillbirth
- disability (the loss of a sense of the future and of security)
- the birth of a baby with a disability (parents may grieve for the 'normal' child they were expecting)
- caring for people with dementia or Alzheimer's disease

Each loss may be viewed as a preparation for greater losses. How the individual reacts to the death of a loved one will depend on how they have experienced other losses, their personality, their religious and cultural background and the support available.

Grief

Grief is a normal and necessary response to the death of a loved one. It can be short-lived or it can last for a long time. Grief at the death of a husband, wife or child is likely to be the most difficult to get over. Grief can take the form of several clearly defined stages:

1 *shock and disbelief:* numbness and withdrawal from others enables the bereaved person to get through the funeral arrangements and family gatherings. This stage may last from three days to three months;
2 *denial:* this generally occurs within the first 14 days and can last minutes, hours or weeks. No loss is acknowledged; the bereaved person behaves as if the dead person were still there. Hallucinations are a common experience. These may consist of a sense of having seen or heard the dead person, or of having been aware of their presence.
3 *growing awareness:* some or all of the following emotions may be felt, and each conspires to make many people feel that they are abnormal to experience such harsh emotions:

   - *yearning:* the urge to try to find a reason for the death;
   - *anger:* directed against any or all of the following: the medical services; the person who caused the death, in the case of an accident; God, for allowing it to happen; the deceased, for abandoning them;
   - *depression:* the pain of the loss is felt, often with feelings of a lack of self-esteem. Crying, or letting go, often helps to relieve the stress;
   - *guilt:* this may be guilt for the real or imagined negligence inflicted on the person who has just died; or the bereaved can feel guilty about their own feelings and inability to enjoy life;
   - *anxiety:* often bordering on panic, as the full impact of the loss is realised. There is worry about the changes and the new responsibilities and future loneliness. There may even be thoughts of suicide.

4 *acceptance:* This usually occurs in the second year, after the death has been relived at the first anniversary. The bereaved person is then able to relearn the world and new situations without the deceased person.

> The most meaningful help that we can give any relative – child or adult – is to share his feelings before the event of death and allow him to work through his feelings, whether they are rational or irrational.
>
> *(Elisabeth Kubler-Ross)*

Research has shown that counselling can help to reduce the damage to physical and emotional health which often follows the loss of a loved one. Most people come through the healing process of grief with the help of relatives and friends. Those who may be in particular need of help are often those:

- with little or no family support
- with young children
- who have shown particular distress or suicidal tendencies

Bereavement counsellors try to establish a warm, trusting relationship with the bereaved person. This is done initially by listening with patience and sympathy; accepting tears as natural and even desirable. Bereavement counselling should not be undertaken by individuals working alone. The support of a group under professional guidance is vital, as close contact with intense grief can be very stressful and emotional demanding.

How to help someone who is suffering from loss

- *do* be available
- *do* let your concern show
- *do* allow them to cry if they want
- *do* allow them to talk about their loss as much as they want
- *do* reassure them that they did everything that they could
- *don't* avoid them because you feel awkward
- *don't* say you know just how they feel, because you don't
- *don't* change the subject when they mention their loss

Expressing grief

Very young children do not understand death, but they do grieve – as we saw in the studies on separation anxiety in infancy (see Chapter 6, page 168). Older children, from about age 6, *do* realise that death is irreversible but will express their grief differently from adults: they will often experience academic difficulties and behaviour problems. Children who are terminally ill often become aware of their situations and use more cognitive strategies of coping as they get older. Adolescents tend to understand death in more abstract terms.

The grieving process varies from one individual to another and is dependent upon many factors. The more unsatisfactory the relationship with the deceased while they were alive, the more disturbed the grieving process is likely to be.

THEORIES OF AGEING

1 *Erikson's psychosocial theory.* Erikson characterised the crisis of old age as a time of **ego integrity versus despair** (see Chapter 6, page 165). Successful ageing is seen as resolving this conflict, so that the individual will end their life with greater ego integrity than despair. **Ego integrity** involves:

   - the conviction that life does have a meaning and does make sense
   - the belief that all life's experiences had some value, even if they were viewed unfavourably at the time
   - an improved understanding of one's own parents because of similar experiences
   - the belief that death is inevitable and something which can be faced without fear
   - the understanding that what happened during one's life was also somehow inevitable and could not have happened in any other way

   Despair is the opposite feeling; that is, that life is meaningless, that it is too late to undo the past, and that death is something to fear.

2 *Social disengagement theory.* Cumming and Henry (1961) describe what happens to us socially as we grow old as **social disengagements**. This theory claims that the following social changes take place in old age:

   - Society withdraws from the individual:
     - compulsory retirement, usually at the age of 65;
     - children growing up, leaving home and starting families of their own;
     - the death of friends and maybe their spouse.

- The individual withdraws from society:
  - There is a reduction in social contacts and in social activity;
  - Life becomes more solitary.

Cumming and Henry view this mutual disengagement as inevitable and beneficial: they believe that being able to cast off social and emotional responsibilities in the later years leads to contentment. Others claim that whilst disengagement *does* take place, it is more a reflection of a society which has a negative attitude towards elderly people than it is a natural and voluntary process.

3 *Activity theory.* **Activity** (or **re-engagement**) **theory** is the chief alternative to disengagement theory. Activity theory proposes that successful ageing involves staying active and participating in as many social activities as possible (Havighurst *et al.* 1968). Other studies have also supported the activity theory. In particular, Langer and Rodin (1976) (see below) noted that declining physical skills and a lowered sense of usefulness can create in elderly people a feeling of lack of control over their fate, and that the generally negative attitudes towards elderly people in this society further enhances their dependency and lack of autonomy.

Langer and Rodin's study

Langer and Rodin attempted to assess the effects of enhanced personal responsibility and choice in a group of patients in a nursing home. They selected two groups on separate floors of the large nursing home who were matched for similar health and socioeconomic status. Each group was given a talk by the nursing home administrator, in which he introduced some information about the home:

- *the experimental group:* the main points of the talk were:
  - The patients had responsibility for caring for themselves;
  - They could decide how they wanted their rooms arranged;
  - They could decide how they wished to spend their time;
  - They were told: 'It's your life';
  - It was their responsibility to make complaints known. They were also offered a plant as a present, told that there was a movie showing in the home on Thursday and Friday, and asked which night, if any, they would like to go.
- *the control group:* a similar talk was given, but with important differences:
  - There was no emphasis on personal responsibility;
  - They were not encouraged to take control in the nursing home. They were *given* the present of a plant rather than offered it, and told that they were scheduled to see the movie one night or the other, and told how the staff tried to make their rooms nice.

Questionnaires and interviews were used to assess the sense of control, happiness and level of activity each group had both one week after the talk and three weeks later. The research assistant and the nurses were unaware of the hypothesis and the methods of the experiment.

The results

Substantial differences between the two groups were reported by the patients, the interviewer ratings and the nurse ratings. The experimental group were found to be happier, more active, more alert and generally much more socially active than the control group. They also spent less time watching the staff.

The researchers went back to the home after 18 months and found that the experimental group were *still* improved in comparison to the control group. Also, they were in better health, and fewer had died. It was concluded that a minor intervention had achieved a remarkable effect on the health and well-being of the residents in the nursing home.

activity

Stereotyping and personal responsibility in relation to elderly people:

1 From magazines and television, collect as many advertisements as possible that include elderly people. For each advert, discuss the aim and the specific role of the elderly person. Can you spot any stereotypes, and if so, how could these be avoided?
2 Try to visit a residential or nursing home for the elderly.
   - Make a list of the features that contribute to a sense of **loss of control** in an institution
   - As a group, discuss ways in which day centres and residential homes for the elderly can avoid the problem of too little stimulus in the day-to-day lives of their clients

References and resources

Ainsworth, M. D. S., Blehar, M. C., Waters, E. and Wall, S. (1978) *Patterns of Attachment*, New Jersey: Lawrence Erlbaum Associates.

Ainsworth, M. D. S. (1989) 'Attachments Beyond infancy', *American Psychologist* 44: 709–716.

Bandura, A., Ross, D. and Ross, S. A. (1961) 'Transmission of aggression through imitation of aggressive models', *Journal of Abnormal and Social Psychology* 63: 575–582.

Barnes, P. (ed) (1995) *Personal, Social and Emotional Development of Children*, Oxford: Blackwell.

Bee, H. (1992) *The Developing Child*, New York: HarperCollins Publishers.

Bowlby, J. (1975) *Separation, Anxiety and Anger*, London: Hogarth Press.

Bruce, T. and Meggitt, C. (1996) *Child Care and Education*, London: Hodder & Stoughton.

Cole, M. and Cole, S. R. (1993) *The Development of Children*, New York: Scientific American Books.

Coleman, J. C. and Hendry, L. (1990) *The Nature of Adolescence* 2nd edn. London: Routledge.

Coopersmith, S. (1967) *The Antecedents of Self-esteem*, San Francisco: Freeman.

Cox, M. (1991) *The Child's Point of View*, Hertfordshire: Harvester Wheatsheaf.

Cumming, E. and Henry, W. E. (1961) *Growing Old: the Process of Disengagement*, New York: Basic.

Cunningham, J. (1993) *Child Development*, New York: HarperCollins Publishers.

Dunn, J. and Kendrick, C. (1982) *Siblings: Love, Envy and Understanding*, Cambridge (Mass.): Harvard University Press.

Eisenberg, N. and Mussen, P. H. (1989) *The Roots of Prosocial Behaviour in Children*, Cambridge: Cambridge University Press.

Erikson, E. H. (1968) *Identity, Youth and Crisis*, London: Faber and Faber.

Fox, N. (1977) 'Attachment of Kibbutz infants to mother and metapelet', *Child Development* 48: 1228–1239.

Gilligan, C. (1982) *In a Different Voice: Psychological Theory and Women's Development*, Cambridge (Mass.): Harvard University Press.

Gross, R. (1996) *Psychology: the Science of Mind and Behaviour*, edn, London: Hodder & Stoughton.

Hall, E. (1983) 'A conversation with Erik Erikson', *Psychology Today* 17(6): 22–30.

Hardy, M. *et al.* (1990) *Studying Child Psychology*, Oxford: Oxford University Press.

Harter, S. (1985) *Manual for the Self-perception Profile for Children*, Denver, Colorado: University of Denver.

Havighurst, R. J., Neugarten, B. L. and Tobin, S. S. (1968) 'Disengagement and patterns of ageing', in Neugarten, B. L. (ed) *Middle Age and Ageing*, Chicago: University of Chicago Press.

Hayes, N. (1994) *Foundations of Psychology: an Introductory Text*, London: Routledge.

Hoffman, M. L. (1982) 'Development of prosocial motivation: empathy and guilt', in Eisenberg, N. (ed) *The Development of Prosocial Behaviour*, New York: Academic Press.

Holmes, T. H. and Rahe, R. H. (1967) 'The Social Readjustment Rating Scale', *Journal of Psychosomatic Research* 11: 213–218.

Kanner, A. D., Coynes, J. C., Schaefer, C. and Lazarus, R. S. (1981) 'Comparison of two modes of stress measurement: daily hassles and uplifts versus major life events', *Journal of Behavioural Medicine* 4: 1–39.

Karmiloff-Smith, A. (1994) *Baby It's You*, London: Ebury Press.

Kohlberg, L. (1968) 'The child as a moral philosopher', *Psychology Today*, 2: 25–30.

Langer, E. J. and Rodin, J. (1976) 'The effects of choice and enhanced personal responsibility for the aged. A field experiment in an institutional setting', *Journal of Personality and Social Psychology* 34: 191–198.

Lewis, M. and Brooks-Gunn, J. (1979) *Social Cognition and the Acquisition of Self*, New York: Plenum Press.

Marcia, J. (1966) 'Development and validation of ego-identity status', *Journal of Personality and Social Psychology* 3: 551–558.

Mead, M. (1928) *Coming of Age in Samoa: a Psychological Study of Primitive Youth*, New York: Morrow.

Montemayor, R. and Eisen, M. (1977) 'The development of self-conceptions from childhood to adolescence', *Developmental Psychology* 13: 314–319.

Murray Parkes, C., Stevenson-Hinde, J. and Marris, P. (ed) *Attachment Across the Life Cycle*, London and New York: Routledge.

Mussen, P. and Eisenberg-Berg, N. (1977) *Roots of Caring, Sharing and Helping*, San Francisco: W. H. Freeman.

Oates, J. (ed) (1994) *The Foundations of Child Development*, Oxford: Blackwell.

Parten, M. B. (1932) 'Social participation among preschool children', *Journal of Abnormal and Social Psychology* 27: 243–269.

Piaget, J. (1932) *The Moral Judgement of the Child*, Harmondsworth: Penguin.

Rutter, M. (1981) *Maternal Deprivation Reassessed*, 2nd edn, London: Penguin.

Smith, P. K. and Cowie, H. (1991) *Understanding Children's Development*, Oxford: Blackwell.

Stern, D. (1977) *The First Relationship: Infant and Mother*, Glasgow: Fontana/Open Books.

Sullivan, H. S. (1953) *The Interpersonal Theory of Psychiatry*, New York: W. W. Norton.

Thomas, A. and Chess, S. (1977) *Temperament and Development*, New York: Brunner/Mazel.

Tizard, B. and Hughes, M. (1984) *Young Children Learning: Talking and Thinking at Home and at School*, London: Fontana Press.

Turner, J. S. and Helms, D. B. (1989) *Contemporary Adulthood*, 4th edn, Florida: Holt, Rinehart & Winston.

Waterman, A. S. (1982) 'Identity development from adolescence to adulthood: an extension of theory and a review of research', *Developmental Psychology* 18: 341–358.

Useful Address

British Psychological Society
St Andrews' House
48 Princess Road East
Leicester LE1 7DR
Tel: 0116 254 9568

PART IV

Provision for the Development of Children

Chapter 8

Provision *of* Health, Social Care *and* Education

Health care may be divided into statutory provision, in other words that which must be provided by law, **and non-statutory provision**. Under 'Statutory Provision' the changing structure of the National Health Service is described.

The care provided by the NHS can be classified as **primary**, **secondary** or **tertiary care**. **Primary care** is the first line of patient care, providing comprehensive, non-hospital care in the community. Examples of this type of care include that given by general practitioners, dentists, pharmacists, opticians, health visitors, district nurses and School Health Services.

Secondary care is the care provided when an ill child cannot be treated by the primary health care team. It is usually provided in hospitals which, ideally, should have a number of features such as specially skilled staff, which enable them to meet the particular needs of children.

Tertiary care is specialised care, which is not normally provided at a district general hospital, but at a specialised centre.

Non-statutory health care includes both private and Independent-Voluntary provision. The buying of medicines in chemist shops and supermarkets can be considered as part of private provision, as well as paying for 'alternative' or 'complementary' medicine, and private treatment by doctors. Independent-Voluntary (or 'not-for-profit') organisations, are those which have been created by their members and not by the state. Those concerned with health care may fund-raise, campaign on various issues, or actually provide health care. They may obtain their funding from central government, local authorities, by selling services, or through charitable funding.

Social care may also be divided into statutory provision, and non-statutory provision. Statutory care is provided on a local level through the Personal Social Services Departments of local authorities. These departments have responsibility for the care and protection of children; day care services and childminders; fostering; residential accommodation; adoption; and the provision of services for children with disabilities, including visual impairment, hearing impairment, and learning disabilities. Statutory social care provision also includes social security. There are some benefits to which all children are entitled, and many others to which children and their families may be entitled depending on circumstances.

Non-statutory social care may be provided by local authorities (i.e. the care that they provide other than that which they are required to provide by law); privately (for example, private fostering and children's homes); by Independent-Voluntary organisations; and informally (for example, by friends and neighbours).

Education provision may be divided into three sectors. These are the maintained sector (i.e. that funded solely by the state); voluntary provision and private provision, although there is considerable overlap between these. For the under 5's it is difficult to separate day care and education, and there are a number of different types of organisation which offer these. As far as possible, where appropriate, children with special needs are educated in mainstream schools, with the provision of extra staff and necessary services and resources. Children may, however, attend a special school, or a special unit attached to a mainstream school or hospital.

There is an overlap in services provided for the health care, social care and education of children. It is important that there is good coordination between the various agencies.

There are four main sources of funding for health and social care and education. These are central government; local government; registered charities; and private funding.

There are many important changes being made to the provision of care for children. These include an increased multi-disciplinary approach to assessment and provision; the empowerment of service users; and an increased spectrum of care (for example, new methods due to scientific advances, and complementary medicine linked to a more holistic approach to care).

The structure and development of health and social care services is described in detail in several health and social-care texts. Sources for further reading are given at the end of Chapter 9 on page 287.

Provision of health and social care for children and their carers occurs through a combination of **statutory**, **voluntary** and **private organisations**, with **informal care** playing an important part. Education similarly follows a pattern of public, private and voluntary provision.

activity

What do you understand by the terms:

- statutory
- voluntary
- private
- informal?

Give examples of each type of provision. (See Appendix A for answers.)

Provision of Health Care

STATUTORY HEALTH PROVISION

Central government is responsible for providing statutory provision. The government department responsible for health and personal social (welfare) services is the Department of Health (DoH). This is headed by the Secretary of State for Health who is responsible for the broad policy and central administration of health and welfare services.

On a local level, the provision of health services is the responsibility of the regional and district health authorities of the National Health Service (NHS), and the welfare services are provided through Personal Social Services (or social work) Department of local authorities.

The NHS is a central part of the country's 'health care system', but as will be explained below, it is not the only agent or organisation which provides health care. Individuals, families, communities, the personal social services, the private sector (e.g. the pharmaceutical companies and private hospitals), the media (in health-promotion campaigns), the trade unions, local government and international organisations (such as the Red Cross) can also all be said to be providing resources for improving people's health.

Figure 8.1 summarises the current structure of the NHS in England, Scotland, Wales and Northern Ireland. In the NHS and Community Care Act 1990, the government attempted to improve efficiency and quality in health services by separating the **purchasers** of health care from the **providers**.

Purchasers and their organisations were divided into four groups:

1. *purchasers of primary care:* family health service authorities;
2. *purchasers of secondary care:*
   - district health authorities
   - GP fundholders
3. *regional health authorities;*
4. *special health authorities.*

Providers in the NHS were divided into three groups:

1. *primary care:*
   - the general practice system
   - community health services
   - indicative prescribing budgets (the amount of money GPs are allowed to spend on drugs for their patients)
   - the dental service
   - pharmacists
   - opticians

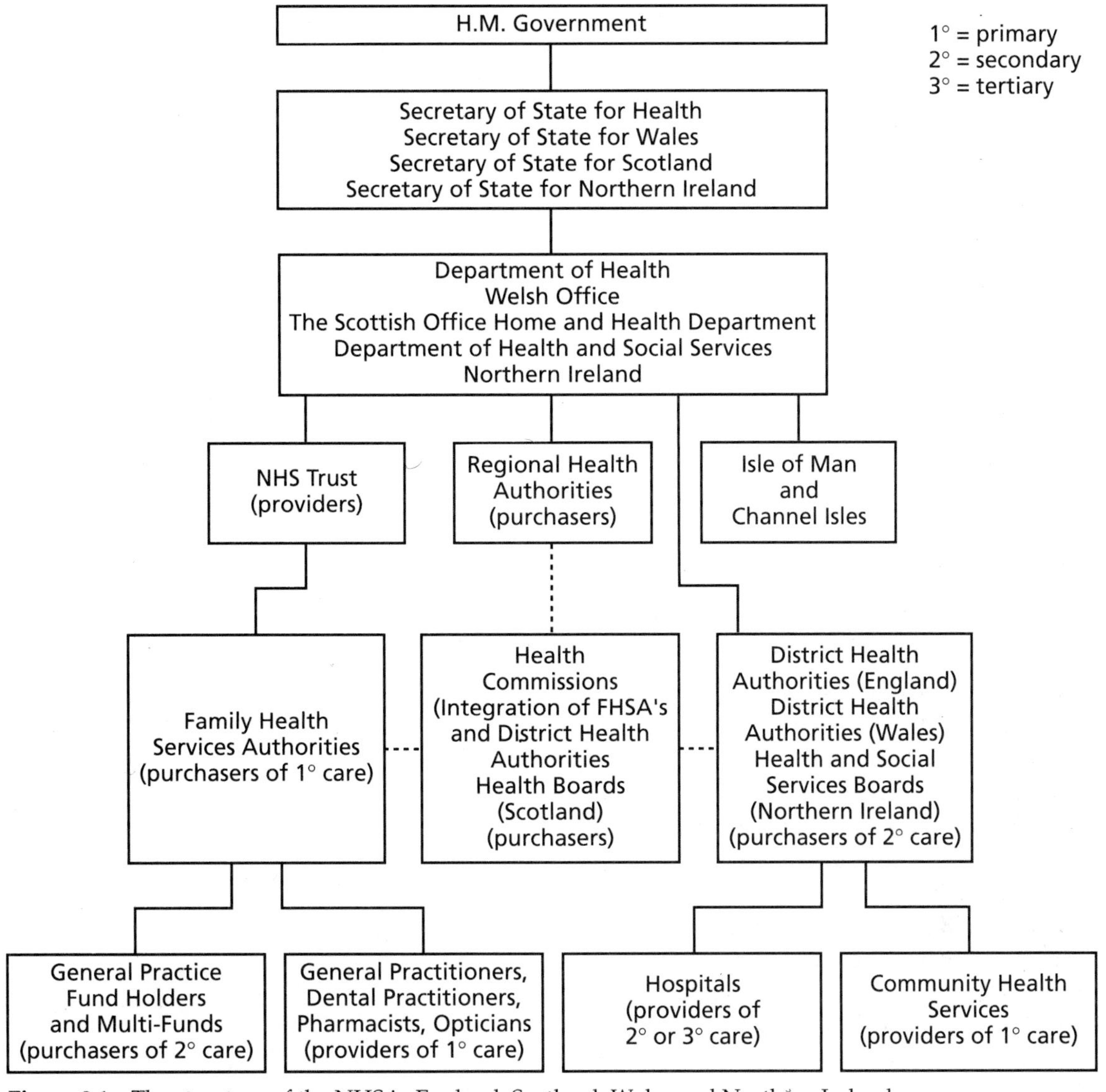

Figure 8.1 The structure of the NHS in England, Scotland, Wales and Northern Ireland

2 *secondary care:*

- hospitals
- NHS Trusts
- directly managed units
- waiting lists
- the independent sector

3 *tertiary care:*

- specialised treatment in a highly developed unit

activity

The structure of the NHS has been constantly changing over the past few years. Because of this, you should check whether there have been any significant actual or proposed changes since the publication of this book.

Check that you are clear about the roles of the following:

- the Department of Health (England) (or the Welsh Office; the Scottish Office Home and Health Department; the Department of Health and Social Services Northern Ireland)
- Regional Health Authorities (England)
- District Health Authorities (England and Wales)
- Health Boards (Scotland)
- Health and Social Services Boards (Northern Ireland)

Use the above information, and your local library, to make a poster to show the structure of the NHS in your particular area.

Primary care

At the first level, most care of sick children is provided solely by parents. **Primary care** can be considered, however, to be the first line of professional patient care. It provides comprehensive non-hospital health care in the community. In the UK, primary care is offered by two complementary service providers: those that come under the control of the Family Health Services Authorities (i.e. **general practitioners**, **dental practitioners**, **pharmacists** and **opticians**), and the Community Health Services (CHSs) which come under the control of the District Health Authorities (DHAs) in England and Wales, and the Health and Social Services Boards in Northern Ireland. Because primary care is provided from these two separate sources, there is now a move to create a more seamless service by combining the District Health Authorities with the Family Health Services Authorities to form Health Commissions (see Figure 8.1). (This situation already exists in Scotland with the Health Boards.)

The importance of primary care is illustrated by the fact that general practices and Community Health Services together deal with 90% of patient contact with the NHS.

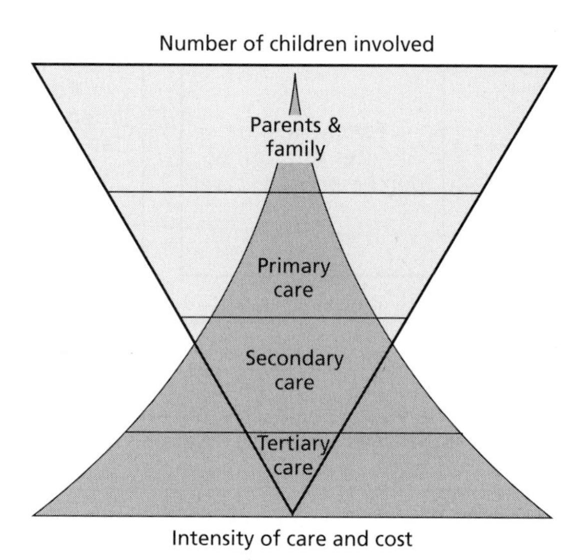

Figure 8.2 Levels of care

Family Health Services Authorities

There are 90 Family Health Services Authorities (FHSAs) in England, and their areas usually correspond to non-metropolitan counties, metropolitan districts and groups of London boroughs.

FHSAs are small authorities which consist of 11 members: the chairman, the general manager, and nine additional members including a general practitioner (GP), a **community pharmacist**, a dental practitioner and a **nurse** with experience of managing community services. The Family Health Services Authorities are responsible for purchasing the primary care services. These services have important preventative as well as diagnostic and curative roles to play in medical care.

The providers of these services are:

- general practitioners (there are about 32,000 GPs in the UK)
- dentists (there are about 17,000 dentists)
- opticians (there are about 9,000 ophthalmic opticians)
- pharmacists (there are about 12,000 retail pharmacies under contract for prescriptions with the NHS)

activity

In the area covered by your Family Health Services Authority, find out:

1 About GPs:

- How many of the residents are registered with a GP?
- How many GPs are there in the area? (How many males/females?)
- Calculate the average number of patients per GP.
- How many practices are there in the area?
- How many of the practices have wheelchair access?
- How many of the practices have practice nurses; health visitors; district nurses; a psychiatric nurse; a chiropodist; a speech and language therapist; other health professionals?
- How many of the GPs carry out minor surgery?
- What screening services do the GPs in the area provide?
- What percentage of children are immunised?
- What is your GP's policy on night visits?

(For information about Fundholding GPs, see Thomson *et al.* (1995) *Health and Social Care*, 2nd edition.)

2 About dentists:

- How many dentists are there in the area? (How many males/females?)
- How many of these dentists give NHS treatment?
- How many of these dentists will take on new NHS patients? (NB: some will take new children on for NHS treatment, but not new adults.)
- Find out how much dentists are paid for various treatments (a) under the NHS, and (b) privately.

(NB: dental treatment is free to all children under the age of 18, and to students under 19 in full-time education.)

3 About pharmacists:

- How many pharmacies are there?
- What is the role of the pharmacist?

(NB: children under 16 and full-time students under 19 do not pay a prescription charge.)

4 About opticians:

- How many opticians are there? (NB:

the FHSA has no control over the location of opticians.)
- Distinguish between opthalmic opticians, ophthalmic medical practitioners and dispensing opticians.

(NB: free eye tests are available to all children under the age of 18, and to students under 19 in full-time education. If they require glasses, they will be provided with a voucher for a basic pair. They then have the choice of paying on top of this for a more expensive pair. Suppliers of glasses may be either registered opticians or unregistered persons. However, only registered opticians may supply glasses for children under 16 and for people who are registered blind or partially sighted.)

Community Health Services

The purpose of the Community Health Service is to deliver local health care. Its aims are to provide the following:

- a personalised service
- a client-centred approach to care
- accessible services available to all
- a quality service to agreed standards
- a highly trained workforce to deliver such a service
- a widely available written statement of service provision
- an integrated service with other agencies, in particular general practices

The fact that both GPs and Community Health Services provide primary care leads to a number of complexities. For example:

- Both GPs and the Health Promotion Units of the Community Health Services seek to promote healthy living and to prevent illness
- Both **district nurses**, who are provided by Community Health Services, and **GP nurses** may care for the same patient
- Family planning is provided by both GPs and the Community Health Clinics
- There are self-employed **general dental practitioners** and salaried **community dental officers**, both of whom may see schoolchildren

Because of these, and other, complexities, considerable coordination between the GP system and Community Health Services is required to:

- avoid duplication of services
- prevent patients falling between the two components of the primary-care sector
- provide the patient with a 'seamless' service

There are a number of different systems used to achieve this coordination:

- In many localities, the main group of community nursing staff (district nurses and health visitors) operates as part of a primary-care team by being attached to a particular GP practice
- In other localities, these nurses work a particular geographical area where residents are registered with a number of different GP practices
- In some localities, many **paramedics**, such as **clinical psychologists**, **speech therapists** and **physiotherapists**, also work as part of a primary health-care team

activity

In every locality, there will be working groups, spanning FHSAs, GPs, dentists and NHS Trust Community Health Services, which are making efforts to coordinate the provision of primary care. Find out what groups are functioning in your area. How successful are their efforts considered to be:

- by the group members
- by patients?

School Health Services

(See also the 'Health and developmental checks at school entry' and 'Subsequent health and developmental checks' sections in Chapter 3 on page 71.)

The Community Health Services provide each school with a School Health Service. The aim of this service is to work with parents and teachers to help every child to make the most of their educational opportunities. Each school will have a School Doctor (School Medical Officer) and a named School Nurse who is responsible for visiting their schools regularly, helping to monitor the children's general health and well-being. The School Nurse also works alongside teaching staff in Health Education throughout the school, covering topics such as growth and development, diet, hygiene, immunisation, exercise and hair and foot care. School health teams may also have one or more of the following members:

- a school dentist
- a health visitor
- an audiometrician
- a physiotherapist
- a speech therapist
- a dietician
- a community orthoptist (who screens vision)

activity

1 Children's consent to health surveillance has not been researched, but it appears that neither pre-school, primary- nor secondary-school children are asked if they wish to be examined. Do you think they should have a choice, and if so, at what age?
2 Children have limited access to health-care services if seeking information and help in their own right. This may be because they are restricted to visiting health professionals such as a GP with a parent, or because their ability to travel to a clinic is limited. It has been shown that, because of these restrictions, a school nurse can be a useful resource. In a group, discuss what issues a child may want to discuss confidentially, and how their access to professionals could be improved.

Secondary care

Secondary care is the care provided when an ill child cannot be treated by the primary-care team. This kind of care is usually provided in **hospitals**. Wherever possible, the hospitalisation of children is to be avoided, but sometimes this type of care will be necessary. When a child requires secondary care, they will be referred to a **consultant**. Secondary care in a general hospital follows referral from either a GP, a hospital accident and emergency (A&E) department or a maternity department.

Some facts from the Audit Commission's study of children in hospital, *Children First*, are as follows:

- There are about 14 million children and young people aged 18 and under in England and Wales – about 28% of the population. In-patient admissions occur at the rate of about 1 per 11 children per year, amounting to about 16% of all in-patient admissions to hospitals.
- 42% of these children are under the care of **paediatricians** (consultants specialising in the care of sick children) (see Figure 8.3).

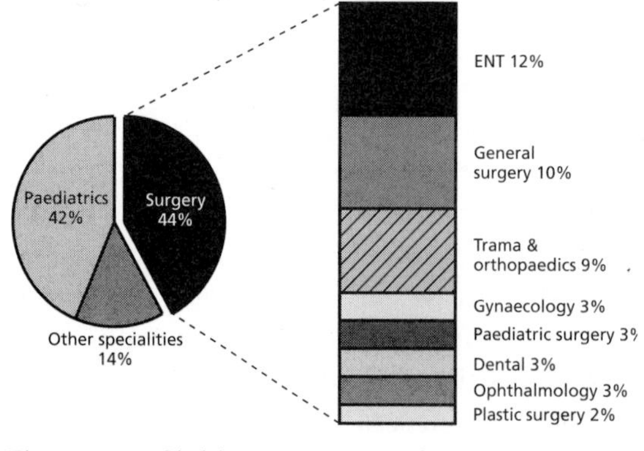

Figure 8.3 Child in-patients aged 0–18, by speciality, England and Wales 1990/91

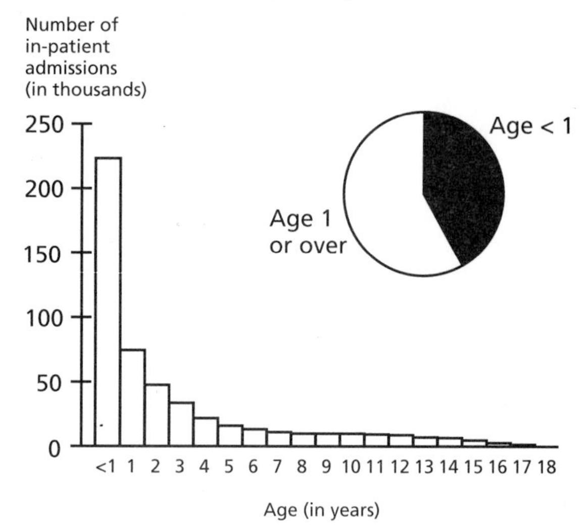

Figure 8.4 Numbers of children admitted to paediatrics, by age

- 44% are under the care of eight surgical specialities (see Figure 8.3).
- 42% of children admitted to paediatrics are under 1 year old (see Figure 8.4).
- Children admitted to surgical specialities are more evenly spread across the age groups, although there is a peak at 5 years due to ear, nose and throat (ENT) surgery (see Figure 8.5).

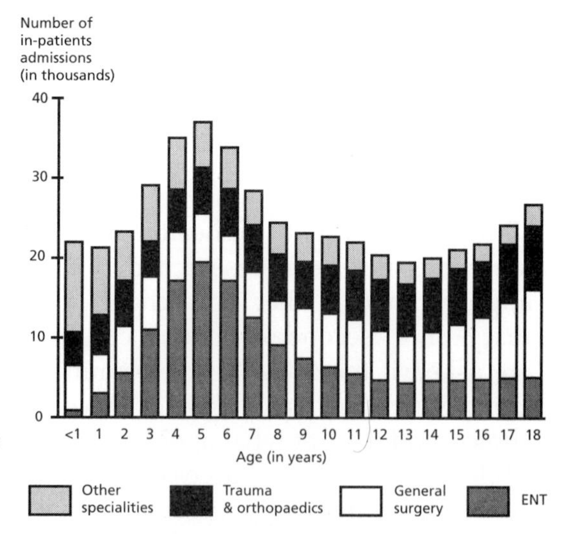

Figure 8.5 Numbers of children admitted to surgery, by age

- Most surgery is carried out on children by surgeons who also operate on adults. Only a small proportion is performed by paediatric surgeons who specialise in surgery for children, predominantly very young babies.
- 93% of admissions to paediatrics are emergencies, whereas to surgery, only 68% of admissions are emergencies.
- The average length of stay in hospital is currently about 4 days, although there are considerable local variations in both this and the admission rates of children to hospitals.
- About 1 child in 4 attends an accident and emergency department in any one year. (See the 'Accident prevention' section in Chapter 3, page 81.)

Because children are physically and emotionally different from adults and need the constant care and support of their parents, it should be remembered that in hospital they will have special health-care needs. To meet these needs, the Audit Commission has identified six principles which should underlie the care of children in hospital (see Figure 8.6).

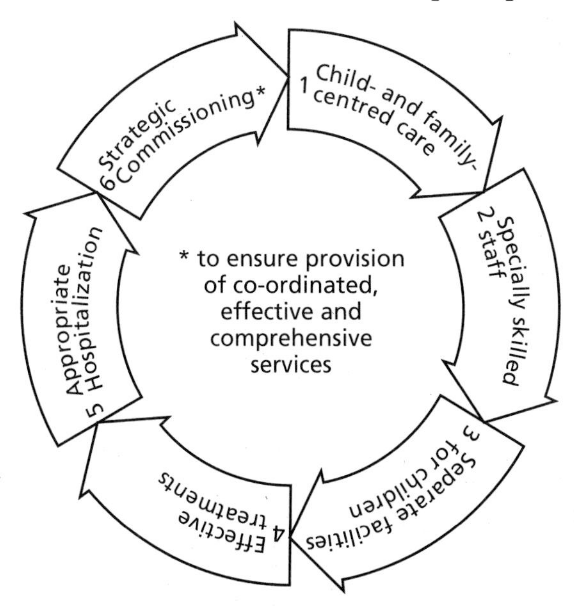

Figure 8.6 The Audit's Commission's six principles which should underlie services for sick children

Child and family-centred care

As much attention should be given to a child's needs for care and support, as to their medical or surgical needs. Caring for a child means involving parents and siblings. Many young children can perceive the separation and pain of hospital treatment to be a kind of punishment. In an effort to prevent this, an explanation of what the treatment will involve can be given to the child through play. Older children and young adults will need counselling, emotional support, peer-group contact and a greater degree of involvement in decisions about all aspects of their care. A child's right to be involved in these decisions is a major principle of the Children's Act 1989 (see Chapter 9, page 275 below).

Specially skilled staff

All the staff who are involved in the health care of children should be aware of the special needs of children and their families. The basic qualified person for nursing children is a Registered Sick Children's Nurse (RSCN). The Department of Health target standard is that there should be 'at least 2 RSCNs – or nurses who have completed the child branch of Project 2000 – on duty 24 hours a day in all hospital children's departments and wards ... and a RSCN on duty 24 hours a day to advise on the nursing of children in other departments ...' (Department of Health 1991). However, this standard is frequently not attained. The provision of **play specialists** is poor in many hospitals. Although it is important that all staff who work with children be aware of the need and purpose for play, there should also be trained staff available who have completed a course recognised by the Hospital Play Staff Examination Board. These specialists should organise play; be a source of advice on play; develop play facilities; and teach other staff about play. In some hospitals, **teaching staff**, employed by the local education authority, work with children aged 5 and over.

Separate facilities

The physical environment of a hospital caring for children and young people should be safe and secure. It should include facilities for play, leisure and recreation. Special facilities for children should be kept separate from those for adults, as should special facilities for adolescents. Facilities should be provided for parents so that they can remain with children at all times. This means that facilities must be provided for parents to sleep, make drinks, wash and sit quietly. All hospitals should have a room set aside for the family with a seriously ill or dying child.

Effective treatments

All hospitals need to ensure that the care and treatments they give are effective. To do this, they must consider the following:

- Have they achieved the desired improvements in the health and well-being of the child?
- Are there alternative ways of reaching the same outcome
  - with less stress and disruption to the child and family?
  - at a lower cost to the NHS?

Appropriate hospitalisation

The aim in delivering health care to children should be to minimise both the number of times a child needs to attend hospital and the length of each stay. Good primary care obviously plays an important part in achieving this aim. In recent years, the number of admissions has been increasing, but the average length of stay has been decreasing. This fall has been due to:

- more day surgery;
- nurses becoming more involved in teaching and supporting parents as prime caregivers;
- more care being given at home, either because of an earlier transfer to primary care or because of continuing secondary care at home. Examples of the latter include the use of high-technology therapies that require the support of a hospital team, and the care of terminally ill children such as those with AIDS.

Strategic commissioning

The main commissioning authorities are the District Health Authorities in England and Wales; the Health and Social Services Boards in Northern Ireland; and the Health Boards in Scotland. These authorities should develop a strategy specifically for the provision of services for children and their families. They should ensure that each hospital has a written policy for the care of sick children, and that there are systems in place for its implementation and monitoring. The commissioning authorities must work towards improving links with providers, particularly in complex cases where a number of different providers may be involved. Because commissioning authorities control the funds used to provide the services, they are the main catalysts for change in the NHS. This means they have a considerable responsibility to monitor the effectiveness of treatments and services.

Action for Sick Children (formerly the National Association for the Welfare of Children in Hospital, NAWCH) supports and represents all sick children and their families. NAWCH drew up a document of rights for children which has now been adopted as the European *Charter for Children in Hospital*. It sets out a number of good practices, including the following:

- Children in hospital shall have the right to have their parents or parent substitute with them at all times;
- Accommodation should be offered to all parents, and they should be helped and encouraged to stay;
- Children and parents shall have the right to be informed in a manner appropriate to age and understanding. Steps should be taken to mitigate physical or emotional stress;
- Children and parents shall have the right to informed participation in all decisions involving their health care. Every child shall be protected from unnecessary medical treatment and investigation;
- Children should be cared for together with children who have the same developmental needs, and shall not be admitted to adult wards;
- Children shall have full opportunity for play, recreation and education suited to their age and condition, and shall be in an environment designed, furnished, staffed and equipped to meet their needs;
- Children shall be treated with tact and understanding, and their privacy shall be protected at all times.

In 1994, Action for Sick Children followed this initiative up with a document specifically on standards of care for children undergoing surgery.

activity

1 Role-play a situation in which hospital treatment is explained to a young child through play.

2 If possible, informally interview the parents of a child who has had a stay in hospital. For example, ask them:

   - Did they feel involved in the child's care?
   - Did information leaflets/notices in the ward encourage parents to stay?
   - Was there a *named* qualified nurse allocated to the child for the shift/entire stay?
   - If they were included in the care of the child, what did they think the purpose of this was? (e.g. to provide support and reassurance/to provide continuity of care/to substitute for a lack of staff.)

   You may find ideas for further questions in Table 8.1 below, and in the points from the *Charter for Children in Hospital* above.

3 If you have a period of work experience in a hospital, find out:

   - Does it have a written policy to ensure that requirements for child and family-centred care are understood by all those involved?
   - Is there a management team with:
     - a consultant with overall responsibility for policies for all children's services?

		Measurement (examples)			
Indicator	**Standard**	**Objective data**	**Child/parent view**	**Staff view**	**Auditor observation**
Overall responsibility for ward.	A consultant with overall responsibility.	Is there a consultant with overall responsibility?		Does it work – e.g. is there one consultant who can decide to close the ward in an infection alert?	
Encouragement and support of parents.	Encouraged and supported to participate in care.	Does it say so in information leaflet?	Do the parents feel 'part of the ward team'?	Can parents come and go as they please? Are parents present – e.g. when doctor takes blood?	Are parents staying? – especially parents of under 5s.
Nursing Responsibility.	One named nurse per patient.	Does it say so in information leaflet?	Do they know they have a named nurse?	Do nurses work to this policy? How does handover take place between shifts?	Is there a notice-board showing which nurse goes with which child?
Pain relief.	Pain-prevention guidelines in place.	Are there written guidelines?	Is the child/parent involved in discussions about pain relief?	Do nurses think children have different pain thresholds? How is this assessed?	Are there charts that could be used with young patients to assess pain?
Respect for privacy.	Blinds and screens are used in ward.	Do all beds, cubicles and bathrooms have blinds or screens?	Do parents close blinds/screens as they wish?	Do doctors and nurses use blinds/screens before examining a child?	Are there times when children are not given privacy?
Information.	Full range of 'high content' leaflets and posters.	Are leaflets readily available, e.g. in out-patient departments for elective admissions?	Has the child/parent received a general information leaflet about the ward?	Do staff ask children and parents what information they need?	Are leaflets and notices up to date, relevant and appropriate to the ward and age range?
Junior doctors.	Continuous cover by 'experienced' staff.	Assessment of medical rosters.		Ask nurses: how often is the consultant called in? Can junior doctors put up drips and take a lumbar puncture?	Are there regularly times when consultants are the only emergency cover above 'inexperienced' SHO grade?
RSCNs.	There should be at least 2 RSCNs on duty per shift.	Assessment of nursing rosters.		Ask senior nurse about RSCN recruitment and retention policy.	How many shifts have no RSCNs or only one on duty?
Ward sensitive to the needs of different ages.	Ward imposes no unnecessary rules on children.	Is there a play specialist?	Ask children: what are the best and worst things about the hospital?	Are children of similar ages put together?	Are a range of basic facilities available for babies, children and adolescents?
Facilities for parents.	No gaps in facilities.	Are parents able to: make tea or coffee, wash and shower?	Have parents suggested any improvements?	Are there sufficient facilities for all parents who want to stay?	Check facilities.

Table 8.1 Ten indicators for measuring the quality of care
Source: Audit Commission: 'Children first, a study of hospital services'

- a senior children's nurse above ward-sister level, to provide the focus for implementing consistent policies for the care of children in all parts of the hospital?

Use Table 8.1 to check other aspects of the quality of care.

4 The numbers of adolescents admitted under the care of paediatricians are increasing as the survival rates for adolescents with chronic illnesses, such as cystic fibrosis and cancer, continue to improve. There are also many adolescents admitted under the care of surgeons. It is recommended that separate facilities be provided for this group. What facilities do you think should be available?

5 Under the 'Appropriate hospitalisation' section on page 238 above, it was explained that children may be transferred to primary care which allows them to return home. Can you think of specific examples of the type of primary care which may be given? (See Appendix A for example of answers.)

Tertiary care

Tertiary care is specialised care, and is provided to children following a referral from a consultant paediatrician, surgeon or GP. Because of the very small numbers of children involved, it is normally provided not at a district general hospital but at a specialised centre.

The advantages of providing specialised care at large tertiary centres are that:

- it allows staff to see sufficient numbers of children to develop the necessary specialised skills
- there is good evidence that for the treatment of some cancers and for the intensive care of very-low-birth-weight babies, mortality is lower for children treated at tertiary centres than it is at general hospitals
- as a result of economies of scale, treatment of relatively rare conditions can be provided more efficiently

The disadvantages are that:

- children and families are more likely to have to travel long distances for treatment. This may lead to physical discomfort and high costs
- where there is shared care of a child between tertiary and secondary centres, there may be problems with communication and the provision of 'seamless care'
- specialist care in separate centres brings the threat that an overview of the 'whole' child will not be considered

To avoid the problems associated with children and parents travelling long distances, some specialists from tertiary centres have links with local hospitals to provide advice and to treat patients in out-patient clinics. In this way, tertiary centres should reach out to the whole population they serve.

To encourage the treatment of the 'whole' child and to avoid focusing only on the disorder itself, a 1993 review of the provision of tertiary care in London recommended that tertiary services for children be based only in hospitals that can provide a full range of child health services, i.e.:

- an A&E service with a separate admission space for children
- a paediatric medical service
- a paediatric surgical service
- maternity services with neonatal intensive care
- a children's intensive-care service (paediatric intensive care)

- children's support services, therapists, teachers, etc.
- a home nursing service, and a parent-care approach

Look at the list of areas of health-care specialities below. For each of these: describe what is meant by the term (see Appendix A for answers); find out about the current provision for children in your locality (e.g. is treatment provided at a secondary or tertiary centre? How far do they have to travel? Are any changes planned for the future?)

- cancer services
- cardiology and cardiothoracic services
- neurology and neurosurgery
- nephrology
- plastic surgery and burns
- neonatal and specialist paediatric surgery
- paediatric intensive care
- endocrinology
- gastroenterology
- haematology
- ear, nose and throat surgery
- opthalmology

Coordination of care

It was explained above that it is essential that the two branches of primary care be well coordinated to avoid duplication of care; to prevent patients falling between the two components of care; and to provide the patient with a 'seamless' service. For the same reasons, it is essential that the different *levels* of care – primary, secondary and tertiary – also be well-coordinated. Meeting the needs of children and their families should not be affected by artificial organisational barriers.

It has been agreed that the following guiding principles should underpin all child health services to ensure that they are effectively integrated:

- The role of each party is clear to the parents of children who use the service, as well as to the staff who provide the service
- Services are provided in a coordinated and consistent way
- Wasteful duplication and inefficient use of resources is avoided

NON-STATUTORY HEALTH PROVISION

Private health provision

In its broadest sense, private provision includes pharmaceuticals bought over the counter ('off-the-shelf products') and alternative medicine, as well as private treatment by doctors.

'Off-the-shelf products'

Commercial 'off-the-shelf' sales of medicines, drugs and appliances in chemists' shops or supermarkets (informal or self-care) have an estimated value of well over £1,000 million (see Figure 8.7). However, because children receive free prescriptions, the amount spent on medicines bought over the counter is proportionately less for under-16 year olds than is the amount spent on products for adults.

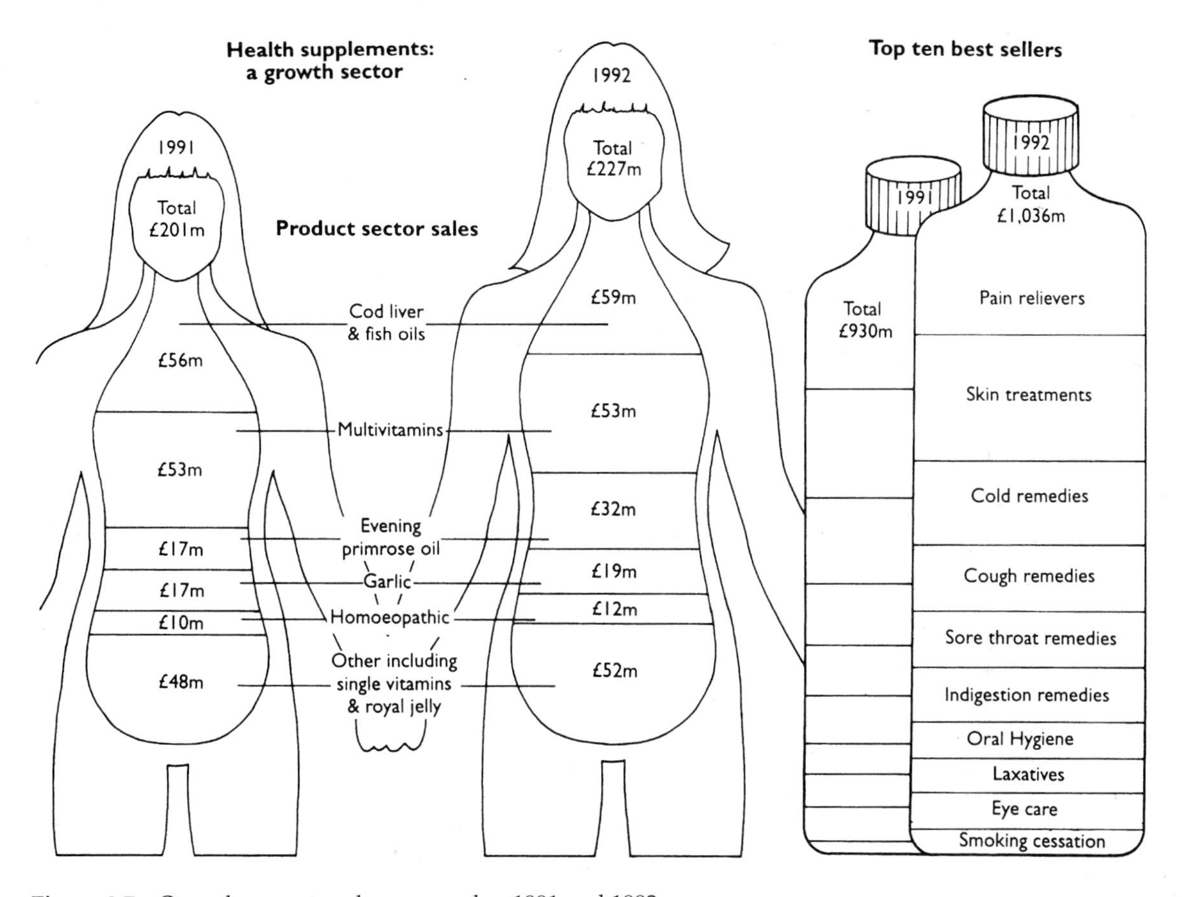

Figure 8.7 Over-the-counter pharmacy sales, 1991 and 1992

activity

Carry out a survey to compare the amount spent on 'off-the-shelf products' for children and adults. (NB: think carefully about confidentiality before carrying out your research.) What products (including health supplements such as vitamins) are bought for children, and why are they obtained in this way rather than by prescription? How do parents, or other carers, decide which products to buy?

Private treatment by doctors

Treatment in private general practices is rare because, under the terms of their NHS contract, GPs are prevented from treating their NHS patients privately. However, this is not the case with their hospital-consultant colleagues. 'Pay beds' may be reserved for the latters' private, fee-paying patients. Patients using 'pay beds' are generally in single rooms, and may be offered more attractive food than standard NHS food, but the treatment they are given will be the same as that given to an NHS patient. There are also about 200 private hospitals and nursing homes in the UK, but because of the number of elderly people in long-term care, the proportion of beds occupied by children is very small.

Frequently, private treatment is financed by insurance (over 70% of private hospital admissions are covered by insurance). There are many policies available which include all members of the family.

activity

1. Find advertisements for private health-care insurance schemes and compare the services offered.
   - How do the costs vary with the age of the insured and the number of family members?
   - Can you find examples of employers that provide health insurance for their employees and their families?
2. If possible, interview the parents of a child who has received hospital treatment privately. Compare the experiences of their child with a child having similar treatment in an NHS hospital.
   - Why did the parents choose private treatment?
   - Did it meet with their expectations?
3. Organise or role-play a debate on the motion: 'The private sector should play no part in the provision of health care to children.' Each side should be given time to prepare a list of the main advantages and disadvantages of the private sector.

Complementary medicine

Some areas of complementary medicine, such as osteopathy and chiropractic, are quite well established and are practised by well-trained professionals who provide treatment where orthodox medicine has often been weak. Other areas of complementary medicine are less widely accepted and less scientific.

There is no law controlling the qualifications of practising complementary therapists. This means that it can be difficult to choose a reputable therapist, although some organisations can give some guidance (for example, the Institute of Complementary Medicine and the Council for Complementary and Alternative Medicine: see the 'Useful addresses' section at the end of Chapter 9, page 288). An increasing number of GPs are now practising alternative therapies such as acupuncture and homeopathy.

activity

1. Have a 'brainstorming' session to list all the areas of complementary medicine you can think of.
2. Question parents who have used complementary medicine for the treatment of their children to find out:
   - why they chose complementary medicine
   - how they chose the therapist
   - how happy they were with their child's treatment

Independent voluntary health provision

A **voluntary organisation** is an association or society which has come into existence of its own accord; it has been created by its members rather than by the state. Within voluntary organisations, some workers are **salaried** (i.e. voluntary organisations are not staffed solely by volunteers). There are a substantial number of such bodies offering, for example, services, education, campaigns, fund-raising for specific diseases and problems, or types of health-care need. Many of them are self-help organisations set up by those experiencing, or affected by, particular illnesses or conditions.

Voluntary organisations may obtain their funds from central government (current funding totals approximately £24 billion); by selling services to purchasers in the NHS, local authorities, or privately; or through charitable funding. These organisations are sometimes classed as **'not-for-profit' organisations**. Not-for-profit organisations differ, however, from voluntary organisations in that:

- the boards that run them consist of *salaried members*
- they do not involve the giving of *voluntary effort* either in time or in money
- many are staffed by ex-local-authority personnel and provide services under contract to social-services departments

The term 'not-for-profit' originated in the USA, where it is used instead of 'voluntary sector'. The structure of not-for-profit organisations varies widely all over the UK, but it is a growth area within care organisations, and the services provided overlap with those of statutory, private and voluntary organisations.

activity

Below is a list from the *Voluntary Agencies Directory 1995/96* for voluntary organisations concerned with the health of children. (Refer to this publication for a list of addresses, and please remember to include an SAE if writing to voluntary organisations for information. See the 'References and resources' section at the end of Chapter 9, page 287.) Select one (or a few) organisations each, and find out about:

- the services provided (for example: are they a pressure group? Do they lobby for improvements/recognition of need?

Are they a provider of services not available through other routes?)
- if these services are also available from other agencies. And if so, is there evidence that the present organisation better meets the needs of its clients?
- the roles of salaried and volunteer staff
- staff training
- how the organisation is financed
- the history of the organisation

Action for Sick Children
Association for All Speech-Impaired Children
Association for Brain-Damaged Children and Young Adults
British Institute for Brain-Injured Children
Cancer and Leukaemia in Childhood Trust (UK)
Child Growth Foundation
Childhood Cancer and Leukaemia Link
Children's Head Injury Trust
Children's Liver Disease Foundation
Cystic Fibrosis Research Trust
Great Ormond Street Children's Hospital Fund
Heart Line Association
Hyperactive Children's Support Group
Malcolm Sargent Cancer Fund for Children
Research Trust for Metabolic Diseases in Children
Sick Children's Trust

Provision of Social Care

STATUTORY PROVISION

(See also the section 'The Children Act, 1989 – specific duties imposed on local authorities' on page 276 below.)

At the start of this chapter, it was explained that the Department of Health is responsible for the broad policy and central administration of welfare services, which are provided on a local level through the Personal Social Services (social work) Departments of local authorities. These local Social Services Departments provide caring services to improve the quality of life for, amongst others, children and young people and their families and carers, so they can live as independently and as safely as possible.

The services provided include:

- assessing needs
- providing personal help
- social work
- day-care facilities
- residential and respite care facilities
- occupational therapy (OT)
- rehabilitation
- supplying specialist equipment
- an emergency service, 24 hours a day, 365 days a year

activity

Write a paragraph to demonstrate that you understand what is meant by each of the services listed above. For example, what are respite care, occupational therapy and rehabilitation?
(See Appendix A for answers.)

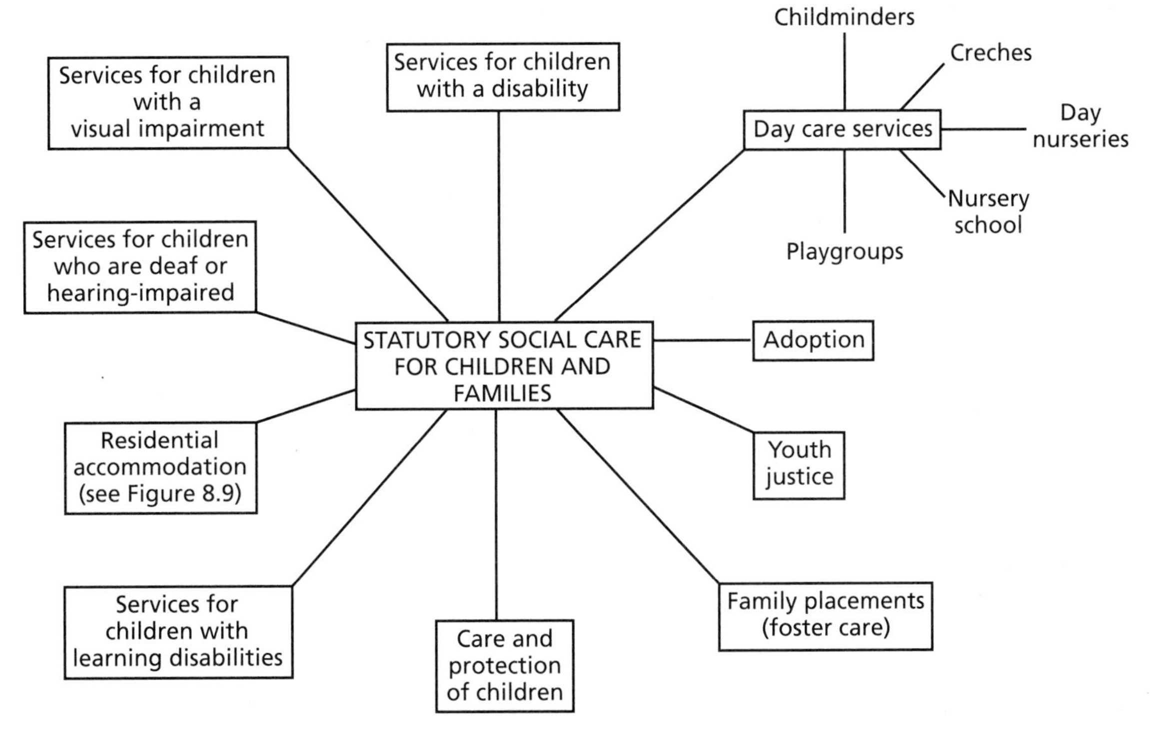

Figure 8.8 A summary of statutory social care for children and families

These services may be provided directly by Social Service Departments, or, increasingly, they are provided in partnership with voluntary organisations or purchased from the private and other independent-sector providers (see page 255 below). Social Services Departments are also responsible for regulating the provision of day care for children by voluntary and private organisations, and of residential care by private organisations.

The Children Act 1989 (see Chapter 9, page 275 below) has had a considerable impact on the provision of social care for children.

Students are referred to the *Guide to the Social Services 1996* from which the following summary of the role of Social Services Departments in the care of children is largely drawn. (See the 'References and resources' section at the end of Chapter 9, page 287.)

Care and protection of children

Where children may be at risk of harm, the social services will work in cooperation with the other agencies concerned – the police, family doctors, health authorities, education departments and local voluntary organisations. Depending on the particular case, they may then be required to, for example, take a child into care or to provide a supervisor to 'advise, assist and befriend the supervised child'. (See the 'Provision for the protection of children' section in Chapter 9 on page 282 for more information.)

Day-care services and childminding

Anyone who acts as a **childminder** at home, or who provides day care for children under 8 years old on premises that are not domestic premises, must be registered and then inspected and registered annually by the local authorities. The local authorities will specify certain standards. For example:

- The number of children who can be cared for is limited
- Where appropriate, a ratio of staff will be specified
- The premises must be suitable for child care
- A childminder and people resident in the childminder's house must be fit to be in charge of, or in proximity to, children under 8
- Records must be maintained, and notification given of changes

Day-care registration covers services such as day nurseries, nursery schools, creches and some playgroups. The local authority keeps a register of childminders and day-care providers.

Family placements (fostering)

The Children Act 1989 states that the local authority must make arrangements which enable children to live with their family, unless this would harm the child's welfare. Where care with the family is not possible, the preferred option is to place children with an alternative family. These arrangements should take place as part of a **care plan**.

The authorities must be satisfied, when making such a placement, that the child's needs and wishes are met, such as those arising from racial origin and cultural and linguistic background. Where possible, the religious background will also be considered.

Foster carers may be approved by either a local authority or an approved voluntary organisation. Foster carers may be approved for a particular named child or for a particular number and age range of children, or for placements of a particular kind, or in particular circumstances. A foster household is normally limited to 3 children, although exemption may be given to allow siblings to stay together. If carers wish to care for more than three children, they should register as a **children's home**. Approval must be reviewed annually. To approve foster carers, the authority must:

- take account of the carer's ability to work with children of different religious, linguistic and cultural backgrounds
- make a compulsory check on criminal records
- obtain a medical record
- check that carers are willing to help the child maintain contact with the natural family

Local authorities are required to keep a register of foster carers in the area, and to keep records of the children placed with them.

Residential accommodation

Figure 8.9 summarises the **residential accommodation** for which the Social Services Department of the local authority has at least some responsibility.

Community homes

These are provided by local authorities or voluntary organisations for residential care of children. They are covered by the Children Act 1989 and the Children's

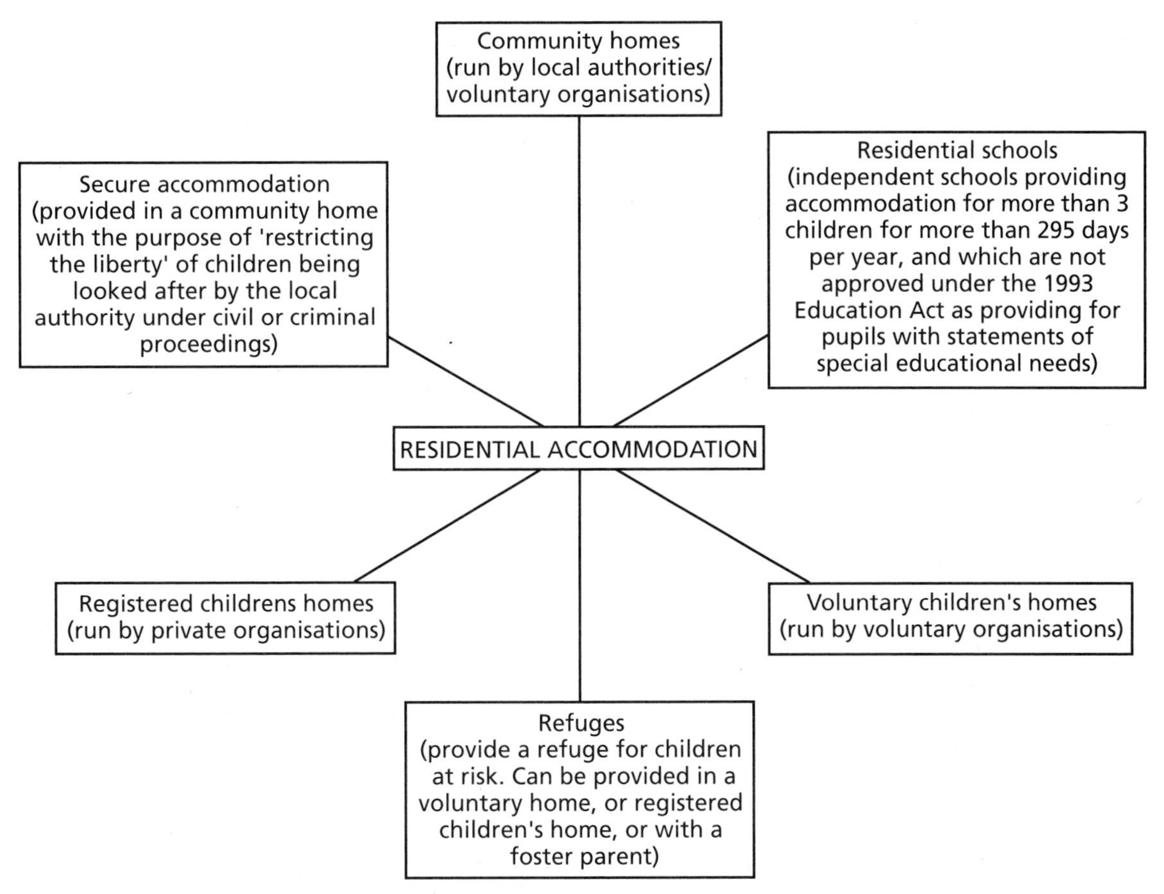

Figure 8.9 Residential accommodation for children

Homes Regulation 1991. These regulations cover:

- the facilities for visiting children
- the records which must be kept
- the control and discipline methods which cannot be used
- health and safety matters
- some aspects of care

Community homes must be visited at least once a month, and a written report, again once a month, made by a responsible manager from the organisation running them.

Registered children's homes

These are run by private organisations, but if they provide care for 4 or more children, they must be registered with the local authority. These homes are also covered by the Children's Homes Regulations 1991, and the proprietors, managers and premises must all be approved by the local authority. An inspection is carried out twice a year. Children must be able to give their comments and complaints about their care to an independent person.

Voluntary children's homes

These homes are run by voluntary organisations and are also subject to the Children's Homes Regulations 1991. They are registered with the Secretary of State for Health, and are subject to inspection by the Social Services Inspectorate. Under the Children Act 1989, local authorities have to ensure that the voluntary organisations are 'safeguarding and promoting' the welfare of children accommodated by them.

Residential schools

Only those schools which provide accommodation for more than 3 children and for more than 295 days a year, and which are not approved under the 1993 Education Act as providing for pupils with statements of special educational needs, are required to be registered as children's homes. Other independent boarding schools, although not registered by the local authority, must still be inspected. The purpose of this inspection is not to monitor the educational standard but to ensure that the welfare of the children is adequately safeguarded and promoted.

Secure accommodation

This means accommodation in a community home which is provided for the purpose of 'restricting the liberty' of children. There are two quite different homes of **secure accommodation**: that which may be provided for children who are being looked after, and that which constitutes a form of criminal detention (see the 'Criminal Justice Acts' section in Chapter 9 on page 279 below). It must be approved by the Secretary of State as secure, and no child under 13 must be placed in secure accommodation without the permission of this official. Usually, children may not be placed in this type of accommodation unless:

- they have a history of absconding, and are likely to suffer significant harm if they continue to do so
- they are likely to injure themselves or others

Additionally, the following restrictions apply to the placing of children in secure accommodation:

- No child must be kept in secure accommodation for more than 72 hours in total in any period of 28 days without the authority of a court.
- A **court order** may initially authorise the use of secure accommodation for a maximum of only 3 months, and after this for a maximum of 6 months at a time
- The local authority must appoint 3 people, one of whom must not be employed by the authority, to review the holding of a child in secure accommodation in a community home
- The first review must take place within 1 month of the placement, with subsequent reviews at not less than 3-monthly intervals

Refuges

These provide a refuge for children at risk, and can be provided in a voluntary home or a registered children's home, or with a foster parent. **Refuges** have to be issued with a certificate from the Secretary of State.

Adoption

The law relating to **adoption** (Adoption Act 1976 and Children Act 1989) is complex, so only a brief summary of the main points is given here:

- An **adoption order** transfers all the responsibilities of parents to the adopter(s)
- Adoption orders cannot be reversed, unless set aside on appeal, by legislation or by readoption
- A child who is under 18 and not mar-

ried may be placed for adoption by an approved adoption society, a local authority or a parent or guardian

- An adopter must be:
  - at least 21
  - resident in the UK
  - able to meet the criteria of the relevant adoption agency or local authority
- If parental agreement is denied, parental responsibility must be transferred by court order to an adoption agency
- The child will be freed for adoption without parental agreement if the parent:
  - cannot be found, or is incapable of giving agreement
  - is withholding agreement unreasonably
  - has persistently failed, without reasonable cause, to 'discharge parental duties in relation to the child'
  - has abandoned or neglected the child
  - has persistently or seriously ill-treated the child
- Similar standards and safeguards operate with children adopted from abroad

activity

1 There have been many recent changes in local government structure. Use your local library to find out about the structure of local government in your area, and then produce a poster explaining the system. (NB: there may be more than one tier – e.g. county and district and even parish councils.) Show how many representatives there are on each council, and how they are elected.

2 There have been a series of revelations concerning the abuse of children in residential accommodation. Look back over some of these cases (if possible, using a *Times*, *Guardian* or *Independent* CD-ROM). Summarise the lessons which can be learnt from these tragic cases, and suggest possible improvements to the management and day-to-day running of these homes.

3 Anyone over the age of 18 has the right to obtain a copy of their original birth certification which will allow them to know the names of their natural parents and their addresses at the time of the birth. However, before this information is provided, counselling by the local authority is compulsory for those adopted before 12 November 1975, and is offered to those adopted after this date. An Adoption Contact Register enables adopted children and their parents to be put in touch with each other.

Discuss the problems that may arise as a result of relatives tracing one another.

4 What particular problems do you think there may be in fostering:

- young babies
- teenagers?

What do you think a fosterer may gain from the arrangement?

5 List the differences between fostering and adoption.
(See Appendix A for answers.)

Services for children with disabilities

All Social Services Departments are required by the Children Act 1989 to set up and maintain a confidential register of children with disabilities. Children and young people who require special services because of an identified disability are eligible for registration, and such registration is voluntary. 'Disability' may include a physical disability, a hearing impairment, a visual impairment or learning or communication difficulties. This register helps the local authority to plan and provide the necessary services, in cooperation with the Education Department, the District Health Authority and voluntary organisations.

The services provided can be divided into those services designed to help disabled children live with their family as independently as possible in the community, and those which provide residential care (see page 248 above).

Community-based services

In accordance with the Chronically Sick and Disabled Persons Act 1970 and the Community Care Act 1990, if the local authority is satisfied that a person has any of the following needs, they must be provided with them, or assistance must be given in obtaining them:

- practical assistance in the home
- radio, television, library or similar recreational facilities
- games, outings or other recreational facilities outside the home
- travel to use specialist facilities
- adaptation in the home for greater safety, comfort or convenience
- holidays

In reality, provision varies between local authorities.

The local authority also has the discretion to levy any charges it considers reasonable.

activity

To find out what services are provided in your particular area for disabled children, you could contact the relevant Social Services Department; the Citizens' Advice Bureau; or your local disability association or advice service.

Services for children with a visual impairment

Social Services Departments are responsible for compiling registers of blind and partially sighted people in a particular area. As with the disability register, registration is voluntary. Social Service Departments are also responsible for the coordination of the provision of statutory and voluntary services to help people with a visual impairment. Many local authorities employ staff who are specialists in working with people with a visual impairment, such as **mobility and rehabilitation officers**. Some local authorities use local societies for people with a visual impairment as their agents for delivering services.

activity

Find out if your local authority employs specialist staff to work with people with a visual impairment. If they do, and if there is an opportunity to meet these staff, write a description of the work done by these professionals.

Services for children who are deaf or hearing-impaired

Most local authorities, or voluntary organisations acting as their agents, employ staff specially qualified to work with people with a hearing impairment. These staff provide support for the person with a hearing impairment and their family, and provide information about local and national services.

activity

Find out what provision is made by your local Social Services Department for children who are deaf or hearing impaired.

Services for children with a learning disability

(See also the 'Special education' section on page 259 below.)

Local authorities, or voluntary or private organisations acting on their behalf, provide residential services for children needing such care. Residential respite care will also be available to give carers a break from their responsibilities. Some local authorities recruit and train families to provide either permanent or short-term care for children with learning difficulties in a family setting.

Social security

The Department of Health is not the only government department concerned with social-care provision. The Department of Social Security (DSS) also plays a major role. This department is responsible for the national administration of **social security**, and has regional and local offices.

The benefits which all children and their families are entitled to include the following:

- free dental treatment and prescriptions
- free sight tests and vouchers for glasses
- child benefit

Depending on circumstances, the following benefits may also be available:

- one-parent benefit
- family credit
- income support
- free milk and vitamins
- Disability Working Allowance
- Disability Living Allowance
- unemployment benefit
- Home Responsibilities Protection
- Invalid Care Allowance
- Severe Disablement Allowance

- Attendance Allowance
- hospital travel costs
- Widowed Mother's Allowance
- housing benefit
- council tax benefit
- payments or loans from the Social Fund

activity

Choose one or more of the benefits listed above and find out:

- who can get it
- how much they can get
- how to claim

This information can be found in leaflets such as FB 8, FB 27, FB 31 and FC 10, which can be obtained from your local Social Security office, or Citizens' Advice Bureau.

NON-STATUTORY PROVISION

Local authorities

It is usually assumed that **local authorities** provide only statutory care (i.e. care they are required to provide by law). However, they also provide some non-statutory care. For example, many local authorities provide training for childminders.

activity

Find examples of non-statutory care provided by your local authority. What impact has funding had on this type of care in recent years?

Private provision

Some social care is delivered through **private provision**. For example, local authorities may pay for children to be cared for in private community homes or, more widely, to be privately fostered. Private day nurseries and childminding are further examples of private care for children.

Although privately run as profit-making schemes, these arrangements are regulated by Acts of Parliament, and they have to be registered and inspected by the local authority (see page 248 above).

activity

1 Find out what private provision for children is available in your locality.
2 What links with the local authority do these private establishments have?
3 What do you consider to be the advantages and disadvantages of the private provision of social care for children?
4 Compare the cost of private day nurs-

eries with state day nurseries in your area, and the number of places provided by each type of provision. How are the places allocated in each type of nursery?

Independent voluntary provision

The provision of social care to children by voluntary bodies, charities and volunteers is considerable. Organisations here may be pressure groups aiming to bring about changes in statutory care, or they may directly provide care to clients. Most organisations combine these two functions. Increasingly, local-authority Social Services Departments are contracting out some of their services to local voluntary organisations (see the 'Statutory provision' section above).

activity

1. What do you think are the advantages and disadvantages of voluntary organisations and volunteers providing social care, compared with statutory and private provision?
2. What voluntary provision is there for children in your locality? To what extent does the local authority use such voluntary bodies as agents to provide statutory services?
3. For the voluntary organisations involved, find out about:
   - the services they provide
   - the roles of salaries and volunteer staff
   - how they are financed
   - the history of the organisations
4. Below is a list from the *Voluntary Agencies Directory 1995/6* of voluntary organisations concerned with the care of children. (Refer to this publication for a list of addresses (see the 'References and resources' section at the end of Chapter 9), and please remember to include a large SAE if writing to voluntary organisations to request information.) Select one (or a few) organisations each, and find out about:
   - the services provided (e.g. are they a pressure group? Are they a provider of services which are not available through other routes? Are they agents for the local authority?)
   - if these services are also available from other agencies, and if so, is there evidence that the selected organisations better meet the needs of their clients?
   - the roles of the salaried and volunteer staff
   - staff training
   - how the organisations are financed
   - the history of the organisations

Children/child care

Barnardo's
Boys' and Girls' Welfare Society
Careline
Child Accident Prevention Trust
Child Poverty Action Group
Children's Country Holidays Fund
Children's Society
Day Care Trust/National Childcare Campaign Ltd

Kids' Clubs Network
National Association for Children of Alcoholics
National Childminding Association
National Children's Bureau
National Council of Voluntary Child Care Organisations
Salvation Army
Save the Children
Working for Childcare

Child abuse
ChildLine
Kidscape Campaign for Children's Safety
Lifeline – Help for Victims of Violence in the Home, Sexual Abuse and Incest
National Society for the Prevention of Cruelty to Children
NCH Action for Children

Disabled children
Contact a Family
Council for Disabled Children
HAPA – Adventure Play for Children with Disabilities and Special Needs
National Association of Toy and Leisure Libraries – Play Matters
STEPS – National Association for Children with Congenital Abnormalities
VIEW – Association for the Education and Welfare of the Visually Impaired

5 It has been suggested by people that charities, particularly those concerning children, create images which encourage people to pity disabled people rather than to value them. Using examples, to what extent do you agree or disagree with this point of view?

Informal provision

Much of the care of children is organised on an informal basis. For example, many friends, neighbours and relatives, such as siblings or grandparents, are involved in either paid or unpaid childminding. Even parental care is sometimes classed as **informal provision**. There are also informal groups, such as parent and toddler groups organised by neighbours.

There are many national and local groups concerned with offering support to informal carers:

- Official statistics show that there are 500,000 children with special needs and disabilities, almost all of them living at home with their families. Local authorities and voluntary organisations may provide **respite care** for the carers of these children. This may involve the child going into temporary residential care, or it may simply mean that the child is taken out for a few hours by a trained volunteer.
- Organisations may provide **advice** – e.g. the National Council for One Parent Families (see the 'Useful addresses' section at the end of Chapter 9, page 288).
- Organisations may provide **support**. For example, they may help carers get together for mutual support, friendship and social activities. For example, Contact a Family (see again the above-mentioned 'Useful addresses' section) provides support for families who care for children with disabilities and special needs.
- Organisations may act as **pressure groups** by working towards influencing policy-makers and planners of services and increasing awareness of the problems faced by informal carers. For example, the Carers National Association campaigns for and represents all carers (see again the above-mentioned 'Useful addresses' section).
- Organisations may provide **training** for carers.

activity

1 Produce a questionnaire aimed at working mothers. Use it to assess how much they rely on the informal provision of child care. If their children are usually cared for under a formal arrangement, e.g. by a registered childminder or at a nursery, what happens when the child is ill?
2 Interview at least one person who regularly baby-sits on an informal basis (this may be paid or unpaid). What problems have they faced with either the child or the parent – or both? How have they overcome these problems?
3 Find out what organisations there are in your area to provide support to informal carers. Choose one of these organisations and design a poster to publicise the services they provide.
4 Find out if there is a scheme in your area in which volunteers care for children with special needs for a few hours each week. If possible, interview such a volunteer to find out about both their training and the benefits to them, to the child and to the child's family.

Provision of Education

Public provision (maintained sector)

In England, the Department of Education and Employment is the central government department responsible for education. In Wales, this is overseen by the Secretary of State for Wales, and in Scotland, which has a different educational system from England and Wales, it is overseen by the Secretary of State for Scotland.

On a local level, education is organised by the Education Department of the relevant local authority.

Pre-school education

For the under-5s, it is difficult to separate education and day care. Tables 8.2 and 8.3 show the main types of early care and education provision in England and the UK, and the main differences between them. (The tables also contain information on private provision – see pages 262–63 below.)

Local education authority state nurseries

The compulsory school age is from 5 to 16 years old. However, local education authorities currently provide, on a non-statutory basis, nurseries giving education to children below school age. These are not provided primarily for children with social problems, but because the number of places are limited, priority may be given to such children. Day nurseries and children's centres offer full-time provision.

Nursery classes

A **nursery class** is attached to a primary school. A child will usually attend for half days, at least to start with.

Type of provision in England, 1991	Number of places	Changes in number of places since 1980
Nursery education schools and classes	177,863	Increased by $\frac{1}{3}$
Reception classes	272,178	Increased by $\frac{1}{3}$
Local authority day nurseries	27,039	Down by 5%
Private nurseries	79,029	More than trebled
Pre-school (formerly playgroups)	428,420	Increased by $\frac{1}{6}$
Childminders	233,258	More than doubled

Table 8.2 Early care and education provision in England, 1991
Source: Bruce and Meggitt (1996)
These figures are based on those given by Peter Moss in the RSA Start Right Report, 1994.

Nursery units

These are also attached to a primary school, but in a separate building and with a separate coordinator, although, as above, they will come under the management of the primary-school head teacher.

Family centres

These are jointly funded by the Education, Social Services and Health Departments. The provision they offer is as much for parents as for children. **Family centres** are staffed by a multi-professional team, including teachers, nursery nurses, social workers and health visitors.

Nursery vouchers

From April 1997, all parents of 4 year olds will receive a voucher for £1,100 which can be exchanged at validated institutions for three terms of pre-school education. These institutions may be provided by the local authority or by the private or voluntary sectors (see page 262 below). In the former types of institution, the vouchers will cover the complete cost, but in the latter types of institution, parents will be able to 'top up' the vouchers if necessary. This voucher scheme began in four volunteer authorities in 1996, and the House of Lords has voted that the scheme should not be extended until these pilot schemes have been evaluated. Critics of the scheme point out that 93% of 4 year olds already had a nursery place before the vouchers were introduced; that the scheme may jeopardise the places currently taken by 3 year olds; and that most of the cost of the scheme is clawed back from what local authorities already spend on 4 year olds. The main political parties have both pledged to extend the voucher scheme for pre-school education to 3 year olds, although the means by which this will be paid for have not been identified.

Primary education

Primary schools may take children from 5 to 11 years old, or they may be split into infant schools (5–7 years) and junior schools (8–11 years). Increasingly, primary schools may also contain nursery classes for children under 5 (see page 257 above).

Secondary education

In most cases, children transfer to a **secondary school** at age 11. However, in some cases they may attend a 'middle' school from the age of 8–13. Most local authorities have comprehensive education, but a few still have a system of grammar and secondary modern schools.

Special education

Under the 1993 Education Act, governing bodies of all maintained schools are 'under a duty to use their best endeavours to ensure that appropriate provision is made to meet a child's special educational needs'. Local authorities are responsible for identifying children whose needs are not being met by mainstream schools. Every effort should be made to identify special needs as early as possible, and to keep a close working relationship with the parents.

Special education for children with learning difficulties may be provided in a number of ways:

- Where appropriate, practicable and in accordance with the wishes of the parents, children with special needs are educated in mainstream schools. Extra staff and necessary services and resources will be made available.
- Children may attend a special school.
- Children may attend a special unit attached to a mainstream school or hospital.

activity

1 Find out the following about primary schools in your area:
   - What nursery provision do they have?
   - At what age do children start their compulsory education?
   - What steps are taken to integrate young children into the school? For example, are visits organised? Do they start off with half days?
   - Is any after-school care provided?
   - What steps are taken to help children with the transition to their next school?

2 If possible, interview children of different ages and ask them what they like and dislike about their school.

3 (a) The 1988 Education Reform Act introduced the National Curriculum into state-maintained schools. Interview a primary-school teacher to find out what core subjects and what foundation subjects have to be covered.
   (b) The Act also requires that state-maintained schools provide a daily act of collective worship for all pupils except those withdrawn by their parents. Find out what form this act of worship takes.

4 Children are tested at 7, 11 and 14, and there are plans to introduce testing for 5

Provision	Time spent	Age of child	% of children	Cost for the family
EDUCATION				
Pre-preparatory schools, private nursery and other schools	Usually about 9 am–3.30 pm	2½–4	3–5%	The fees vary
Reception classes in primary schools	9 am–3.30 pm during the school termtime	4	21%	Free
Local education authority nursery schools and classes	Usually morning or afternoon sessions, but some are full time. During the school termtime	3–4	26%	Free
Pre-schools (formerly known as playgroups)	Two or three sessions a week, usually. Sessions are usually 2½ hours. Some are full time.	2½–4	60%	£1.70 or more per session
CARE				
Local authority day nurseries, children's centres, family centres	Some sessions are part time. Some are all day	0–4 (only a few children are 0–2)	1%	This is means tested
Childminders	Usually all day	0–4	7%	They vary between £1.50 and £50/week
Workplace nurseries, partnership programmes and private day nurseries	Usually all day, but there is variation	0–4	2.5%	This ranges between £45 and £150 each week. Some places are subsidised
COMBINED				
Combined nursery centres	Part time or all day	0–4	50 centres approximately	Although education places are free, day care is means tested
Family centres	Part time or all day	Usually 0–4, but there is variation	500 centres approximately	These vary
Holiday schemes and extended hours schemes, clubs and out-of-school clubs	During the school holidays. Before and after school	A wide range	700	These vary

Table 8.3 Provision of care and education services in the UK
Source: Bruce and Meggitt (1996)

Who makes the provision?	Who are the staff?	Qualifications of staff	Adult: child ratios
Commercial organisations, private individuals	Not specified, but often NNEB	Not known	3–4 yrs 1:8 5+ 1:20/30
Local education authority	Primary teachers. Sometimes a teaching assistant or a nursery nurse	Degree and PGCE/ BEd/BA (QTS) NNEB, GNVQ, SNNB, SCOTVEC, NVQ	1:30/40 (1:15/20 if a trained nursery nurse is employed)
Local education authority	Nursery teachers Nursery nurses	Degree and PGCE/ BEd/BA/(QTS) NNEB, BTEC, SNNB, SCOTVEC, NVQ	3–4 years 1:10/13
Parents and voluntary groups	Playgroup leader	Diploma in pre-school practice	3–5 yrs 1:8
Local authority social services	Mostly nursery nurses	NNEB, DPQS, GNVQ, SNNB, SCOTVEC, NVQ	0–2 yrs 1:3 2–3 yrs 1:4 3–5 yrs 1:8
Private arrangement	Registered childminder	No national requirements	0–5 yrs 1:3 5–7 yrs 1:6
Private individuals, organisations/employers	Some staff are untrained. Some nursery nurses	50% of the staff must be trained	0–2 yrs 1:3 2–3 yrs 1:4 3–4 yrs 1:8
Local authority education and social services usually, but sometimes voluntary organisations and health authorities	Nursery teachers Nursery nurses	Degree and PGCE/ BEd/BA (QTS) NNEB, GNVQ, SNNB, SCOTVEC, NVQ	1:10/13
Local authority social services, health authorities, voluntary organisations	Nursery nurses, social workers, health visitors, wide range of staff	Very varied	This varies, and depends on the kind of work in the centre
Schools, voluntary organisations, Departments of Leisure	Volunteers, community workers, playleaders	Not known	5–7 yrs 1:8

year olds. Talk to teachers, parents and children to find out their views on these tests.

5 Find out about the role of **Education Welfare Officers** (also known as **Education Social Workers**).

6 List what you consider to be the advantages and disadvantages of educating a child with special educational needs in a mainstream school compared with a special school.

VOLUNTARY AND PRIVATE PROVISION

Pre-school education

(See again Tables 8.2 and 8.3.)

The contribution of voluntary and private provision is particularly significant in pre-school education. However, under the Children Act 1989, these are subject to local-authority inspections and regulations. Voluntary organisations also play an important role in campaigning for better pre-school education (see the 'Useful addresses' section at the end of Chapter 9, page 288).

Voluntary provision

Charitable trusts offer education and care to children and their families. Examples include Barnardos, RNIB and SCOPE. This provision may be in the form of **community nurseries** and **parents and toddler groups**, or it may be home-based.

Pre-schools (previously known as **playgroups**) are usually organised and run by parents. Provision is usually for 2 or 3 half days a week, and a small charge is made.

Private provision

Private day nurseries, **private nursery schools**, **preparatory schools** and **kindergartens** all offer care and education. There are also a few **workplace nurseries** which offer subsidised places to children of their staff.

activity

In your area, compare the number of places available to pre-school children in the maintained sector with the number available in the private sector.

School education

In education, as in health and social care, there are many cases in which state, voluntary and private provision overlap, as illustrated by the following types of school.

Voluntary schools

These are usually **denominational** (e.g. Catholic or Church of England). The voluntary body and the local education authority usually share the costs.

Grant-maintained schools

These are schools which have voted to receive a grant from the Secretary of State rather than funding from the local education authority.

City technology colleges

Industrial and commercial sponsors contribute significantly to the setting-up of these colleges, and are then represented on the governing body. They provide education for 11–18 year olds.

Independent schools

These are outside the state system, and they charge fees. Many have **private endowments** and **scholarship funds**. They must be registered with the Department of Education and Employment, which can inspect them. Some **independent schools** provide assisted places which are paid for in part by the Department of Education.

activity

Interview parents to find out what factors contributed to their selection of schools for their children.

Interaction of Agencies

(See also the 'Coordination of care' section on page 242 above.)

There is considerable overlap in the services provided for the health care, social care and education of children. In some cases, this overlap is well-organised. For example, in the provision of School Health Services there is an important link between health care and education; and Education Welfare Officers play an important part in the link between education and social care. However, as the first extract on page 264 illustrates, the links between the various agencies providing different aspects of care for children are often not adequate.

activity

1 List the five services mentioned in the article which have some responsibility for the welfare of children.
2 What suggestions would you make to improve the links between agencies?
3 Read Kelly and Martin's story on p. 264. What services may be provided, and with which agencies will the social worker have to coordinate her work? (See Appendix A for answers.)

Resourcing of services

There are four main sources of funding for health and social care. These are:

1 central government
2 local government
3 registered charities
4 private funding.

For too long social services departments, which hold the lead responsibility for working with children in need, have been left to operate in isolation. Other services, including education and housing, the NHS and the voluntary sector, ought to be part of the action. Not surprisingly, many children's services provided by social services departments have been unable to respond adequately to children's needs.

The children looked after by social services departments often suffer from psychological problems, sometimes involving significant psychiatric illness. It is still not uncommon, though, to find that social workers in residential homes are left on their own to deal with very damaged children, with no help from health professionals. Similar difficulties exist for social services departments in obtaining adequate teaching services for looked-after children, even though these children are in law the corporate responsibility of local authorities.

(The Guardian, 6 December 1995)

Kelly and Martin's Story

Kelly is 4 and Martin is 18 months old. Their father, Mike, was made redundant a year ago and, just recently, the mortgage on the family home was foreclosed and the family made homeless.

For six weeks now they have been living in a one-bedroom flat on the tenth floor of a dilapidated tower block. The flat is cramped and damp, with mould growing on the walls. The kitchen is infested with cockroaches and the electricity supply has been cut off for non-payment.

Their mother, Kaye, is suffering with severe depression, and she and Mike have been having serious arguments. Mike has moved out to live with his brother. Kaye is finding it impossible to cope with the two children on her own. She asks for help from her health visitor. She is especially worried as Martin has become very sickly. She finds it very difficult to leave the flat to go shopping as the lift often does not work.

The health visitor contacts social services. Martin and Kelly are identified as children in need. This places the local authority under an obligation to arrange welfare services for the family.

(Stainton Rogers and Roche 1994)

Central government

The money available for public expenditure comes from:

- taxes
- National Insurance contributions (paid by employees, the self-employed and employers – in fact, a form of taxation)
- charges (direct payment by client, e.g. rents, health-service charges etc.; see Table 8.4)
- government borrowing

Figure 8.10 shows the relative importance of these as sources of NHS funding.

Services	Charges (£m)							
	1981	1985	1986	1987	1988	1989	1990	1991
All services	524	808	930	925	1,020	1,072	1,441	1,606
Hospital	54	78	86	91	97	107	399	471
Pharmaceutical	71	122	128	170	167	203	191	206
General dental	92	171	195	223	240	291	367	335
General ophthalmic	29	44	12	1	–	–	–	–
Personal social services	277	393	509	440	516	471	484	544

Table 8.4 National health and personal social services in England: charges to persons using the services (years ended 31 March)
Source: HMSO

activity

1 Discuss within your group to what extent services should be resourced by the individual who needs the service, and to what extent services should be resourced by the nation through the taxation system.
2 Discuss what charges may be made by each of the five services listed in Table 8.4. What is provided free to all users?
3 Where possible, find out the amount individuals may be asked to pay (for example, current prescription charges).
4 What exemptions are made for children?
5 If possible, interview a professional from each of the five areas to help you check your findings.
6 In 1995/96, the National Health Service spent nearly £41 billion providing health-care services for around 58 million people in the UK. From this, calculate the amount spent per person.

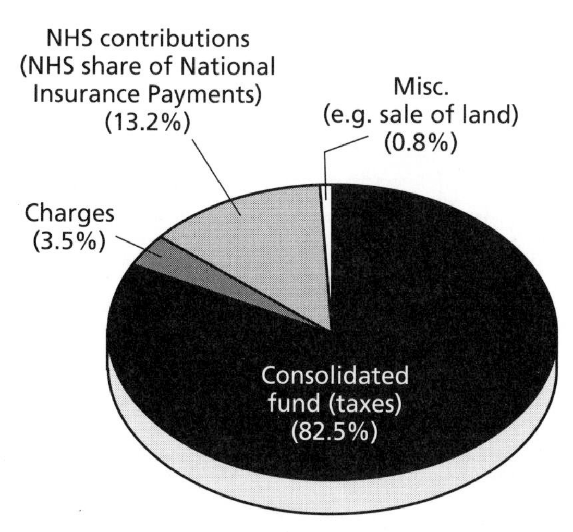

Figure 8.10 Sources of NHS funding in 1993/94

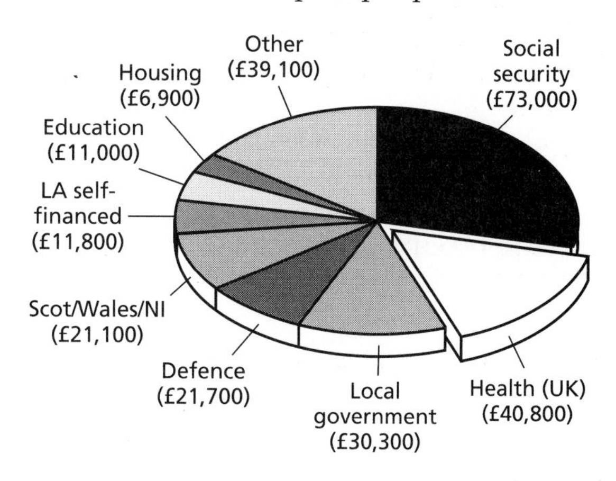

Figure 8.11 National shares of public spending 1995/96

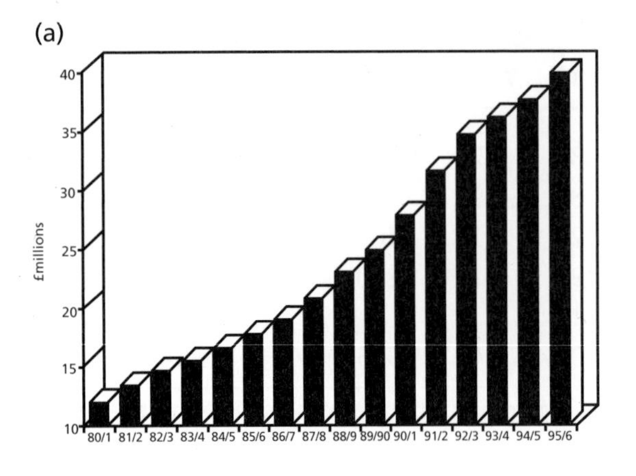

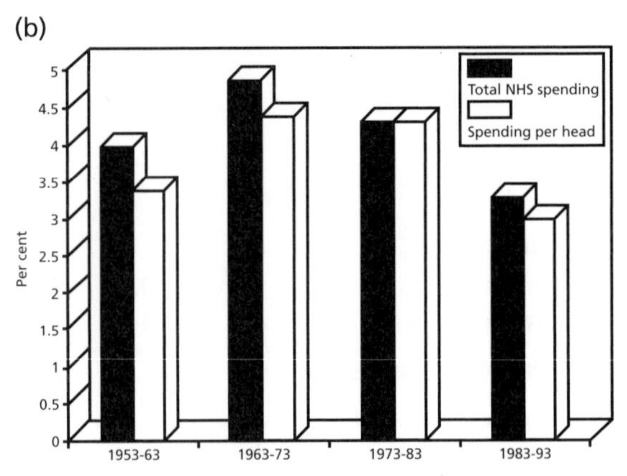

Figure 8.12 (a) Total UK NHS spending (cash terms) 1980–96 (b) Average annual real UK NHS spending 1953–93 (adjusted for inflation)

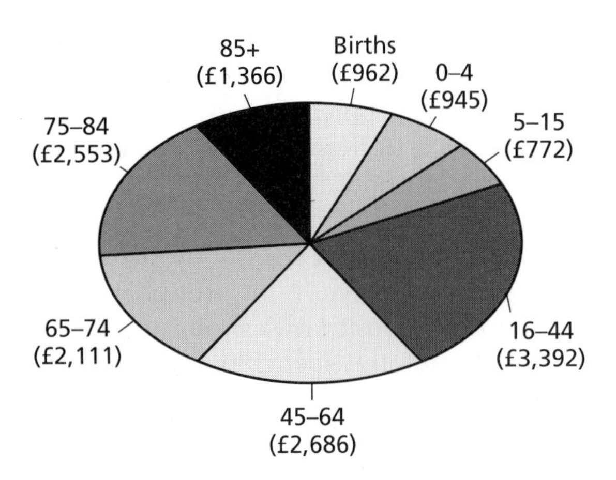

Figure 8.13 English hospital and community health services spending by age group: 1990/91

7 Figure 8.11 shows the national shares of public spending. Calculate the percentage of total spending which goes on:

- health
- social security
- education

8 Figure 8.12 shows the changes in UK NHS spending in cash terms and real terms (i.e. adjusted for inflation). Explain in words how spending has changed over the periods shown.

9 From Figure 8.13, calculate the percentage of spending on hospital and Community Health Services that is on children (i.e. under 16s).
(See Appendix A for answers.)

Figure 8.14 shows the sources of revenue and the main categories of expenditure. Figure 8.15 shows how finance flows from central government down to health and social-care services.

Local government

Local authorities obtain their funds from council tax (previously poll tax or community charge and, before that, rates) and grants from central government.

These grants are weighted, depending on the needs within the local authorities. Financial penalties are imposed on local authorities which overspend.

activity

Discuss the arguments for and against local freedom in collecting taxes and managing services. Compile a list of each.

REGISTERED CHARITIES

In the UK there are at present 175,000 **registered charities**, and this number is continually growing. Central government contributes a great deal to charities:

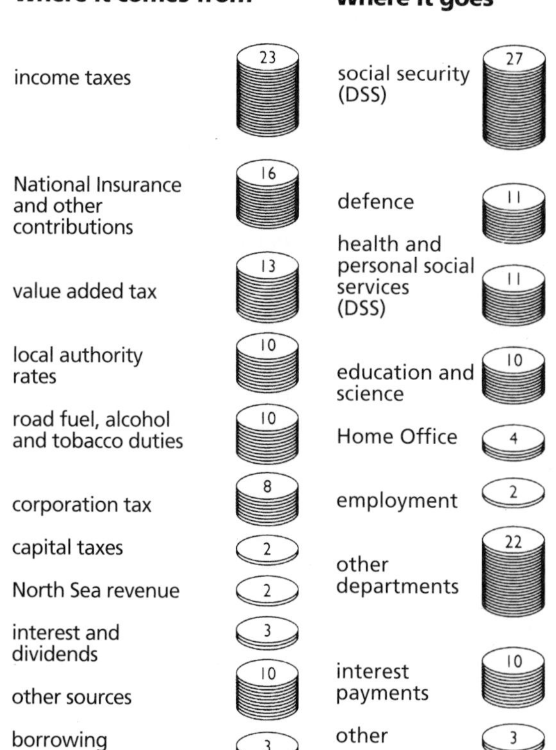

Figure 8.14 UK public income and expenditure, 1987/88, pence in every pound (to the nearest penny)
Source: Financial Statement and Budget Report 1987/8; Economic Progress Report Supplement, March–April 1987

- **Charitable status** confers exemption from taxation, which amounts to about £3 billion of tax forgone per year.
- Various government departments may also give grants directly to charities; for example, the Department of the Environment funds many inner-city projects.

Local authorities, too, fund many charities. This may be through grants or, increasingly, with the introduction of the government's 'Care in the Community' programme, through payment for services provided (see page 247 above).

It is often thought that charities obtain most money through **donations**, but in fact this accounts for less than 40% of charitable income. Such donations may be gained:

- in the form of endowment
- on flag days (street and door-to-door collections)
- from employees at work who regularly donate part of their wage
- from corporate sponsorship
- from charity shops
- in response to appeals in the media
- from the National Lotteries Charities Board

Some fund-raisers worry that as services provided by charities replace those previously provided by the state, people will be less willing to donate money.

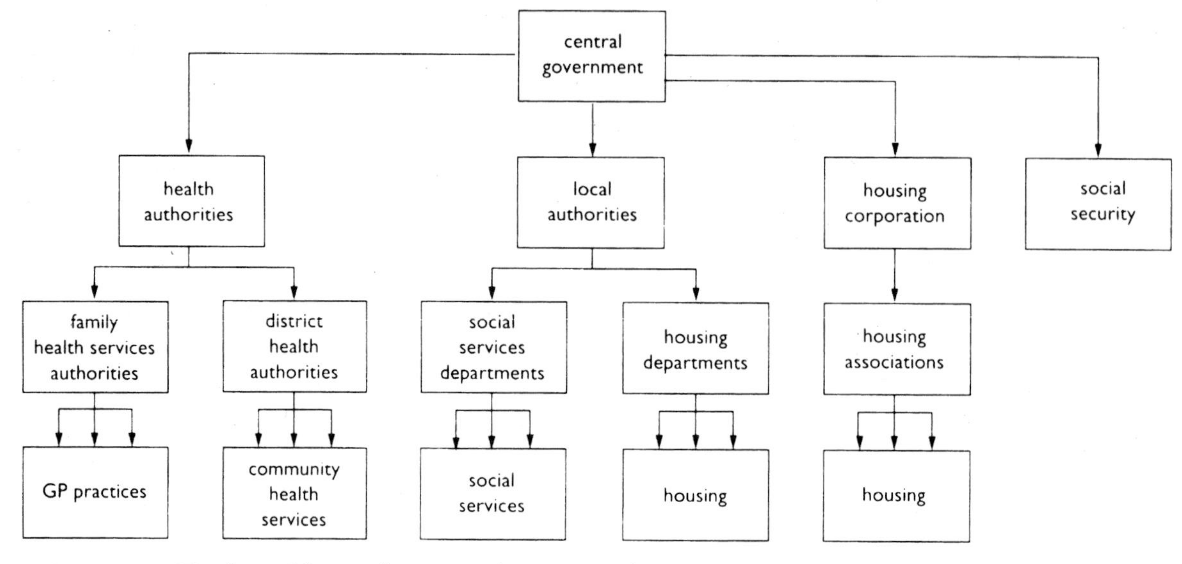

Figure 8.15 The flow of finance from central government

activity

1 Look at Figure 8.16. Discuss the distribution of charity donations. Why are some causes more 'popular' than others?

2 Find out how the National Lottery Charities Board decides on the distribution of money.

Charitable funding of the NHS

Charitable fund-raising is not limited to voluntary organisations. Before the NHS was funded in 1948, charity was at the forefront of health services. After this, up until 1980, charity in hospitals ceased to be of any significance.

In 1980, the Health Service Act empowered health authorities to fund-raise, and the amounts collected through this activity doubled every year during the late 1980s. Proceeds are now used to pay for basic patient care and hospital-building, not just for small comforts for patients and staff and for research.

activity

1 What examples can you find of charitable funding of the NHS in your area?

2 What are the merits and drawbacks of the charitable funding of health care?

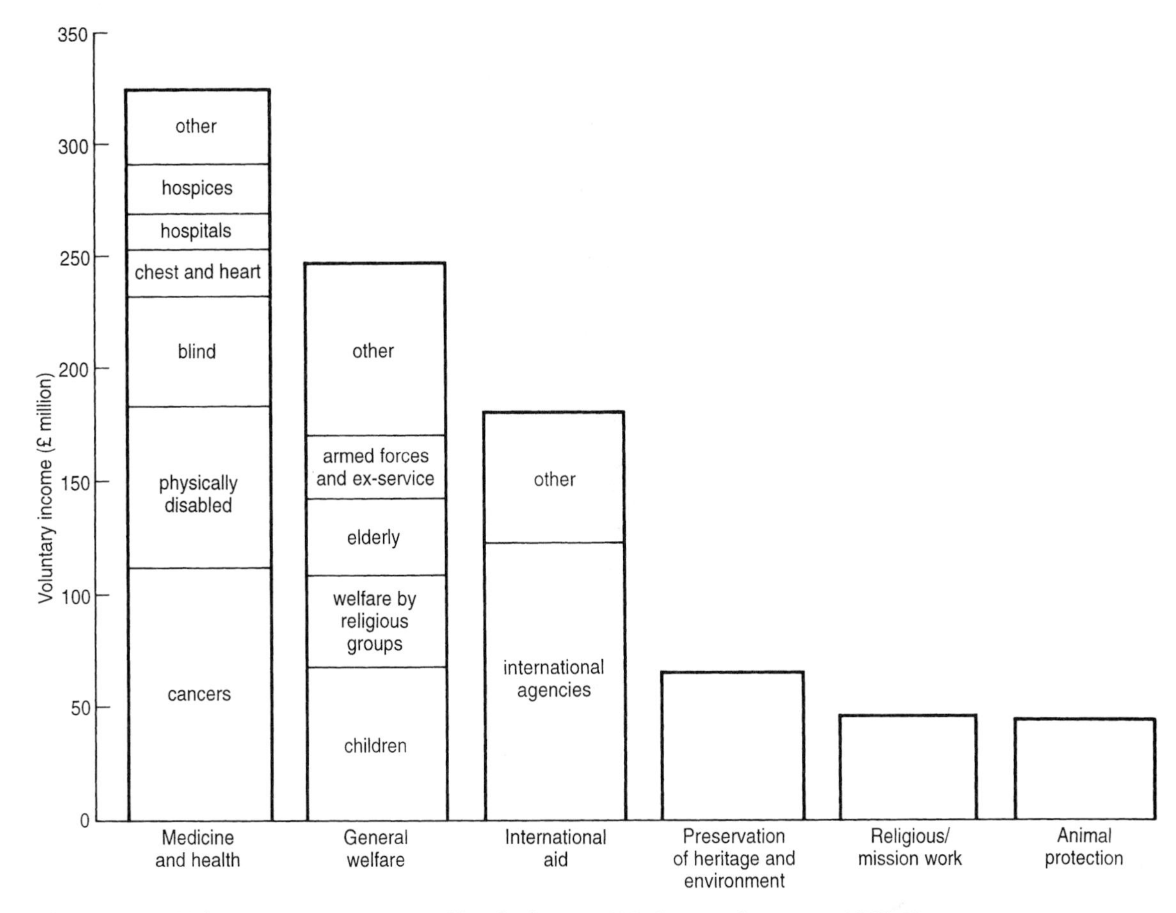

Figure 8.16 Voluntary income received by the largest 200 charities by sector, 1987–88

PRIVATE FUNDING

Corporate sponsorship

An important aspect of charitable fund-raising is **corporate sponsorship**. It is now common for local businesses to fund building programmes and pay for items of equipment in hospitals.

In another example, in an effort to boost the take-up of child immunisation, St Helen's and Knowsley Health Authority on Merseyside struck up a deal with Iceland frozen foods to distribute £6,000 in grocery vouchers to families in the worst-performing neighbourhoods who completed all immunisation courses before their child's third birthday.

West Middlesex University Hospital marked its first day of NHS trust status by signing a deal for a new state-of-the-art endoscopy unit which will allow them to treat patients more efficiently.

Lister BestCare Limited are funding the building of the unit which can diagnose and treat conditions of the stomach and intestine without surgery.

(Richmond and Twickenham Guardian, April 1993)

activity

1 Discuss the advantages to a business of donating funds.

2 Can you find examples of corporate sponsorship in your locality?

Profit-making schemes

(The selling of goods and services and private insurance schemes has been covered earlier in the chapter, in the sections on private provision – see pages 242–45.)

The private sector also invests in **profit-making schemes** in hospitals; for

First private hospitals for NHS

The first scheme in which the private sector will design, finance, build and operate a hospital directly for the National Health Service is due to be announced by Kenneth Clarke, the Chancellor of the Exchequer, in tomorrow's Budget. The proposal would mean that Granada, more commonly associated with television and motorway service stations, would run a 150-bed section of a hospital.

Mr Clarke is expected to give the go-ahead to the £35m project to rebuild large parts of Wycombe and Amersham General Hospitals, which are part of the South Buckinghamshire NHS Trust . . .

The scheme will be announced to off-set capital cuts in the Budget which are expected to hit not only NHS hospitals but the roads programme, housing, schools and other parts of Government spending . . .

The private consortium will finance and run the buildings, but, as with the other projects, medical care will continue to be provided by directly employed NHS staff.

Thereafter, Stephen Dorrell, the Secretary of State for Health, expects about one scheme a month to go through over the next year . . .

Mr Dorrell said last week that in the 'overwhelming majority' of cases, NHS Trusts will continue to be the direct employer of clinical staff – a claim which is aimed at heading off Labour's charges that the schemes will lead to the privatisation of the NHS.

The projects are at the core of a big boost to the Government's Private Finance Initiative across departments, which Mr Clarke will unveil in a budget speech that Tory MPs firmly hope will provide the basis for a political recovery between now and the general election.

In a tough spending round, which has seen cuts of around 5 per cent in the costs of all spending departments, ministers have been told that many pet capital projects will have to be privately financed if they are to go ahead.

(The Independent, 27 November 1995)

NHS takes top position in private healthcare

The NHS has become the largest provider of private healthcare in Britain. The boom in the construction of private wings attached to trust hospitals and the opening of new pay beds has put the health service at the top of the private hospital league for the first time.

In 1995 the NHS earned £225 million from private work, just ahead of the £222.3 million earned by Bupa, its nearest rival, latest figures show. Its estimated 16.5 per cent share of the total private market has grown from 11 per cent in 1988. At the present rate it could claim 20 per cent by 2000 . . .

In some quarters there was embarrassment at its achievement, [William Fitzhugh, the publisher] said. 'The NHS has mixed feelings about its role in the private sector. Whilst it wants the revenues it does not always want to be seen to be attracting the revenues.' . . .

(The Times, 3 September 1996)

example, there are privately managed shopping malls.

Recently, the use of private finance has widened still further. The first article below describes how, through the Private Finance Initiative, private-sector organisations are now building entire hospitals which will be leased back to the NHS.

The second article explains that through the construction of private wings attached to trust hospitals and the opening of new pay beds, the NHS is now the largest provider of private health care in Britain.

The Changing Pattern of Provision for the Care of Children

The multi-disciplinary approach to assessment and provision

To become more effective and efficient in the delivery of services, many providers are now moving towards providing a **skill mix**. This means that teamwork is encouraged so that skills can be used in a complementary way. For example, many GP practices are now grouped together so that resources can be pooled and GPs can afford to buy in the additional services of other health professionals such as **occupational therapists**, nurses, health visitors, physiotherapists and alternative medicine practitioners (see page 273 below). The Patient's Charter (Department of Health 1992) emphasises a 'service provision' approach and a move away from the generic health-care worker who views patients and clients as 'my patients' or 'my families'.

Advantages of the skill mix are:

- It can create new opportunities for practitioners, e.g. learning management skills
- It can lead to more opportunity for the practitioner or team leader to focus on wider issues, e.g. health promotion
- It may lead to greater job satisfaction for team members
- Patients and clients may benefit from the collective experience shared by the team

Disadvantages of the skill mix are:

- Support workers are replacing trained nurses, de-skilling nurses and eroding the professional role
- Supervision of untrained staff is more difficult to carry out effectively in the community than on a hospital ward
- It can lead to job dissatisfaction if the practitioner feels 'de-skilled'
- It may make the concept of the 'named nurse' (enshrined in the Patient's Charter) more difficult to implement
- Without good integration and communication (see the 'Interaction and Agencies' section on page 263 above), adequate care may not be delivered

Empowerment of service users

Increasingly, children and their informal carers are being encouraged to have a role both in their own care planning and in the kind of interventions implemented (see Thomson *et al.* (1995) *Health and Social Care*, pages 333–334). In the most recently built specialist children's hospital, children were asked for the first time what features they wanted to be incorporated in the new building. Examples of those requested included waterfalls, plants and furniture designed specifically for children.

There are still many examples, however, in which children's power over the care they receive is limited. It was mentioned above (see page 235) that children may find it difficult to gain access to a health or social-care professional. It may also be the case that their wishes regarding their treatment are overruled. For example, children can overrule their parents if they refuse to allow them to have life-saving treatment, but they cannot overrule their parents if the children wish their treatment to stop and their parents don't. Many health-care professionals feel that children are the best judge of how long this type of treatment should be continued (for example, chemotherapy and radiotherapy, and transplants), and that their wishes should be respected.

Advocacy is one means of empowering people. This has been defined as 'pleading the cause of another' or 'a means of transferring power back to the patient'. In practice, it involves an **advocate**, who is someone independent from the services, befriending a child and their informal carer(s) and representing their interests to professionals.

activity

Our **social rights**, i.e. the rights that we all expect to have in a social setting, are:

- dignity
- privacy
- the right to be alone
- the right to choose diet, dress and activity
- the right to choose whom we associate with
- the right to have a say in the organisation of the care setting

If you have the chance to carry out a period of work experience on a child's hospital ward, consider to what extent these rights are met. Give specific examples of when efforts are taken to ensure that these rights are met, and specific example of when they are not.

INCREASED SPECTRUM OF CARE

There are increasingly more types of care and treatment available to clients. Some of these new methods may be due to scientific advances, e.g. organ transplants. Other increases to the spectrum of care have occurred because some professionals are taking a more **holistic** approach to care. Holistic care involves the treatment of the whole person. It takes into account the social, psychological and environmental influences, including nutrition, exercise and mental relaxation, that affect health.

Complementary medicine is often linked to the holistic approach (see page 244).

Chapter 9

Legislation *which* Relates *to the* Care *of* Children

There is much legislation relating to the care of children. The most relevant acts are The Children Act, 1989; the NHS and Community Care Act, 1990; Criminal Justice Acts; and Education Acts.

Provision for the protection of children, which draws together the legislation and the services provided, is an important theme.

Readers are referred to the description of 'The legal framework of health and social care' in Holden *et al.* (1996) *Further Studies for Social Care*. Because legislation is constantly changing, readers should check for relevant updates.

Purposes of Legislation

The law is woven into all of our daily lives. It aims to ensure that children are provided with the following:

- health and social care
- support
- information
- education
- protection

activity

To protect children's rights, the United Nations has drawn up an international agreement called the United Nations Convention on the Rights of the Child. The UK government is bound by the Convention, which means that all relevant UK laws must meet standards laid down in the Convention. Send for the booklet produced by the Department of Health (1993) – see the 'References and resources' section at the end of this chapter. Read the list of rights which should apply to all children. Check the treatment of children in this country against the standards set.

Relevant Acts

An overview of the main features is given below. (NB: dates of Acts may differ in Northern Ireland.)

THE CHILDREN ACT 1989

This is the most significant piece of legislation relating to children. It came into force on 14 October 1989, and is about how children should be brought up and cared for. It is a very large piece of legislation. Even the *Guidance and Regulations on the 1989 Children Act* produced by the Department of Health runs to eight volumes.

The description of the Act below is taken from *The Teenager's Guide to the Law* (Posner 1995).

Parental responsibility

This is a new concept introduced by the Act. The following are the most significant of the powers, rights, duties and responsibilities that parents have in relation to their children:

- a responsibility for the physical care and control of the child
- the authority to discipline the child
- a responsibility to maintain the child
- a responsibility to ensure that the child receives an efficient full-time education suited to their needs and abilities
- the authority to consent to the child being medically examined or receiving medical treatment
- the authority to appoint a **guardian** (although a guardian will not acquire parental responsibility unless both parents are dead)
- an entitlement to be treated as a parent by the child's school, including being eligible to stand as a parent-governor

Some aspects of parental responsibility require the consent of *both* of the child's parents. These include:

- the authority to agree to the child being adopted
- the authority to consent to the child getting married if the child is over the age of 16
- the authority to remove the child from the UK

(**Note:** in some circumstances, foster parents or local authorities may hold parental responsibility.)

Orders

The Children Act repealed (cancelled)

[The Act] is about how you should be brought up and cared for. It rests on the belief that children are generally best looked after within their families with both parents playing a full part and without the courts becoming involved unless there is no alternative. It aims to strike a balance between your right to express your views on decisions about your life, the rights of parents to exercise their responsibilities towards their children and the duty of the state (in other words the courts and the social services department of the local authority) to intervene where your welfare requires it. It encourages co-operation between parents, and between parents and social services, in order to promote the welfare of all children and young people.

(G. J. Posner, The Teenager's Guide to the Law, 1995)

much of the previous law relating to children. Terms such as 'custody', 'care and control' and 'access' are no longer used. Instead the Act introduces a range of 'orders', which are instructions saying what must or must not be done.

activity

Find out about the following orders:

- residence orders (refer to Posner 1995 – see the 'References and resources' section at the end of this chapter, page 287)
- contact orders (refer to Posner 1995 – see the 'References and resources' section at the end of this chapter, page 287)
- emergency protection orders (EPOs) (see page 285 below)
- child assessment orders (CAOs) (see page 285 below)

Specific duties imposed on local authorities

Under law, a **duty** is something that must be carried out. Below is a list of the duties imposed on local authorities by the Children Act.

- The identification of children in need (see page 282 below) and the provision of information
- The maintenance of a register of disabled children
- An assessment of children's needs
- The provision of accommodation (to a suspected abuser) in order to protect the child
- Provision for disabled children
- Provision to reduce need for care proceedings etc. (i.e. to take steps to avoid any child being involved in court proceedings)
- Provision for children in need living with their families
- Maintenance of the family home (to enable a child in need to live with their family, or to promote contact between the child and the family)
- The duty to consider racial groups to which children in need belong
- Regulating and registering the following services:
  - day care
  - family centres
  - childminders
  - private fostering

Children in need are children with a disability; children whose health and development are likely to be significantly impaired or maintained; and children without the provision of services

Principles upon which the courts must act

- The child's welfare is the paramount consideration
- A decision must be made as quickly as possible
- Children are entitled to be protected if they may suffer 'significant harm', but an order (see above) must not be made unless it is really necessary
- A court must take into account, and give equal importance to, the following list of factors:
  - the child's physical, emotional and educational needs

- the likely effect of any change in circumstances on the child
- the age, sex, background and any other relevant characteristics the child has
- any harm which the child has suffered, or is at risk of suffering
- the capability of the parents, and any other adults who may be involved, in meeting the child's needs
- the range of powers available to the court

- Children must be consulted about their feelings and wishes

THE NHS AND COMMUNITY CARE ACT 1990

This Act was passed in 1990 and is now fully implemented. A key concept in the new legislation is 'care in the community': the provision of support services to people who need help to live as independently as they can in the setting of their own choice. This could be in their own homes, in a residential home or local-authority sheltered housing.

The Act has six identified 'key objectives':

1. to promote domiciliary, day and respite services to enable people to live in their own homes wherever feasible and sensible;
2. to ensure that service providers make practical support for carers a high priority;
3. to make the proper assessment of need and good care management the cornerstones of high-quality care;
4. to promote the development of a flourishing independent sector alongside good-quality public services;
5. to clarify the responsibilities of agencies, and so make them more accountable;
6. to secure better value for taxpayers' money by introducing a new funding structure for social care.

Under this new Act, the NHS no longer carries the main responsibility for service provision: instead, local authorities now have the major function of providing social care for the elderly, for those with physical disabilities and for people with learning difficulties.

These changes have implications for the roles of social worker and community nurse. A key feature in implementing the Act is that of **care management**: the central elements of this are

- assessment
- the implementation, monitoring and review of a **care plan**

activity

The Patients' Charter applies to all users of the NHS, including children. Obtain a copy of this, and then list the entitlements it describes.

The Criminal Justice Acts

Criminal justice legislation (e.g. the Criminal Justice Acts of 1988 and 1991 and the Criminal Justice and Public Order Act of 1994) details criminal offences as identified by Parliament. Such legislation encompasses thousands of laws which, if broken, may result in the restriction of liberty, including imprisonment. It also frequently sets out sentencing guidelines for magistrates and the judiciary, and outlines particular requirements concerning the treatment and sentencing of offenders. (Health and social-care workers will need to keep appraised of the legislation as it affects their particular field of practice and assessment of risk.)

Successive legislation has demonstrated a rather contradictory attitude towards juvenile offenders. It has been recognised that young offenders have special needs if their first offence is not to become their introduction to a lifetime of offending. The younger the offender, the more vulnerable they are deemed to be and the more they are in need of social workers and probation officers to act as advocates for them. The Police and Criminal Evidence Act 1984 sets out strict guidelines on the treatment of young offenders and requires that an appropriate adult (possibly a social worker) always be present. However, it is also the case that the UK has one of the youngest ages of criminal responsibility in the world (10 in England and Wales and 8 in Scotland) and the 1994 Criminal Justice Act provides for custodial sentences of up to 14 years for children who commit robbery, rape or assault, or handle stolen goods.

The two main ways in which the Criminal Justice Acts impact upon children is in the legislation concerning the way child witnesses are dealt with; and in the provision of criminal law which places certain children and young people in local-authority accommodation.

Child witnesses

- Children under 14 will give their evidence without having to take the oath.
- A child will be treated as competent to testify, unless shown otherwise.
- If the child is a victim or witness in a case of violence or sexual abuse, the **committal stage** (during which the case is tested to see if it should be brought before a jury) is bypassed so that the child does not have to give evidence twice.
- Children, up to the age of 17 in the case of a sexual offence, and up to 14 in the case of a violent offence, can give their evidence on video. A live video link can be used in crown courts to allow children to be cross-examined. (The child sits in a room next to the court, and technical equipment allows the child to see and hear whoever is questioning them, and the court to see and hear the child.)
- Criminal trials where a child is a victim or witness will go ahead as quickly as possible.

activity

1 Look through newspapers to find an example of a court case in which a child has given evidence on video. What do you think are the advantages of using this technique compared with face-to-face cross-examination?

2 If possible, interview a social worker or police officer to find out about the advice they are given on how to conduct interviews with children, in order to enable the child's account to be used, if necessary, in subsequent criminal proceedings.

(See Appendix A for answers.)

Young offenders

Young people between 10 and 17 years old will be dealt with in the Youth Court, unless they are facing a charge of murder or manslaughter, in which case it will be dealt with in a crown court. Although the Youth Court is a criminal court, it still has a duty to consider the welfare of the children and young people with whom it deals. It has the power to impose various sentences depending on the seriousness of the offence and the child's age. (A child under the age of 10 is treated by law as being incapable of committing a criminal offence and cannot therefore be prosecuted. The same applies to children who are younger than 14 if the prosecution are unable to prove that they know right from wrong.)

Sentencing and penalties

(The following information is taken from Posner (1995) *The Teenager's Guide to the Law*.)

1 *Absolute discharge.* If a child has been found technically guilty but punishment is not thought necessary, no penalty will be imposed.
2 *Conditional discharge.* Again, no penalty is imposed, but in this case, if another offence is committed within a set period of up to 3 years, the young person will be punished for both the original and the later offences.
3 *Binding over.* The young person makes a written agreement to 'keep the peace and be of good behaviour' for a set period (of up to 3 years). If this promise is broken, a fine is paid.
4 *A fine.* Children between 10 and 13 can be asked to pay a maximum fine of £250. Young people between 14 and 17 can be asked to pay a maximum of £1,000. Parents are ordered to pay the fine for children under the age of 16, and may be ordered to pay the fine for 16 and 17 year olds.
5 *Compensation orders.* A child or young person may be asked to pay **compensation** to the victim of a crime (up to a maximum of £5,000), as well as, or instead of, any other sentence.
6 *Community sentences.* These include one or more of the following **community orders**:

- attendance centre orders: attendance centres are usually run by the police, and activities may include physical exercise or craft work. Young people are usually ordered to go for 2 hours on alternate Saturday afternoons.
  - 10–15 year olds: maximum number of hours 24
  - 16–20 year olds: maximum number of hours 36
  - 14 and over: minimum number of hours 12
- *supervision order:* this places a young person under the supervision of a local-authority social worker for not more than 3 years. The order may require you to live with a named person or in a particular place (including local-authority secure

accommodation. You may also be required to take part in particular activities.

- *probation order:* this places a young person of 16 or over under the supervision of a **probation officer** for between 6 months and 3 years. Requirements can be attached, such as living in a probation centre or undergoing treatment for alcohol or drug dependency. Consent from the young person is required before this type of order can be made.
- *community service order:* this type of order is placed on young people of 16 or over, and requires them to carry out unpaid work in the community for between 40 and 240 hours.

7 *Custodial sentence.* This type of sentence deprives a young person of their freedom. It will only be given if the court considers that:

- the offence is so serious that it justifies such a sentence; or
- the offence is a violent or sexual offence, and the sentence is necessary to protect the public.

If the young person is aged over 15 and under 21, they will be sent to a **young offender institution**.

8 *Destruction order.* The court can order items such as controlled drugs and offensive weapons to be destroyed.

9 *Exclusion order.* This is designed to deal with the problem of football hooliganism. The court has the power to prevent a young person from attending league and cup football matches.

10 *Deferred sentence.* The court can delay **sentencing** for up to 6 months if there is about to be a change in the young person's life – e.g. they are about to commence employment.

11 *Secure training order.* The Criminal Justice and Public Order Act 1994 introduced a new sentence for 12, 13 and 14 year olds. This is a period of **detention** in a secure training centre followed by a period of the same length under **supervision**. The total period must be between 6 months and 2 years, and the offender must have been convicted of three or more offences which would be punishable with imprisonment in the case of an adult, while on supervision order.

The Criminal Justice Act allows police to hold 15 and 16 year olds, but not younger people, where no local authority secure accommodation is available, and where keeping them in any other local-authority accommodation would not be adequate to protect the public from serious harm from them.

activity

1 If you are interested in finding out about criminal procedures, you can visit the public gallery of a magistrates' court. This will not, of course, be dealing with young people under the age of 18, and proceedings will be more formal than those in the Youth Court. (The Youth Court is not open to the public.)

2 There was considerable controversy over the introduction of secure training camps which were based on American 'boot camps'. If you have access to a

national newspaper on CD-ROM, look back over the arguments and list the points made for and against these institutions. What is your opinion on their likely effectiveness?

3 Whenever a child under the age of 16 is sentenced for an offence, their parent(s) are bound over to take proper care of the child, or to exercise proper control over them to prevent them from re-offending for up to 3 years. In some cases, parents are also responsible for paying the child's fine or compensation payment (see page 279 above). To what extent do you think parents should be held responsible for their children's crimes?

THE EDUCATION ACTS 1981, 1993

(See also the 'Provision of Education' section in Chapter 8, pages 257–63.)

All children must receive education while they are of compulsory school age. This is from the term after their 5th birthday until they are 16. It is the parent's legal responsibility to ensure that their child receives an adequate full-time education. Young people have the right to receive a full-time education until they are 19, but parents cannot force young people to stay in education once they have reached the age of 16. Education is a complicated area of law, and it is not within the scope of this book to cover the legislation in depth. However, readers are referred again to Posner (1995) *The Teenager's Guide to the Law* which contains an excellent summary of the main points of education legislation (see the 'References and resources' section at the end of this chapter, page 287). These are grouped under the following headings:

- compulsory attendance at school and the right to receive education
- free education, transport and school meals
- staying on after school-leaving age
- the young person's say in educational matters
- truancy and education supervision orders
- punishment and discipline
- exclusion and expulsion from school
- reports and records
- safety at school
- discrimination at school
- special educational needs

activity

1 If you are working in a group, divide the 11 headings above between you, and prepare on a poster a bulleted list of the main points of legislation covered by each heading.

2 Parents do not have to send their children to school, provided that they make arrangements that are satisfactory to their local education authority (LEA). For example, they may educate them at home, either themselves or with a tutor. What do you think are the advantages and disadvantages of this type of education?

3 Legislation gives children and young people certain rights and duties at cer-

tain ages. List these for the following ages (refer to Posner (1995) *The Teenager's Guide to the Law*):

- 5 years old
- 7 years old
- 10 years old
- 12 years old
- 14 years old
- 15 years old
- 16 years old
- 17 years old
- 18 years old
- 21 years old

Provision for the Protection of Children

Children have the right not to be physically, sexually or emotionally abused. The Children Act 1989 (see pages 275–77 above) provides the majority of the legislation dealing with child protection. The main emphasis is on **prevention** rather than on dealing with the aftermath of the detection of abuse. Equally, children should be protected from the overanxious interference of the state (i.e. local authorities). Wherever possible, the child should be helped to remain living at home safely, without the need for court proceedings. There are well-defined **child protection procedures**, the main points of which are set out below.

Referral of concerns about a child's safety

By law, local authorities have to investigate any concerns about a child's safety. These concerns may be referred to them from a variety of sources. For example:

- the local authorities' own casework with a family may lead to concerns.
- court proceedings may lead to concerns about a child's welfare.
- Neighbours, relatives etc. may report their suspicions, either directly or via an **independent voluntary group** such as the NSPCC (see page 283 below).
- Professionals such as those involved in child care and health care may report their concerns. (By law, the establishments these professionals work in must have written procedures for dealing with suspected child abuse.)
- The police may report suspected cases of abuse to the local authorities. If the police have reasonable cause to believe that a child would suffer 'significant harm', they have the power to place the child in suitable accommodation and to keep them there for up to 72 hours. This is known as **police protection**. (Where possible, it is the suspected abuser, rather than the child, who is removed from the family home.)

The investigation process

Although it is the statutory duty of the local authority in which the child lives or is found, to carry out an investigation into a case of alleged child abuse, the authority in question usually works in close association with the police, especially where sexual abuse is suspected. This is because, as well as seeking to discover whether the child has suffered 'significant harm', there may be a possibility of pursuing a **criminal prosecution** against the suspected abuser(s). Most local authorities have set up joint police/social-work child-protection teams in which both the social workers and the police officers are especially trained to deal with offences committed against children.

As well as receiving assistance from the police, the investigating local authority also requires other local authorities and Education and Housing Departments to provide information, except 'where doing so would be unreasonable in all the circumstances of the case'. Wherever possible, the professionals will aim to work together with the parents, although inevitably, if a parent is suspected of abuse, this leads to a conflict of interests.

Figure 9.1 summarises the typical stages in the local authorities' investigation procedure.

THE PROTECTION PLAN

Once all the necessary information has been gathered, a **child protection conference** will be organised by the Social Services Department. This is a meeting of all the professionals concerned with the case, including social workers, police and the NSPCC where they are involved. Other professionals involved may include probation officers, teachers, nursery staff, doctors, nurses and health visitors. Increasingly, parents and children will also be invited to attend and given support to enable them to take part. This is a formal meeting which allows relevant information to be exchanged and an assessment to be made of the degree of risk to the child.

It will be decided at this meeting whether or not to place the child's name on the **Child Protection Register**. This consists of a list of the names and details of children who are considered to be 'at risk' of possible harm from:

- physical injury
- sexual abuse
- emotional abuse
- neglect

(In 1993, there were 36,000 children in England, Wales and Northern Ireland on the register, over a third of whom were considered to be at risk from physical injuries.)

If a child's name is put on the register, they will then be allocated a **key worker**. This is usually a social worker, from either the local authority or the NSPCC, who is then responsible for coordinating the drawing-up of a **child protection plan**.

The child-protection conference formulates advice to the agencies involved. As mentioned above, wherever possible, the aim of the conference is to find a way to solve the problem in a way that enables the child to remain at home safely and without the need for court proceedings. However, in some cases, legal action may be recommended (see below).

Every 6 months, a **child protection review meeting** will be held, at which a decision is reached as to the continued need for registration of the child, and future plans are agreed for any necessary work by the relevant agencies.

THE ROLE OF THE COURTS

Depending on the circumstances, the child protection conference may decide to recommend:

- leaving the child at home
- removing the child temporarily from the family home
- removing the child permanently from the family home

If the first, and preferable, action is taken and the child remains in the home, then

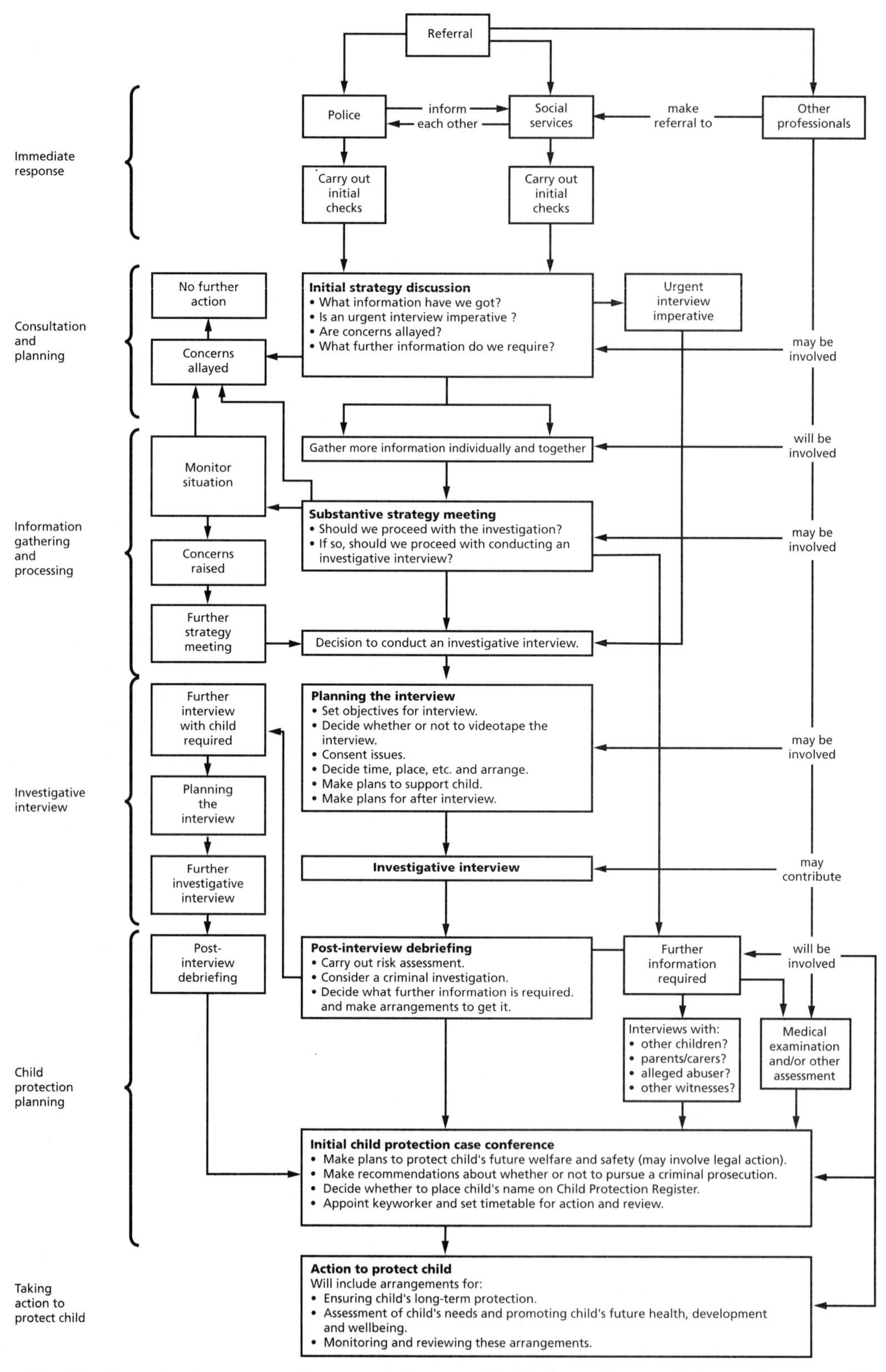

Figure 9.1 The investigation process in suspected cases of child abuse; Source: Stainton, Rogers and Roche

where possible, legislation will be avoided. For example, a comprehensive assessment will be taken of the child's and family's needs, and services will be provided to alleviate stresses and to support families coping with difficult times and demanding children. In this way, situations may be avoided in which the child is exposed to harm. Where the child is at risk of harm, voluntary agreements will try to be met with parents about ways of making sure that their children are kept safe. However, in some cases when the child is to remain in the home, it will be considered that legislation is necessary, and the local authority or NSPCC will apply to the **family proceedings court** for a **supervision order** (see above).

If the child is to be removed from home, either permanently or temporarily, the place where they will live is clearly an important aspect of the care plan. The Social Services Department may place the child:

- with a foster family (see page 248 above), or
- in a community home, or
- in a voluntary home, or
- in a registered children's home, or
- at a special school which is a boarding school, or
- with a suitable adult family member or friend who is willing to have them.

The Social Services Department has a duty, wherever possible, to place a child near their home, and to keep brothers and sisters who are being looked after together. Any of the following pieces of legislation may be used to remove a child from their home:

Child assessment order

A social worker does not have the right to enter a child's home without the permission of the parents. If the parents are not prepared to cooperate in an investigation, and if there is reasonable cause to suspect that the child is suffering, or is likely to suffer, 'significant harm', the local authority or NSPCC may apply to the family proceedings court for a **child assessment order** (**CAO**). This lasts for up to 7 days and can be made on a child or young person under the age of 18. It involves an assessment of their state of health and development, or of the way in which they have been treated. During this period of assessment, the court can direct that they live away from home if this is necessary.

Emergency protection order

If concerns are more urgent, such a CAO is not appropriate because it cannot be used to gain access to see a child who is suspected of being at immediate risk. In such a case, an **emergency protection order** (**EPO**) must be sought to gain access to the child. This is a short-term order that removes the child from the home for up to 8 days initially, with an extension of up to 7 days if necessary. The EPO is intended to be used for two purposes:

1. by any person to deal with an urgent crisis where the child is in immediate danger, by removing the child from that danger (e.g. removing the child from their home where they are in danger of physical abuse), or by keeping the child somewhere safe (e.g. on a hospital ward if they require urgent treatment and the parents are trying to remove them);
2. by a local authority or the NSPCC, in order to allow them to conduct an investigation when there are immediate concerns about the child's safety.

Recovery order

This is sought when a child either is removed or runs away when they are protected by an emergency protection order or when they are in either police protection or the care of the local authority.

Care order

A court order can be made if the child or young person is suffering, or is likely to suffer, significant harm, and if this is because of either a lack of care being given to the child or the child being beyond parental control. If a child is subject to a **care order**, the local authority shares parental responsibility with the parents. The court has the power to determine the extent to which parents are allowed to be involved in caring for the child. The local authority has the power to decide where the child lives, and to make other decisions about their life and upbringing. However, there are certain restrictions on how the local authority can exercise its parental responsibility. For example, the local authority cannot have the child **adopted** (see page 250 above) without a proper application to the court for an adoption order being made.

Before making a care order, the court must give consideration to the arrangement for contact between the child and their parents or guardian.

A full care order lasts until the person is 17 or gets married at 16, or until the court **discharges** (i.e. terminates) it.

If, for any reason, the full **court hearing** cannot take place, an **interim care order** may be made. This will be made only if the court believes that there are grounds for the full care order, but it does not necessarily mean that there will be a full order. An interim order may not last for longer than 8 weeks.

INDEPENDENT VOLUNTARY GROUPS CONCERNED WITH CHILD PROTECTION

The most significant group here is the NSPCC (or RSSPCC in Scotland) as this is the only voluntary organisation with statutory powers to apply to a court for protection orders for a child (see above). The NSPCC runs a Child Protection Helpline which is a free national 24-hour service that anyone can call if they suspect a child is at risk. They have a number of local centres, and as can be seen above, their social workers (**Child Protection Officers**) work closely with local authorities. They also maintain a national register of abused children. As a charity, 85% of their income comes from donations, so fund-raising is a significant part of their work.

Childline is a voluntary organisation which operates a 24-hour telephone helpline free of charge for children to call to discuss with trained counsellors situations which place them under stress.

Kidscape is an organisation which works with schools to devise **assertiveness training programmes** to give young children protection from abuse. For example, children are taught that in some situations, it is appropriate for them to shout and kick in order to avoid harm.

(See the 'Useful addresses' section on page 288 below for the addresses of the above organisations.)

activity

1 The two functions of the local-authority investigation into a suspected case of child abuse are:

- to establish whether the child is at risk of harm, and to devise a plan for protecting the child
- to establish whether a crime has been committed against the child, and to determine whether to pursue a prosecution against the alleged offender

It is often said that these two functions are frequently incompatible. Discuss why you think this could be.

2 If possible, interview at least one of the following professionals about their child-protection work:

- a Child Protection Officer from the NSPCC
- a social worker
- a specially trained police officer

References and resources

Allen, N. (1990) *Making Sense of the Children Act*, London: Longman.

Audit Commission (1993) *Children First: A Study of Hospital Services*, London: HMSO.

Audit Commission (1993) *Report of an Independent Review of Specialist Services in London: Children*, London: HMSO.

Brayne, H. and Martin, G. (1991) *Law for Social Workers*, London: Blackstone Press Ltd.

Bruce, T. and Meggitt, C. (1996) *Child Care and Education*, London: Hodder & Stoughton.

Charities Digest 1996, London: Waterlow Information Services Ltd. (Lists national and regional charities.)

Comprehensive and Practical Guide to Childcare Law, London: Longman, in association with the NSPCC. (A legal guide for child-care practitioners, updated regularly.)

Department of Health (1991) *Welfare of Children and Young People in Hospital*, London: HMSO.

Department of Health (1993) *The Rights of the Child. A Guide to the UN Convention*, Leaflet CAT 9, available from BAPS, Health Publications Unit, Storage and Distribution Centre, Heywood Stores, Manchester Road, Heywood, Lancashire OL10 2PZ.

Directory of Independent Hospitals and Health Services, 1995, London: Longman.

Family Welfare Association (1996) *Guide to the Social Services*, London: Waterlow Information Services Ltd.

Holden, C. *et al.* (1996) *Further Studies for Social Care*, London: Hodder & Stoughton.

Howland, G. (ed) (1995) *The Institute of Health Services Management Health Services Year Book*, London: (An annual record of the hospitals and health services of the UK and Northern Ireland.)

NAHAT (1996) *NAHAT (National Association of Health Authorities and Trusts) NHS Handbook 1995/6*, 10th edn, Tunbridge Wells: JMH Publishing.

Office of Population Censuses and Surveys (Beverley Botting ed) (1996) *The Health of our Children. Decennial Supplement*, London: HMSO.

Posner, G. J. (1995) *The Teenager's Guide to the Law*, London: Cavendish Publishers Ltd.

Stainton Rogers, W. and Roche, J. (1994) *Children's Welfare and Children's Rights*, London: Hodder & Stoughton.

Thomson, H. *et al.* (1995), *Health and Social Care for Advanced GNVQ*, London: Hodder & Stoughton.

The Voluntary Agencies Directory 1995/6, London: National Council for Voluntary Organisations Publications.

Useful addresses

British Agencies for Adoption and Fostering
Skyline House
200 Union Street
London SE1 0LY

British Association for Early Childhood Education
111 City View House
463 Bethnal Green
London E2 9QY
Tel.: 0171 739 7594

Carers National Association
20/25 Glasshouse Yard
London EC1A 4JS
Tel.: 0171 490 8818

Childline
2nd Floor
Royal Mail Building
Studd Street
London N1 0QW
Tel.: 0800 1111

Contact a Family
170 Tottenham Court Road
London W1P 0HA
Tel.: 0171 383 3555

Council for Complementary and Alternative Medicine
Suite 1
19A Cavendish Square
London W1M 9AD
Tel.: 0171 409 1440

Day Care Trust/National Childcare Campaign
Wesley House
4 Wildcourt
London WC2B 4AU
Tel.: 0171 405 5617

Institute for Complementary Medicine
PO Box 194
London SE16 1QZ
Tel.: 0171 737 5165

Kidscape
World Trade Centre
Europe House
London E1 9AA

National Campaign for Nursery Education
BCM Box 6216
London WC1N 3XX

The National Childminding Association
8 Masons Hill
Bromley
Kent BR2 9EY
Tel.: 0181 464 6164

National Council for One Parent Families
255 Kentish Town Road
London NW5 2LX
Tel.: 0171 267 1361

National Early Years Network
77 Holloway Road
London N7 8JZ
Tel.: 0171 607 9573

National Foster Care Association (NFCA)
Leonard House
5–7 Marshalsea Road
London SE1 1EP
Tel.: 0171 828 6266

National Organisation for Counselling Adoptees and their Parents
3 New High Street
Headington
Oxford OX3 7AJ

NFCA Scotland
1 Melrose Street, off Queen's Crescent
Glasgow G4 9BJ
Tel.: 0141 332 6655

NSPCC
National Centre
42 Curtain Road
London EC2A 3NH

Practical Alternatives for Mums, Dads, and Under-Fives
c/o 162 Holland Road
Hurst Green
Oxted
Surrey RH8 9BQ

The pre-school Learning Alliance
(formerly the Pre-school Playgroups Association)
69 King's Cross Road
London WC1X 9LL
Tel.: 0171 833 0991

RSSPCC
Melville House
41 Polwarth Terrace
Edinburgh EH11 1NU
Tel.: 0131 337 8539

Appendix A

Answers to Activities

Page 2

3 Mitosis involves one division of the nucleus to give two genetically identical daughter cells with the diploid number of chromosomes. Meiosis involves two divisions of the nucleus to give four genetically different daughter cells with the haploid number of chromosomes.

Page 3

Weight gain is most rapid in adolescence.

Page 4

2 As children grow, their head becomes proportionately smaller, and their arms become proportionately longer.

Page 5

1 Using norms helps in the understanding of patterns of development. For example, they are useful in helping parents and carers know what to expect at certain ages, especially when planning a safe, stimulating environment. A disadvantage of their use is that the wide range between individuals may be ignored, and children may be labelled as 'slow' or 'bad' if they fall behind the norm.

3 97%

Page 7

2 23 chromosomes in ovum;
23 chromosomes in sperm;
23 pairs (46) chromosomes in nucleus of zygote.
Sex is determined by the 23rd pair of chromosomes. Females have 2 identical X chromosomes in each cell; males have an X chromosome, and a smaller Y chromosome in each cell. Each individual inherits an X chromosome from their mother, and an X chromosome (in the case of a female) or a Y chromosome (in the case of a male) from their father. (Half the sperm contain an X chromosome and half the sperm contain a Y chromosome.)

Cross-sectional study	Longitudinal study
Advantage Completed in much shorter time	Advantages: Easy to choose representative sample. Takes into account factors like nutrition which may change from generation to generation.
Disadvantages: Difficult to choose representative sample. Does not take into account factors which may change from generation to generation.	Disadvantage: Time consuming.

Page 9

Ectopic implantation is when the zygote becomes implanted in the fallopian tube instead of in the uterus. The pregnancy will then have to be terminated.

Page 10

A tail is present until about the 54th day after conception, and the developing embryo has gill clefts, which are retained in adult fish for gas exchange.

Page 13

Diffusion is the process by which a substance moves from a region of high concentration of that substance to a region of lower concentration of that substance.
Active transport requires energy because the process involves moving molecules against a concentration gradient (i.e. from a region of low concentration to a region of higher concentration).

Chapter 2

Page 43

1 Gene: The length of DNA that codes for one polypeptide chain.
DNA: Deoxyribose nucleic acid. Along with proteins, forms the chromosomes. Determines the sequence of amino acids in a polypeptide chain.
Polypeptide: A chain of amino acids.
Protein: Made up of one or more polypeptide chains.
Enzyme: A protein which catalyses a biochemical reaction.
Metabolism: The chemical reactions which occur in the body.
3 There would be a 50% chance of each offspring being a tongue roller (heterozygous), and a 50% chance of each offspring being a non-tongue roller.

4 Parent's phenotype:	Male	X	Female
Parent's genotype:	XY	X	XX
Gametes:	(X) (Y)	X	(X)
Offspring genotype:	XX		XY
Offspring phenotype:	Female		Male

5 N represents the 'normal' allele; n represents the haemophilia allele.

Name:	Genotype:
Victoria	$X^N X^n$
Beatrice	$X^N X^n$
Irene	$X^N X^n$
Frederick William	$X^n Y$

Page 45

- If the father has never had a job, or does not have a job now, this classification of social class is not accurate.
- The occupation of the mother is not taken into consideration.
- All members of the family are ascribed the same social class. It fails to recognise that some members of a family (particularly children) may experience poorer social and economic circumstances than others.

Chapter 3

Page 103

1 Cervical screening

Page 67

3 Blood clotting:

PKU

Cause: Genetic mutation means a particular enzyme is not produced. This means that a PKU sufferer cannot convert the essential amino acid phenylalanine into another amino acid, tyrosine.

Symptoms: The accumulation of phenylalanine results in the brain and other organs and tissues such as muscle and cartilage failing to grow and develop normally.

Treatment: A blood test identifies PKU at birth. The child can then be fed a special diet with just enough phenylalanine to allow normal growth without it accumulating in the body.

Hypothyroidism

Cause: Underactivity of the thyroid gland. This may be caused by a lack of iodine in the diet.

Symptoms: The basal metabolic rate falls, leading to a weight increase. There is retardation in mental, physical and sexual development.

Treatment: Addition of iodine to the diet.

Page 77

The rubella virus can cause malformation of the eyes or ears in the foetus, resulting in blindness or deafness.

Page 80

There is a positive correlation between the percentage of food intake used for growth and the relative rate of growth.

Chapter 4

Page 104:

1 Children at this stage of development **attend** to fast-paced action, special effects and sections in which there are rapid changes in scenes and special effects. The commercial is likely to be louder and to use brighter images than the film.
2 The attention shown by the other children to the buyer of the 'Boomer' is the unconditioned stimulus (UCS) for the unconditioned response (UCR) of pleasure.
   The 'Boomer' sweet bar is a conditioned stimulus (CS) which, when paired with the UCS, elicits the conditioned response (CR) of pleasure.
   NB: Repeated showings of the commercial emphasise the conditioning process.
3 Likely factors include: the use of a slightly older child who is powerful and competent enough to go into a shop and buy sweets on his own; the probable use of stylish clothing and an attractive model; the use of a model who, by implication, already has a great many friends; that the model is the same sex as Alex.

Page 117:

2 A: 3, B: 7, C: 2, D: 9, E: 1, F: 8, G: 10, H: 4, I: 6, J: 5.

Chapter 8

Page 230:

Statutory: Must be provided by law; e.g., schools for 5–16 year olds.

Voluntary: Non-government, non-profit making organisations, at a national and local level offering services; e.g., a playgroup.

Private: provision of care with the aim of making a profit; e.g., a privately owned day nursery.

Informal provision: Care organised on an informal basis; e.g., neighbour babysitting.

Page 241:

5 Two possible answers: routine post-operative care – changing dressings etc.; long-term management of children with mild to moderate asthma.

Page 242:

Cancer services: malignant tumours and leukaemia
Cardiology and cardiothoracic: heart and lungs
Neurology and neurosurgery: nerves
Nephrology: kidneys
Plastic surgery and burns: reshaping parts of the body and skin grafts
Neonatal and specialist paediatric surgery: operations on babies and children
Paediatric intensive care: health care for critically ill children
Endocrinology: hormones, and the glands that secrete them
Gastroenterology: the digestive tract, and the liver and pancreas
Haemotology: blood

Ear, nose and throat surgery (commonly known as ENT)
Opthalmology: eyes

Page 246:

Respite care: alternative care given to allow the main carer a break from their responsibilities

Occupational therapy: the treatment of physical and psychiatric conditions through specific activities in order to help people reach their maximum level of function and independence

Rehabilitation: the care given to a person to help them return, as far as possible, to their previous state of health

Page 251:

5 The differences between fostering and adoption:

- When a child is adopted, the legal link between their birth family is broken completely and permanently. This is not the case when the child is fostered.
- The adoptive parents have parental responsibility for the child. For example, they make all the major decisions such as where the child will live and go to school. Foster parents do not have this level of responsibility.
- If a child is not a British citizen, and is adopted by a British person, they will automatically become a British citizen. This is not the case if the child is fostered.
- Adoptive parents can change the child's surname to their surname, and can change the child's first name(s). Foster parents cannot do this.

Page 263:

1 Social Services Departments; education; housing; the NHS; the voluntary sector.
2 Possible suggestions: better staff training; more resources – e.g. staff; better communication; legislation to require public services to fully cooperate in the drawing-up and implementation of joint service plans.
3 Services provided may include rehousing, marriage counselling for Kaye and Mike, a nursery place for Kelly and day care for Martin. They should also receive advice on benefits and getting the electricity reconnected. The social worker will therefore have to coordinate her work with the benefits office, housing department, voluntary agencies and the education department.

Page 265:

3 At the time of writing (1997):

- Each quantity of drug or item on a prescription costs £5.50.
- 'Season tickets' can be purchased for £27.20 for 4 months, £74.80 for 12 months.
- Children under 16 and full time students under 19 are exempt.

6 Around £707 per person.

7 a) 16%
b) 28.5%
c) 4.3%

9 18%

Chapter 9

Page 278

1 The child is spared the trauma of confrontation in court with their alleged abuser, and can therefore tell their stories more effectively.
2 Recommendations may include that: the interview be videotaped; the purpose of the interview be explained to the child; although formal consent is not required, the interview not go ahead without the child's agreement; appropriate equipment be used; tapes be stored securely; the interview progress from the child giving a 'free narrative' account to open and closed questions; leading questions not be used; only one interview take place; it last for no longer than an hour, and that a sensitive approach be taken at the end of the interview.

Appendix B

Relating units from different awarding bodies to chapters in text

Chapter no. and title	**City and Guilds** Optional Unit 11 Provision for the development of children (Advanced)	**RSA** Optional Unit 9 Child development and provision for children (Advanced)	**BTEC** Additional Unit 25 Human growth and development (Advanced)
PART 1			
1. Stages of physical development	11.1.1; 11.4.2	9.1.1; 9.1.2	25.1.1; 25.1.2; 25.1.5; 25.1.6
2. Factors affecting physical development	11.1.4; 11.1.5	9.1.3	25.1.1; 25.1.3
3. Ways of promoting and maintaining good health	11.1.3	9.1.4	25.1.4
Childhood diseases	11.1.2	9.1.5	
PART 2			
4. Cognitive development from birth to adulthood	11.3.1; 11.3.2; 11.3.3; 11.3.4; 11.4.2	9.2.1; 9.2.2	25.1; 25.3; 25.4
5. Language development from birth to adulthood	11.3.1;11.3.2	9.2.3	25.2.2
PART 3			
6. Emotional and social development from birth to late childhood	11.2.1; 11.2.2; 11.2.3; 11.2.4	9.2.4	25.3.1; 25.3.2; 25.3.3; 25.3.4
7. Emotional and social development from adolescence to adulthood	11.2.1; 11.2.2; 11.2.3; 11.2.4	9.2.4	25.3.2; 25.3.3; 25.3.4; 25.3.5
PART 4			
8. Provision of health, social care and education	11.4.1; 11.4.4	9.3.1; 9.3.2; 9.3.5	
9. Legislation which relates to the care of children	11.4.3	9.3.3; 9.3.4	

Appendix C

Glossary

Accommodation The process by which children modify their existing schemas in order to incorporate or adapt to new experiences (Piaget).

Adaptation Fitting in with – and thriving in – the environment. In Piaget's theory, adaptation is achieved through the complementary processes of **assimilation** and **accommodation**.

Adolescence Period during which a sudden spurt in both growth and maturity takes place to produce an adult capable of producing children.

Adoption The permanent transfer of all parental rights and responsibilities from the 'natural' parent(s) to the 'adoptive' parent(s).

Allele One of two or more alternative forms of a gene, only one of which can be present on a chromosome. (For example, brown and blue are alleles for the eye colour gene.)

Allometric growth Organs increase in size at different rates.

Alphafetoprotein See 'maternal serum alphafetoprotein' below.

Altruism Acting in the interests of other people and not of oneself.

Amniocentesis Withdrawal of a sample of amniotic fluid surrounding the embryo in the uterus, by means of a syringe inserted through the abdominal wall, to enable the prenatal diagnosis of chromosomal abnormalities (such as Down's syndrome).

Animism The belief that everything that exists has some kind of consciousness.

APGAR score A method of rapidly assessing the general state of the baby immediately after the birth. A maximum of two points is given for each of the following signs: type of breathing; heart rate; colour; muscle tone; and response to stimuli.

Assimilation The process by which children incorporate new experiences into their existing schema (Piaget).

Asthma A condition, particularly common in children, in which the bronchioles constrict, causing difficulties in breathing.

Attachment An enduring emotional bond that infants form with specific people, usually starting with their mothers, some time between the ages of 6 and 9 months.

Authoritarian personality A collection of characteristics implying a rigid approach to moral and social issues.

Autism A psychiatric disorder of childhood marked by severe difficulties in communicating and forming relationships, in developing language, and in using abstract concepts; repetitive and limited patterns of behaviour; and obsessive resistance to tiny changes in familiar surroundings.

Basal metabolic rate A measure of the rate at which the body breaks down foods, and therefore releases heat, when a person is at rest.

Blastocyst Hollow fluid filled ball of cells formed after fertilisation.

Chorionic villus sampling A very small sample is taken of the tissue surrounding the embryo and tested for abnormalities.

Concept Something formed in the mind based on and linking past, present and future ideas which share some attributes. A child may sit on a variety of chairs, but a **concept** of a chair is an idea which exists in the child's mind.

Continuum A continuous series or whole with no part perceptibly different from adjacent parts.

Correlation When two variables change in the same direction, such that when one is large, the other tends to be large too; or if one is small, the other also tends to be small.

De-individuation The idea that riots and other types of crowd behaviour can be explained in terms of 'mob psychology', in which the anonymity produced by a lack of individual identifiers causes people to abandon such aspects of individuality as conscience, consideration, etc.

Development The general sequence in the way that the child functions in terms of movement, language, thinking, feelings etc. Development continues from birth to death.

DNA Deoxyribose nucleic acid. The chemical of which our genes are made.

Dominant characteristic The genetic characteristic which will mask the recessive characteristic. (For example, the dominant allele of 'tongue rolling' masks the recessive allele of 'non-tongue rolling').

Embryo The term used for the developing human during the first two months after conception.

Empathy The sharing of another's emotions and feelings.

Ethology The study of an animal's behaviour in its natural environment.

Factor analysis A statistical technique, using **correlation**, which is used to reduce a large amount of data to a much smaller amount made up of overlapping characteristics or factors.

Family A group of people living together or apart who have strong emotional relationships and who are significant to one another through blood or other links. Includes 'those people caring for the child', so could be foster parents, adoptive parents or residential carers.

Fertilisation The fusion of the sperm nucleus and egg nucleus.

Foetus The term used for the developing human from the beginning of the 9th week after conception until birth.

Fostering Caring for a child or young person on a temporary basis. The foster parent does not assume all parental rights and responsibilities.

Gametes Sperm and ova (eggs).

Gene The length of DNA which codes for a single polypeptide chain (see below).

Genetic counselling Guidance given (usually by a doctor with experience in genetics) to individuals who are considering having a child but who are concerned because there is a blood relative with an inherited disorder.

Genotype The set of genes an individual possesses.

Gene therapy The treatment of a genetic disease by altering the patient's genes.

Gestation The period between conception and birth.

Glue ear A build-up of sticky fluid in the middle ear.

Growth An increase in size and structural complexity.

Haemoglobin A red pigment found in the red blood cells which carries oxygen around the body.

Human chorionic gonadatrophin Hormone secreted by the developing placenta immediately after implantation.

Ideal self One's perception of how one should be or would like to be.

Identification The process of social learning which involves oneself trying to be the same as, or very similar to, another person and basing one's style of interaction on that comparison.

Immunization The process of inducing immunity as a preventative measure against certain infectious diseases.

Implantation The attachment of the zygote to the lining of the uterus.

Imprinting Konrad Lorenz, an ethologist, believed that imprinting was an inborn ability in goslings and ducks to follow the first relatively large moving object which they saw after hatching – an instinctive reaction and a very rapid attachment.

Independent-voluntary organisations Non-government, non-profit making organisations, offering services at a local or national level.

Maternal serum alphafetoprotein Used to check for the condition of spina bifida in the unborn baby.

Meiosis Cell division which results in the daughter cells having only half the number of chromosomes found in the parent cell. Produces the gametes.

Meningitis Inflammation of the **meninges** which cover the brain.

Menopause Occurs in women, usually between the ages of 45 and 55. Hormone levels change, and the woman no longer ovulates so she cannot become pregnant.

Mitosis Cell division which results in all daughter cells having the same number of chromosomes as the parent (i.e. 23 in humans).

Morula Solid mass of cells formed after fertilisation.

Mutation Any change in the structure or the amount of DNA which can produce sudden and distinct differences between individuals.

Naturalistic observation This narrative method is often called 'specimen description' or 'written record'. Observers must write down (as it happens) as much as they can of what they are seeing. The present tense is used, and the record is structured only by noting the sequence of time.

Norm (or milestone) Used to describe averages which provide a framework for assessing development. They are the result of observations by many professionals in the field of child development.

'Not for profit' organisations See 'Independent-voluntry organisation' above.

Ovulation The release of the egg from the ovary.

Peer group Children of approximately the same age with whom a child associates.

Personality Stable patterns of behaviour, including thought and emotion, that distinguish people from one another.

Phenotype The observable characteristics of an individual, resulting from the interaction between their genotype and the environment.

Phobia One of a group of mental disorders called **anxiety disorders** that is characterised by an intense and, at least on the surface, irrational fear.

Placenta The organ that develops in the uterus during pregnancy, and brings the blood supplies of the mother and baby close enough for the exchange of materials. (Often referred to as the 'afterbirth').

Pleasure principle In Freudian terms, the way in which the **id** operates by demanding immediate gratification of its impulses, regardless of social convention.

Polypeptide chain Made up of amino acids, one or more polypeptide chains are folded in a specific 3 dimensional shape to form a protein.

Premature birth A birth which takes place before 37 weeks of completed gestation.

Primary care The first line of patient care, provided in the community, not in hospitals. For example, the care provided by GPs or dentists.

Puberty The stage at which the secondary sexual characteristics develop.

Reality principle In Freudian terms, the way that the ego attempts to balance the demands of the id and the **superego** with the practical demands of reality.

Recessive characteristic See 'Dominant characteristic' above.

Rhesus factor A group of antigens that may or may not be present on the surface of red blood cells. Most people have the factor (i.e. are rhesus positive; people who do not are rhesus negative). Incompatibility between rhesus positive and rhesus negative blood can cause haemolytic disease of the newborn.

Rubella Or 'German measles'. This condition is particularly harmful to the developing foetus as it can cause deafness, blindness and mental retardation. All girls in the UK are now immunised against rubella before they reach child-bearing age, and this measure has drastically reduced the incidence of rubella-damaged babies.

Schema A mental framework or structure which encompasses memories, ideas, concepts and programmes for action which are pertinent to a particular topic.

Screening The examination of large numbers of apparently healthy individuals, in an attempt to identify those with a particular disorder.

Secondary care Care provided in hospitals

when a patient can not be treated by the primary health care team.

Self-concept The individual's view, acquired through life experiences, of all the perceptions, feelings, values and attitudes that define 'I' or 'me'.

Sex linkage Describes genes carried on the X chromosome, for example colour blindness and haemophilia. These conditions are more common in males than females.

Socialisation The process by which children learn the culture or way of life of the society into which they are born.

Statutory care Care which must be provided by the state by law. For example, education for 5–16 year olds.

Swaddling Wrapping the baby tightly in material.

Syphilis A bacterial sexually transmitted disease.

Temperament This is the style of behaviour which comes naturally to you – e.g. relaxed or easy-going.

Tertiary care Specialised care, following a referral from a consultant, surgeon, or GP. Normally provided at a specialised centre.

Tracking Following a moving object with the eyes.

Ultrasound A process used for, amongst other things, the monitoring of the age and development of the unborn baby, and to check for multiple births.

Vaccine A dose of killed or weakened microorganisms which is introduced into the body, usually by injection, in the process of immunisation.

Variation Differences in the characteristics of individuals caused by either genetic or environmental differences.

Zygote The fertilised egg.

Index